Turning

Turning Silk

A Diary of Chen Taiji Practice,
the Quan of Change

KINTHISSA

Lunival · 2009

First published in 2009 by
Lunival
50 Park Town, Oxford OX2 6SJ, United Kingdom

ISBN 978 0 9562846 0 0

Printed and bound in Italy by
Arti grafiche Litoprint Genova

玄本

For writing Chinese words in Roman letters the modern pinyin system has a bracing simplicity, and an attractive regularity that becomes natural once one has got used to a few surprises. TaijiQuan is pronounced as in the older Wade-Giles spelling T'aiChiCh'uan; Qi is pronounced Ch'i; Laozi and Zhuangzi are familiar to generations of readers as LaoTzu and ChuangTzu.

Contents

CHAPTER 1

Mindful Practice

IT IS January. In the long evenings while the valley sleeps I shall venture to speak from within my practice of TaijiQuan. This little book will be in the form of notes, following the daily rhythms of a practicant; these I will intersperse with a composite selection of reflections from my years with the taiji since 1976. In that year, I began learning the Yang Style 108 long form from Gerda Geddes, known to her students as Pytt, for whom the T'aiChi was a guide to the living of life on this earth, and a preparation for the journey beyond. The allegory that she read in the symbols of her chosen art was inspirational to many who came to study with this Norwegian lady who pioneered the teaching of Yang Style T'aiChiCh'uan* in England.

The old Norse gods never quite let her go, and perhaps her teaching was the deeper for its trans-cultural vision. She above all taught me friendship with one's body, and companionship with one's breathing. The dutiful Asian student that I was, I wrote down just about everything she said in the classes that I attended, first as a weary dance student at The Place – the school in London teaching Martha Graham technique; then as a T'aiChi aspirant, from 1976 until 1989. Pytt enjoyed telling stories in her lessons, including accounts of her dreams. One which all her students will be familiar with was her Dream of the Baskets, from the time when she was working through the section where the snake casts off its skin.

The last time I saw her was in early March 2006. She had been expecting such an event, that a stroke would befall her, and she had prepared well for it: there was in her handbag a letter asking that she be allowed to die naturally, and to be given neither food nor water. To the tremendous credit of the doctors and nursing staff at the hospital, and the perseverance of her family, she died in the best way she could under the circumstances. When I saw her on her fifth day without food or water, her touch was the same as the one I had treasured for years: cool, dry, letting one be. Her eyes were both here and elsewhere. Her right hand kept reaching for the sunlight outside, just as she had recounted of her childhood game, of going from shadow into the light. On the eighth day she joined the *dao*. I am sure she shot goodness into the universe with her last golden arrow.

By 2006, I had been studying TaijiQuan intensively for ten years under another teacher, Chen XiaoWang of the Chen family. The death of my first teacher curiously freed me from dependence on the teacher. Pytt had said to me again and again in those last years, "You do not need a teacher. You must become your own teacher." Her insistence on this point had irked me countless times. I valued Chen XiaoWang's instruction so much that I had gone to Sydney in Australia every winter for seven years. Perhaps Pytt and Chen XiaoWang were two pulls and when one let go, I let go of the other.

In profound gratitude I dedicate this book to my two teachers, the Hon. Gerda Geddes and Grandmaster Chen XiaoWang. They taught me deeply their art, and have set me on an open road to the mountains, the uncharted land beyond the confines of style and form.

Your Own Physician

The first entry happens to coincide with the resumption of proper practice after a long interruption. Nearly a year ago I suffered my first injury since I began Taiji some thirty years ago; it was serious enough to prevent me from exerting my normal fairly strenuous daily effort for ten months. Since my first visit to Australia in 1996, my training had concentrated on the fundamental practices: *ZhanZhuang* the standing qigong; *Chansigong* the 'twining silk' exercises; and the Chentaiji forms, above all *LaoJia* the 'old frame' credited with being the matrix form of the various TaijiQuan forms seen today, and the 'new frame' *XinJia*, and more variously, as inspiration took me, the practice of sabre, sword and spear forms.

This evening's ZhanZhuang: what is the best way to proceed, when the body is at odds with itself? Beginner's mind, open outlook, no expectations. I must practise what I preach, which is: accept things as they are. Be aware of the entire body, do not get caught by any one part. Keep the attention fluid, sweeping over the body from top to bottom, left and right; the front, the back, outside and inside.

Stay light. Mind barely touches body. It is enough simply to know the part you are passing over. Do not fix on the pain. Observe yourself, be your own physician. As a wise old Burmese abbot put it, the doctor does not fall ill alongside the patient! Observe the signs of the malady. Do not jump in.

I feel myself anxious, how am I ever going to find ease again? And what is this dis-ease? Pain in the area around the fifth lumbar and first sacral vertebrae, and the left sacroiliac joint. Intense sensations where ligaments bind the left ilium to the spine.

An old injury from dance school days, thirty-three years ago. Through an enormous amount of effort both on my part and my teacher's over years, I had managed to strengthen the legs and lower back enough to establish centre in *dantian*, in the lower abdomen, and thus develop twining power. Then last year's mishap, as if out of the blue: one crude move by a therapist, and overnight a delicate balance was thrown into disarray and agony, a balance that had served for many years without its precarious nature being clearly appreciated. Yet somehow, during these last ten months, the centre has stayed intact. How can this be?

Now I am immersed in the sensations of tonight's ZhanZhuang. Standing with feet parallel, a shoulder-width apart, knees bent just slightly, arms gently rounded and raised, with palms before my chest. Head up… listening behind… mind balanced, weight balanced, breathing easy, looking for *qi* balance… qi, the wild sister of breath, we shall have much to say about this elusive concept.

Mind is all-important. Attention sweeps through the body, fraught parts and all. Noticing where tightness is, soften; release the breathing a little. Warmth begins to waft around the diaphragm, the waist fills out with a sense of ease. Shoulders begin to unlock, hips also. Mind's decision to stay with the body loosens it, gives it the confidence to explore. Feeling the body begin to flow, the mind in turn calms a little. My heart is no longer so oppressed.

TaijiQuan, or T'aiChiCh'uan as we used to spell it in the 1970s, is sometimes described as meditation in motion. For those interested in it as a martial art, this description may seem feeble. But what use would a warrior be without awareness? The misunderstandings may arise from this word *meditation*. It is a word which comes from the Christian world of the pioneering translators of Buddhist texts, in the nineteenth century. When we apply it to the mind techniques indigenous to the lands east of Afghanistan, we must be alert to the need to qualify, to adjust our terms of reference. Would *contemplation* be a better term? I don't think so. Let us for now simply say *attention*. Studying the teachings of the Buddha is a fine way to learn to appreciate the kind of attention that is cultivated in TaijiQuan.

I can hear a friend saying, "But I thought Taiji was Daoist! Not Buddhist!"

Well, let us look at all this in this little book.

The first part of the name TaijiQuan refers to one of the nearly final stages of creation in Chinese cosmogony, occurring more or less after the unformed and before the manifest. It is the birth of quality – *qualis*, of which sort? Edward Schafer translates* *Taiji* as 'Grand Culmination'. The preceding stages are Grand Interchangeability, Grand Antecedence, Grand Initiation and Grand Simplicity. The culmination expresses itself in differentiation; he describes the infinite potentialities:

> Once started, the world keeps going … the Chinese looked eagerly for the evidence of rhythms and progressions within this final stage of cosmic evolution. What they discovered was cycles – and nests of cycles … The cycles are repeated, but are never identical … Each chimes a different celestial tune … each phase – the formal duplicate of his predecessor – glows somewhat differently. Hue, saturation, intensity, luster, iridescence, brilliance never recur in identical combinations, even through an infinity of time.*

After all my wanderings, I think I may settle for a simple explanation of the name TaijiQuan. *Taiji/T'aiChi* is the pole of the universe; *Quan/Ch'uan*, which means 'fist', is to have oneself within one's grasp. My first teacher said this: one who is master of the *ch'uan* is master of her own energy.

Practising ZhanZhuang, one is tuning oneself to the wavelengths of the pole that connects Earth and Heaven. For a little while one becomes the pole, the connection flows through. Everything that is out of true becomes a little truer, more in tune. That may be why one comes back to this fundamental practice, why one might even feel a kind of hunger for it.

Getting into Stride

Walking, a step at a time, is the object of this morning's practice. In my T'aiChi days, thirty years ago, the challenge was to step softly. Pytt liked to call 'Parting the Wild Horse's Mane'/'Wild Horse Parts its Mane' by another name: the Seven Steps of the Buddha. She was inspired by the story of Prince Siddhattha's birth. His mother, carrying him in her womb, travels back to her parents' country to give birth. While she is resting in a garden on the way, he is born under a tree. The little fellow takes seven steps into the world, and in the place of each step there grows a lotus flower. I grew up with paintings of the little Buddha-to-be at the beginning of his last life, standing on the seventh lotus with a trail blazing behind him. For Pytt the connection between the two names of this section of the T'aiChi form was softness, a gentleness born of freedom from fear. A lesson in how to walk the earth, so that you nurture what can grow beneath your feet. The Wild Horse, to Pytt, was violent force, which could sweep down into China from the steppes beyond the Great Wall. If you can approach this force without fear, you merge with its power and are transformed.

Feeling my ropey back as I start the morning's practice of walking reminds me of beginner's body and beginner's mind. The remnants of last year's mishap make my steps uneven, the weight shift awkward. I wrote in 1981:

> The form of T'aiChi shows you an ideal state. When you actually begin learning, you realize that you cannot take even one step! Instead of flowing, you clunk, and any control that you may have is only through tension.*

So, back to the beginning. As I get into stride, I remember how the walking felt in those days. The aim was to relax the body and the breathing, to imagine oneself suspended from above 'by a silken thread'. Stepping forwards with the knees bent, allowing the legs to do the work, lifting the foot with the ankle loose, articulating in the joint just enough for the heel to touch the ground, before the weight feeds in from the back leg.

> As the foot begins to unclench and learns to articulate itself, a long process of undoing is started throughout the body ... it is simultaneous with the letting go of something in the mind...*

Pain in the body makes one clench interiorly. Unclench, and try to let go of all sorts of ideas of injury and pain!

Even in my beginning-again state today, the stepping is a very different affair; it has been different for many years. The main difference in feeling is due to changes in the posture itself. Those changes are necessary for building *dantian*. For most of us, jinxed by life, the dantian as centre does not exist naturally. It has to be re-constructed. I will say in a moment how specifically this may be done. When it is done, power to move comes, as it originally should, from the centre. The legs are simply the means to ferry the passenger, who rides sovereign in dantian.

In the old days I had a picture of Dantian in my mind: a cauldron with a lively fire burning beneath, lying deep inside the lower belly. As a woman, it was easy to imagine this place as my centre. I had had no experience of dantian being the source of strength and stability empowering me, in a real sense, until I had delved for many months under Chen XiaoWang's guidance into the practice of ZhanZhuang, the standing qigong, and Chansigong, the basic exercises which develop twining power from the centre.

The growing experience of dantian was not the result of the hours of practice *per se*. It arose from the effortful coming together of the body's disparate parts. Here is something that I wrote more recently:

> In order for this spot some three fingers below your navel in the interior of the body to become the fulcrum, certain things must be established. First is the apparently simple direction: your weight perpendicular. Honestly try to do this: is it easy? Chances are, your body's weight is ricocheting off in several directions.
>
> For both sides of your body to flow towards a central core will take time. The work is both mechanical – loosening, altering, refixing the tent pegs as it were – and energetic: as dull areas get incorporated into alignment, there are clear sensations of freshness, moisture, warmth gently moving through you.
>
> The body must be balanced in all directions. What does this mean? The two sides in equilibrium; the upper body's weight directly over the lower body; front and back equally suspended; from centre emanating outwards to hands and feet.*

For all the above to take place, you must rest in tranquillity.

Back to Walking

It is astounding what must be taken into consideration before you can take a single step in Chentaiji. One winter, two students of Chen XiaoWang went to study with him in Sydney. Every day for a month, a two-hour lesson. At the start of each lesson, maybe, if they were lucky, there would be a chance to discuss what the programme for the lesson might be. For the first lesson they asked to work on the forward and backward steps ('Wading Forwards' and 'Step Back Whirling'). Chen XiaoWang beamed at them, saying, "I also wish!" With him in the lead they began, following him to the end of the beaten earth practice area under the shady trees, looking down the slope past the houses into a hazy Sydney. Birds screeched above, the white cockatoos with their yellow crests and the harshest cries. When he reached the neighbour's fence, Chen XiaoWang began to whirl backwards. They quickly changed to stepping back. At each stretch he would get in the greatest possible number of steps. Stepping backwards, he would force the students behind him to retreat up a slope at the edge of the practice area, Chen XiaoWang still looming backwards upon them, his backward walk as commanding as his forward steps. The minutes and the entire morning's lesson passed, Chen XiaoWang entirely absorbed in the stepping forwards and the stepping backwards, the two students following as best they might. Goodness, they thought, will we spend our entire visit to Sydney walking forwards and backwards?

When you have the great fortune to be corrected in your stepping by Master Chen, he may arrest you in mid move saying "Not ready, not ready for step!" Suppose that you are about to shift weight onto the forward leg, your left leg, and your back right heel is still on the ground. Your right arm, the back arm, has begun to fold in, the hand coming to the right side of the head. There is a precise sequence of events, a coordination between weight shift and arm motion. It seems simple enough, but then the teacher places your hips in a surprising position. Much of the posture adjustment in TaijiQuan is in preparation for a moment such as this, when you are transferring weight from one leg to the other. How well you are sitting in your pelvis affects how stable you are in dantian. When you can remain in dantian as you step, the sensation is of the centre not moving, your unified body simply pressing through the air, like a long boat cutting through with the water streaming straight past.

The coordination happens on a subtle level, and part of the subtlety lies in the twining of the arm. There must be no tension in the chest, upper back or shoulders; the arm then can be free in its socket. Relaxed along its length and aligned in its bones, muscles and tendons doing their work smoothly, the arm may learn to twine effortlessly.

There is a mind picture always present when I mull over the Wading Forwards. As he steps, Chen XiaoWang's arms have a sharp-edged appearance, in spite of the thick rope-like twisting of his limbs. For a brief moment this afternoon I have that sensation, an internal experience of the image. Where did it come from? The coordination of upper and lower body mentioned above is only the mechanical starting point of the exercise. The twining I have spoken of is a complex interweaving of pathways of qi knitting together the body: left and right; upper and lower; horizontally, vertically and diagonally. All this will become clearer when I speak more of Chansigong, the exercises to develop twining power. When you remain in dantian as you move, the windings spread out from the waist and lower abdomen freely, precisely. The 'sharp-edged' look and feel come from each arm taking the only correct trajectory for that moment's execution of the movement.

What this correct trajectory is depends on the twining in the legs, twining which also has its origin in dantian. These delicate spirallings through the legs must happen naturally, and it takes years of Chansigong for the technique to develop.

There are surprises in store for people who come from a Yang Style background, as I do. When a person walks normally in a relaxed way, the arms tend to swing loosely in opposition to the step: while the right foot advances, the left arm swings forwards in a balancing motion. The forward stepping that I had learned in Yang Style happens along the same lines, with familiar coordination of opposite arm and leg. In Chen Style taiji, the forward stepping works the other way around. As one wades forward, the arm and leg on the same side of the body advance together. This unexpected pattern, and its indication of internal processes, will be interesting to examine another day.

Now here's a treat for this evening, an exposition on *chansi*, the Chen twining, described in unforgettable English prose in the book *Chen Style Taijiquan* from the Zhaohua Publishing House in Beijing.

> The twining strength is the core of Taijiquan and it is united by two opposite basic twinings. Any action of the whole series cannot leave the twining strength all the time, so it runs through the processes of all actions. There are smooth twining and adverse twining in all actions of the whole series, so they are the basic twinings with universality; while inward and outward, upward and downward, leftward and rightward, forward and backward, greatly and slightly, all these twinings describe the different points of the twinings of all actions in direction and degree, so they are the bearings and twinings with particularity.*

That basic introduction says it all. Never lose the twining strength. Let *chansi* run through all actions.

The years of study and training in Chansigong are to de-jinx our bodies so that one day we may recover nature's rhythms. There is a deep power inherent in the human body. After some years your body begins to change, if you practise correctly. It becomes kind of padded, cloaked by a layer that is firm and yielding at the same time. The skin softens. The fingers and the palm of the hand plumpen like a baby's. This is something remarkable. All the strenuous practice that you do in TaijiQuan does not build up your body in the same way as Western sports or fitness training tends to. There is no exaggerated show of muscle or top-heaviness. A resilient strength is nurtured in the kernel of the body, the strength pliable, the body cushioned. Dantian is home, comfortable, spacious, light, uncluttered by tension created by habit and desire.

The Spirit of the Valley

Occasionally someone asks me, how did you come to the Taiji? Or, why do you do it?

There were glimpses of it in my childhood in Yangon (Rangoon), Burma. Memory has clothed it in mists, but it was simply what was happening in the grounds of the Chinese temple that I passed every day on my way to school, and the mists could have been in the cool season of the year, or in the monsoons as the heat rose out of the earth after heavy rain.

I do not recall seeing it in America, while I was studying there from 1969 to 1973. But during this time I discovered my love of Chinese and Japanese painting and ceramics. Vassar College had a collection of tea ceremony ware and I stored a passion for this for years, until I dared to teach myself how to throw and fire ash-glazed stoneware in a singing valley in Italy.

In 1974 I first saw Pytt Geddes in London; she was the one untired-looking person in the entire School of Contemporary Dance, which made quite an impression. She rented studios in the building for her T'aiChi classes three days a week. I went to a demonstration and was amazed to see her perform what had lived on mistily in my imagination.

It was curiosity about her and a strange sense of homecoming that drew me to her Thursday evening lessons. She told us of her own first glimpse of T'aiChi: in the blisteringly hot season in Shanghai, she and her husband David used to go at the break of day to walk along the Yangtze estuary. Crops were planted there, and one day when these were high, they rounded a bend to find an old man enacting something that made her flesh go bumpy. This was in 1949.

The T'aiChi began its work on me right from the start. Friends and family remarked on how I never missed a lesson, however exhausted I was from the dance training. I had by then 'a bad back'. I think it was actually from something that happened in the first week of the three-year training course, when the ballet teacher had the tallest male in the group stand on the shoulders of the smallest female, for the latter to do pliés at the barre. The female was me. It was meant to be a demonstration of the strength of the spine. We were a bunch of gangly youth with little or no training.

By the time I attended Pytt's classes, my lower back was in constant pain. I left the dance school only at the beginning of the third and final year; I cannot think why I stayed so long. Pytt invited me to attend all her lessons, asking if I would like to teach T'aiChi one day. I was unnerved by the thought, but accepted the reading list she gave me. Several books on that list I was already familiar with, from my Eastern philosophies courses in college. But John Blofeld's books I had not read, nor the one or two T'aiChi books mentioned; in those days there were not so many books on T'aiChi.

Even with the emphasis on slowness and grace that the T'aiChi in those days had, I was aware of its power to deconstruct the practitioner. One was undone by it, and it was up to the person to find a way to put herself together anew. But the 'undone' phase had substance: one's feet really rested on the earth, enabled to receive heaven's blessings.

Thirty years on, the images that Pytt so loved in Chinese art I now find within, particularly when I practise ZhanZhuang; not quite exactly the images, but the Qi permeating form.

Breath and Qi

The breath, our most intimate companion, beckons qi, but is not always answered. Independent-spirited, unbiddable, Qi is the wild sister of Breath.

All the breathing exercises that we carried out in our T'aiChi classes at The Place, standing upright or lying on the floor, guiding coloured pathways around our bodies in our imagination: somehow they did not summon the *ch'i*. It seemed to me that the more visualizations we performed, the more we distanced ourselves from experiencing *ch'i/qi*, 'intrinsic energy'. At least, that is how it was with me. I could not visualize the *ch'i*. She came one day of her own accord.

What passes through our lungs, precious and life-giving as it is, is not the life force. But our vocabulary is limited; shuffling around the words, searching for a way to describe experience, we may appear to go around in circles. The old Chinese masters looked into misty canyons and shrouded mountains: here they saw Qi's domain. Seen fleetingly. Cloud, mist, rain and wind are the vestments veiling her.

Also in our bodies, qi manifests itself lightly. Gung-ho about power, people sometimes do not hear what Chen XiaoWang is telling them – that qi is delicate, that it flows if allowed to be, connecting all parts of the body to dantian, so that all parts support dantian. Its pathways are fine like the veins of a leaf, crisscrossing the entire framework, binding it subtly but firmly, like a spider's web that does not break in the storm.

Qi eludes description. One might very well say, almost, that it eludes experience, at any rate the aspect of experience which seeks to comprehend, to know. It eludes characterization, as a slippery thing eludes the grasp. Sometimes, tempted by the thought of it, I wish to say that qi feels like a sweetness. Is that an imaginary comparison?

My companion, relatively inexperienced as a taiji practitioner, endured patiently a long and detailed correction from Chen XiaoWang. Eventually Master Chen stepped back, took an appraising look at his handiwork and said, "Now good!" My companion, perhaps trying to pin down a little what he was supposed to feel at this point, said "But I'm not feeling any different." Master Chen said, "What do you mean, not feeling any different?" My companion: "Well, I'm not feeling good or anything." Master Chen: "Well, are you feeling bad?" Companion: "No, certainly not feeling bad." Master Chen: "Ah! Not feeling good, not feeling bad, this best!"

And yet, learning to recognize the feeling of qi is an important step along the way. Guided by the teacher's touch, there are sometimes whiffs and surges, a sense of fullness. Then, practising alone, you may recognize its absence. If it can be hard for a beginner to recognize the feeling of qi, it is certainly easier to recognize the loss of that feeling. Chen XiaoWang puts it simply: "First learn feeling of no qi; then learn feeling of qi; then learn to find qi."

Where is it to be found? It is to be found in flowing. "Looking for qi roads", as Master Chen says so often.

Forging and Dredging

I came up with this metaphor during my first years of practice in Chansigong. It describes what the training feels like: pathways of Qi have to be forged, and there is a lot of dredging to be done in the process. My Catalan students had to be persuaded to translate "forging and dredging". Their best efforts produced words which to me conjured up a detergent advertisement:

> Obrint i netejant els canals energètics del nostre cos.

"No!" I had to insist. "It is a process with a lot of fire in it, like blacksmithing! And much clearing of the way, so that qi may travel unobstructed."

For me these words express what this practice can do for us. Because they are a little strange, it makes people stop and think.

In this kind of taiji training we alternate continually between working on postural changes that centre us in dantian, and creating channels through our bodies with persistent pourings of something liquid. Pointing one morning at the dry red earth, Chen XiaoWang remarked that when you first pour water on this, the water disappears; but that if you keep on pouring, there will soon be a channel; and that is how it is with qi in the body. The fiery aspect of this work will become apparent in later chapters of this book.

And where does the dredging come in? This is easy to visualize. A waterway, a stream. There is some movement down its middle. Here and there along its banks are bits and pieces of debris, they are stuck, for they are not in the moving stream. When the flow of water increases, the dead branch, the old shoe, gets jostled and nudged into the main stream, and is carried all the way out to sea.

Years ago, I had a dream. I was living in an old house, it was full of family. Slowly, the house was being suffocated, for inside this house, there were big trees growing, ever more and more contorted. One day I woke up to find the house empty, and the trees growing out in the light.

Dredging can sometimes be major.

A Particularity of Chentaiji

There are many factors which distinguish Chen Style TaijiQuan from the other styles. There are obvious and superficial differences, often noted: the big movements and deep stances, the changes in speed, especially the sudden, explosive actions which may be quite unlike what one had thought of as TaijiQuan.

But what really intrigued me was not the appearance of Chentaiji. When I first met Chen XiaoWang I saw something on the move inside the body that I had not seen before in TaijiQuan. It was difficult to pin down, but it seemed that somewhere there was a hidden impulse, setting off vibrations which linked and transmitted an energy that appeared palpable.

Slowly I began to understand that what had affected me so deeply was partly the result of a mysterious undulation of the spine, a forwards and backwards rolling, what Chen XiaoWang describes as 'chest-waist change place'. The core ripples.

This undulation was nothing like what I had encountered in dance technique. It was not an action being executed, and there was no suggestion of its being a beautiful or sensuous motion. One cannot make it happen. Chen XiaoWang would say, "Natural – first principle!"

To return to nature one must train for a very long time, in the correct frame of mind. The technique arises from gathered energy. Dantian is built day by day. This centre, open and alert in all directions, exquisitely mobile, sends the initial impulse – originating not in dantian – rippling through the rest of the body. Depending on the particular stance and the varying conduct of arms and legs, the twinings happen each in a unique way. This is most clearly shown in the double hand Chansigong, where the rippling core sets off multiple waves, some across the current, each one slightly different in amplitude and timing.

A snake which is all spine is the best image to hold in the mind. Have you ever watched a snake, alive in its own habitat? Last year there was one so regular in its habits that I named it Fedele, Faithful, and not being sure of how many there were in the stone wall opposite our front door, I referred to them as the Fratelli Fedeli, like an order of friars which may have once roamed this wild hinterland.

I usually come across them when I go mushrooming in the woods all around our house. Perhaps because my step is light, I often surprise one as it is basking in the sunshine. When it is all coiled, head and tail are hard to discern. Even when it begins to slither, it is difficult to be sure of parts, for the whole appears to be on the move, all at once. It is not one part pushing or pulling that affects the rest. The slithering is a series of curves and straights straightening and curving, like this it moves, and suddenly it enters its hole in the ground.

This 'chest and waist change place' of Chentaiji, can we say that one moves and the other follows, or do they change place simultaneously? I pondered over this for many months, and one night I had a dream. In the dream, Master Chen gave me certain terms in Chinese to help me understand key Taiji principles. Much of the dream was lost upon awakening, but one detail remained clearly; he said, "this [term] means change comes one after the other. People think same time, but it is not; first one, then the other."

I lived with this for a while, watching myself at practice, watching him when there was the chance. A few years later, when we were discussing such matters in a small group, I told the dream to him and the taiji friends who were present. He said, "Yes, like same time, but not same time."

I would now venture to say that the spark, the initial impulse, is a little below the small of the back, what Master Chen calls 'waist'. It is inseparably linked to dantian in the lower belly. This spark sets off a motion upwards into the chest ~ curved parts straightening, straight parts curving ~ and with a truly supple spine, the entire torso is involved, all the way through neck and head to the sacrum and tailbone.

CHAPTER 2

The Art of Learning

WE BRING such a lot of baggage with us when we come to study something. Partly because it was the fashion, but also because of necessity, the taiji teaching which boomed in the 1970s and 80s was often a therapeutic process. Now therapy is no longer so fashionable, and we are all geared up to learn the 'true secrets' of the art from 'real masters'. Sometimes I think we could do with a little old-fashioned introspection, in order to have some understanding of what we bring with us into the dojo.

The study of TaijiQuan is a long undertaking. Aspects of the training have been mentioned in the previous chapter. I have said that mind is important. Mind is the big mind, awareness, attention, the knowing; but also the little mind that is scurrying all the while eating away what's left of original clarity.

One greedy gobbler is vanity. Not having a realistic awareness of oneself is vanity – you either underestimate yourself, or you overesteem yourself; both are wasteful of energy. All those distractions, "I think I should do better, I don't like it that I can't take a proper step", the talking inside the head. But we're not here in the room to show that we already can do the taiji; we're here to learn.

This book will document some of my struggles. The pictures, also, will show my difficulties. When one sees a picture of a masterly position, it may have the effect of 'closing the book': what is shown appears so far out of reach that we leave excellence to the masters, rather than take on the challenging task of improving ourselves. Here we shall have the opportunity to see, examine and mull over some of the problems that actually arise in the course of ordinary practice.

My first seminar with Chen XiaoWang was in London in 1995 to learn LaoJia, the Chen family's long form. On day 1, I was flummoxed by a bouleversemental adjustment which Chen XiaoWang made to my basic taiji position, standing on two feet a shoulder's width apart, arms down by the sides, the position known by the splendid title, Initiation of the Grand Terminus. It was a small group, about ten people; for a few it was their second course with him, a couple were entirely new to taiji, one or two like me new to Chentaiji. As we stood there, thinking that we were about to do the very first move, he went around all of us, giving a couple of minutes to each person, gently nudging us into a better positioning for attempting to lift the arms.

The unfamiliar place that he put me in brought about an entirely new sensation of a movement that I had been doing for nearly two decades. I did not panic, although I could have done. But I was shocked. Caught by surprise at the very beginning, I felt that I could not remember ever having done any taiji (or even t'aichi) before.

Everyone else seemed to be able to keep it together. In those ten days I sought help from my fellow students, among whom were a policeman, a taxi-driver, taiji instructors. Whoever knew a segment of the form, with gratitude I followed. Someone tried to help by explaining how the Yang Style long form followed the general outline of the Chen form, but that was no help at all. The Wading Forwards, which I have already mentioned, is so different from the Brush Knee and Push Steps of Yang Style that I could not even remotely relate it to a general outline. Even when we got to the stepping backwards, Monkey Steps as Pytt had loved to call them, I could not recognize in them a movement that I had ever done before.

Like in a dream I went through the ten days with Chen XiaoWang, who meticulously taught the whole of LaoJia in three-hour stretches every evening. I had come to London specially for the seminars, and therefore had the rest of the daytime free. I slept. The learning was so intense that I dropped into a state where LaoJia happened in me day and night.

I had had a similar experience years before, when I first went to Bill Williams for Alexander Technique. Learning can happen on a deep level, if we get out of the way. Bill Williams brought this about through saturating his student with the barely audible sounds of the long list of instructions which he repeated, over and over. Slowly one found oneself letting go of the usual props, physical and emotional, that we hold onto without awareness. His whisperings reached far into the mind, and therefore far into the body, and at the lesson's end when one sat up and walked away, one flew. There had been barely a touch. I went home, fell into a deep sleep for the rest of the day, and woke up with every part of my body aching. So much had been shifted and worked through.

With Chen XiaoWang, whether you are alone with him or in a small group, or in a huge auditorium with some fifty folk, the lessons always begin very slowly. The thought crosses your mind, that there's no way he will have time to teach the whole form. With some slight variations, his instructions go something like this:

- head up
- listening behind
- mind balanced
- weight balanced
- inside, your Qi balanced…
- relax chest, relax shoulders, relax hips, relax dantian.

By this point you start sinking, you give up holding because you know he's going to go on and on. You suddenly tune in…

- shoulders looking for hips, elbows looking for knees, hands looking for feet
- Calm Down (uttered very slowly and deep into the "Down").

And if it is ZhanZhuang you are doing with him, you stay on your feet with arms up for thirty, forty, fifty minutes – our friends found themselves standing with him the other day for two hours!

Raum für Bewegung

In 1979, I was invited to teach in a studio by the Rhine in Basel, Switzerland. It was called *Raum für Bewegung*, Room for Movement. A taiji class is such a space. You enter it with respect. There will be a teacher, and a group of people who, like you, want to study TaijiQuan. The first lessons, especially if you join a group that has been going for a while, may be a little tense. Slowly you realize that this learning situation is an unusual one. You learn at your own speed, whatever else others in the group are doing. One class can contain people at all stages of experience. Each person is working for themselves, learning and refining what they have so far absorbed. The standards are your own.

In our classes in London the setting is an aikido dojo. A fine place for taiji. The talk is quite lively before we start the lesson, during the break between the two sessions, and afterwards. During the course of the lesson it is very quiet, the attention inward. We are all training together on the same moves, but each of us is treading our own path. But it is not lonely, as it can be when you train alone. For one thing, without our being conscious of it, there is being nurtured a comfortable abode, a macro-dantian, containing all of us. Here too there are qi roads connecting each of us to one another. This is why the concentration in the class may be less effortful. We link to the Universal Pole which we all are. We take of it, we give to it. We are building a Macro-Wave together!

Now, this wave, it is for riding. Do not cling to your tiny patch, your taiji, your Pound Mortar. Each person's effort performed with goodwill gives energy to another. We help each other to learn. What we are attempting in Chentaiji, be it the fundamental practices of ZhanZhuang and Chansigong, or basic moves like Wading Forwards and Step Back Whirling, or any of the stances in any of the forms: these are in actual fact very difficult. Master Chen has been known to say, "If people know how difficult, they will not want to try." So we need each other; our own practice is fortified by everyone's effort. Just think, if we can absorb what the teacher says to each person in the class at different moments, how much we will have learnt in a single lesson. So do not withdraw thinking, "Oh! The teacher is helping him and not me." Chen XiaoWang insists that we observe each other being corrected. He says, "One person's question, every person's question!" Note all the questions; follow, as much as you can, someone else being adjusted; collect all the answers you can, every time. Stay connected; afterwards, practise on your own.

Apprenticeship

In speaking of my early years of TaijiQuan, I say that I was apprenticed for ten years to Gerda Geddes, my first teacher. I think that for those years, I simply immersed myself in her guidance. She sent me to Bill Williams for Alexander Technique. She herself did not teach *tuishou* (taiji partner work) so she sent me to study with John Kells. She thought I should learn from a Chinese teacher, so I was sent to Rose Li; actually, the way Pytt put it, she thought I should learn from a Chinese body. Miss Li however was not pleased by the fact that I continued my studies with Mrs Geddes so I was packed off after one year, although I pleaded with her, in vain, to let me carry on with the calligraphy lessons which were at the end of the long Sundays that Rose Li taught, after an entire day of TaijiQuan.

It can be useful to submit oneself to one kind of taiji training and really stick to it for a few years. Having some understanding of one's own prejudices and inclinations, one may be able to make a good choice, and that certainly seems better than going through a lot of teachers, feeling dissatisfied. But by all means, you should check out other possibilities. You might have the intuition that the kind of taiji you are looking for is still not in sight. Then go on searching. There are many ways to the top of the mountain, as Pytt said.

I was not brought up on the idea of individuality, so perhaps it was easy for me to accept one teacher and to follow one way for a good length of time. The Burmese have great respect for teachers. A teacher is someone who is able to share with you their craft, in any area of life's endeavours.

Last month I was in Burma. We were travelling on the road to Mandalay when our car broke down. For four hours I watched ox-carts go past, together with lorries overladen with cheap goods from China heading south, or equally weighed down old trucks heading north, many bound for the Chinese border. The road is shaded by enormous trees, planted by the British in colonial times. To each side lie paddy fields. That afternoon, men and women were busy, ploughing with water buffalo, planting and harvesting by hand, with several different stages of rice cultivation all happening at the same time. Two mechanics were called by a relay of messages from passerby to motorcyclist and on, all to no avail, and at dusk which falls very swiftly in the tropics, we were towed by a tractor to a nearby town. We arrived feeling like we too had travelled by ox-cart.

At the mechanic's house that evening, where they generously offered me a place to sleep by the altar, I watched *Sayagyi* (like *Guruji*, Elder Teacher) give a teaching to his two young apprentices. It was on how to thread copper wires into an armature (I think). The boys, about sixteen years old, sat crosslegged, each at the ready with a large coil of copper wire in their hands. Their teacher, the mechanic, sat facing them, with the piece of machinery resting between them. He had one hand on the wire already inside the groovings, while the other moved about freely. Whenever he needed a little more wire to thread into a groove, the two boys responded, letting out just the required length, with not a moment's hesitation. Their eyes were soft and bright. Their hands gentle and poised. This went on for over an hour; the boys' attention never wavered. The teacher said not a word. I went to sleep with a peaceful heart on the teak floor under my mosquito net, while the lesson continued under the lights of the altar.

My companion Ben told me a story. He was walking with his wife and their young son in the heat of the day in Delhi, many years ago.

> We set out in the blistering heat of the mid-afternoon sun. That part of suburban Delhi was then sparsely built, and at one point the road ran alongside a canal for some hundreds of yards, with open ground on either side. About halfway along, there was a man sitting on the pavement with his back against the canal-side wall, tucked into the ribbon of shade. As we came closer, we saw that he was an elderly cobbler. I do not remember whether as we came abreast we greeted him, as well one might, there being no other human beings for a couple of hundred yards in any direction, or whether he greeted us, but I remember clearly that a couple of paces further on, the strap broke on the sandal of our son.
>
> Thanking our lucky stars that a cobbler was so close to hand, we asked him to repair the sandal, immediately done, and we continued our afternoon stroll.
>
> We returned by the same route, some hours later. Dusk was fairly advanced as we passed back along the canal. The cobbler was still there, sitting in the same position. This time however, he was half surrounded by a dozen or more younger men, sitting in rows in front of him, spread across the pavement, all of them apparently cobblers, strong and tough-looking men in their twenties and thirties. He was talking to them, giving them instruction of some kind, holding them spellbound. One of them had brought along a portable stove from which smoke was rising, enveloping the gathering.

A Faithful Copy

There is a painting hanging on the wall of the practice room in our home, ink on silk, of a scene viewed from a distance: far away, you see the outlines of mountains; in the middle ground there are gnarled cypresses; and in the foreground, a man is running, leading a wild horse which has just been lassoed, or so it appears, with two rugged men following behind, one holding something like a spear or a long staff. Chen XiaoWang gazed at it for some time, then pronounced in a satisfied tone of voice, "This famous painting. This good copy."

The study of TaijiQuan is a training in observation. You slowly learn to watch and listen with your entire being. First you must practise the art of copying. At the beginning you may not realize that the tiny details are important. Then gradually, it dawns on you that the degree of articulation in the wrist joint, the angle of the hand's edge, the orientation of the fingers, all of these are indications of something happening inside, and therefore need to be watched with full attention.

If you can copy very closely the appearance of the movement, change can work inwards from the outside. At the start, the direction of qi flow may not be clear, but if the hand is slowly learning to articulate itself like the teacher's, the path is being laid for the qi to eventually follow. If however your hand simply cannot move in the particular way in which the teacher's hand is moving, noticing this gives you useful information. The joints may simply be too tight; but more interestingly, there may be an internal reason for the difficulty. The hand indicates the arm's state, the arm the shoulder's condition, and the shoulder the hip. And so back to the fundamental posture. Like this, the effort to copy as closely as possible is a teaching in itself.

The arms reflect your state of being. When the teacher goes around from person to person during ZhanZhuang, the standing qigong, the arms of each student speak volumes; the teacher listens through her hands, they are her antennae.

Be curious how the hands are, your own, the others', during ZhanZhuang and Chansigong. Each finger tells a story, for one who can read the signs. Perhaps it is better not to get caught in equating a finger with an organ, it would be too worrying too often! But one discovers the connections of the parts of the hand to parts of the body during practice, especially in ZhanZhuang.

And what about the eyes, should they be open or closed during Zhan-Zhuang? There are good reasons for doing it both ways, it is good to alternate. Closing the eyes helps to turn the attention inwards, to sense more acutely one's body, to better follow the internal changes as they occur during the standing. However, the eyes are conduits of energy; the flow through the body needs also to move outwards through the vision.

Seeing the surroundings as one practises ZhanZhuang can also be of practical help, and not only in keeping tab on suspicious characters prowling around as you stand stock-still in a public park. Once during a lesson in Sydney I opened my eyes while standing, and was startled by the sight of the window at the far left end of the back wall of Master Chen's house. From my spot under the pomelo tree, I was used to a view not of this window but of the one to its right. In the previous minutes, my spine had become centred, thereby aligning my vision, so I was no longer gazing slightly right-wards as was my habit.

Attention should flow inwards and outwards, it is a fine division. Many people neglect the outwards; when the teacher is there before the class, communicating through demonstration, many of the students are studiously not looking, concentrating on their own efforts.

The copying of the teacher also has its pitfalls, and comic ones. Master Chen likes to tell a story of a teacher he once knew, back in Asia. This man's students were very devoted to him, and faithfully copied every single detail of their teacher's movements. Because of an old injury, a flicker of pain would pass across the teacher's face, whenever he did a certain kick. The students somehow managed to reproduce this flicker.

So one needs one's wits when studying TaijiQuan. You feel out a teacher with whom you think you can stay for some time. Confidence may slowly build, in the teacher, in the group. As trust grows, so will your practice. The Buddha cautioned his followers, do not believe blindly, but test and learn from your own experience.

Perhaps the test of whether you have found something you love is to see if you can be alone with it. Can the teacher inspire you enough, to practise on your own?

Your Own Patch

It is good to help yourself by practising on your own, regularly, right from the start. Your solo practice is like settling into a room, you get to know its atmosphere, and begin to fill it with your presence. A room of one's own.

It does not matter in the slightest what mood you are in when you begin your practice. Start from wherever you are. Close your eyes and feel the sensations. Pleasant, unpleasant, it is the same, for it will change. When you realize the truth of this experience, you become more free.

A little solo ZhanZhuang, arms up or down. Just stand, like a mountain. You know mountains come in all shapes, some as crooked and cracked as anything.

Can you wait quietly, while the mud settles?* Feel the breathing. Let it stir all over your body. With your breathing too, it does not matter how you find it. Take a few deep breaths, then let it be. Give spirit free rein… let the breath permeate the bones.

If you have had your arms up, lower them slowly. As they sink all the way down, let your chest completely relax, qi from upper body flowing towards dantian.

Stay a little while, enjoy "the sorting which evens things out".*

Breathing

Quite a few people come to the taiji with ideas about breathing techniques. Perhaps it is because of books on the subject which have appeared in recent years. I wonder if it may be more men than women who are interested in the topic; is it to do with building up sexual power? Some of the interest in Daoist practices may also be due to this concern. Happily not being a man, I feel free to explore the subject of breathing, pure and simple! Writing this sentence reminds me of these words, *Spät habe ich gelernt, gerne Frau zu sein** (late have I learnt, to enjoy being woman).

Most of us do not breathe very well. It is easy to recognize a person who breathes freely, you hear it in the way they speak. Pytt always noted the voice of a new person appearing in class. We should listen also to our own voice, it is a way to know oneself.

The way we breathe affects the entire body, and freeing the breath is essential in the work to establish centre in dantian. One cannot build dantian by concentrating only on the lower belly, in isolation. Dantian receives energy from all parts of the body, and sends it forth in all directions. If the chest is tense and breathing is constricted, there will not be enough flow in and out of this area. When we breathe freely, energy from the chest and the belly mingle, the passage between chest and belly is a freeway. In taiji one hears 'waist' mentioned often. Sometimes when Chen XiaoWang uses the term he is zeroing in on a spot just below the small of the back, the fulcrum of the waist. But 'waist' also refers simply to the broad area connecting chest and belly, a wide band encircling the body, a region that one wants to mobilize.

Having a picture of how breathing functions can help change where and how we breathe. The respiratory diaphragm is a thin sheet of combined muscle and tendon spanning the entire width of the torso. Shaped like an open umbrella, a dome, it lies between the chest and the abdominal cavities. In order to draw air into the lungs, the diaphragm presses down onto the abdomen; in order to expel air from the lungs, the diaphragm relaxes and returns to its domed aspect. Thus in easy natural breathing, the inhalation is a downward movement of the diaphragm, expanding the belly. Being aware of the downward aspect of inhalation can change the feeling of it and thus help it to saturate the body.

Master Chen again and again reminds us: "Calm Down". It is mind and qi and breath, settling.

A Bare Attention

When learning in class, or alone with the teacher, if one is able to watch the movement being demonstrated without thinking too much about it, without attempting to copy, one slowly learns that it can be breathed in. The body's sense of it will awaken. Forms may seem complex when they are unfamiliar, but as the body begins to taste the changes, the patterns in the forms will gradually emerge.

To let this happen it helps to find a kind of attention that is very relaxed, without strain, without desire; a bare attention. It may be cultivated during ZhanZhuang practice. The *chansijin* exercises also, when familiarity and ease have grown, may be practised with this kind of awareness. One can watch the processes at work, noting where there is lack, where there is surfeit, without interfering. Slowly passing again over those places which earlier were noted, simply understanding what needs adjusting – this in itself will affect what is happening. The bare attention method. We may think of it as a technique borrowed from Buddhism, but the ways of *dao* are fluidly veiled.

*Frame and Essence**

By the time of Kublai Khan, Buddhists in China had been mingling and jostling with Daoists for a thousand years.

When people talk of Daoism it is usually in reference to philosophical Daoism, and to what is associated primarily with two classics: the *Daodejing* of Laozi ('Old Master', LaoTzu) and the *Zhuangzi*, which is named after its author ('Master Zhuang', ChuangTzu). Laozi appears to have lived in the sixth century BC but nothing is reliably recorded of his life. Zhuangzi lived during the fourth century BC; his personal name was Zhou; he withdrew from public life after having been an official in Qiyuan, 'Lacquer Garden', somewhere in what is now Henan.

Daodejing may be translated as 'Book of the Way and Its Power'.* *Dao* means 'way', *de* means something between virtue and essential power, and *jing* means 'book', but Chinese has the ability (*de*) to put these words together so that they mean both less and more than an English translation can well express. *Dao* was a malleable term used by many of the schools of thought in ancient China, each school teaching its own Way, but the word is associated particularly with the followers of Lao and Zhuang because for them the *dao*, being unnameable and unpinnable-downable, is all-embracing.

> Perhaps it is the mother of ten thousand things. I do not know its name. Call it *Tao*.*

De expresses the outflowing action of *dao*, nurturing and guiding all things arising from the nameless source.*

The *Daodejing*, a mere 5000 words, permeates Chinese civilization and character. Together with the much longer *Zhuangzi*, it influenced all schools of thought in China. It inspired painters and poets throughout Chinese history. Its ideas were taken as guidelines for governing the people, "If he would lead them, he must follow behind",* and the art of warfare, "Marching without appearing to move".* It gave perspectives on all aspects of life and the art of living. Yet it did so subtly, asking of the reader a way of perception that will allow understanding slowly to emerge. It calls us to *stand under*, empty of 'this and that'; to approach indirectly the unending source of sky and earth. Here is the opening of chapter 6:

gu shen bu si : valley spirit not die
shi wei xuan pin : is called profound feminine,
xuan pin zhi men : profound feminine, thereof gate
shi wei tian di zhi gen : is called sky earth thereof root

When Buddhism arrived in China by way of mountains and deserts, around the beginning of the Christian era, it found receptivity amongst the followers of Laozi and Zhuangzi. Buddhist texts brought from India and Central Asia were often translated by these people. The terminology chosen was from native systems of thought, and it becomes difficult to separate out the finely woven fabrics of Chinese Buddhism and Daoism, or either of these from the Confucianism with which they became triply entwined. The last "ism" here is the school associated with Kongfuzi (Confucius), who was a real contemporary of the semi-mythical Laozi. Confucianism is the third leg of the Chinese tripod, one might say the most upright leg. Its philosophy was the ordering of humanity, social ranking, and the proper naming of things. Laozi's nameless Unnameable was a direct and invigorating challenge to Confucian order. In the seventh and eighth centuries Chan (Zen) Buddhism flowered in this climate, from seeds sown by the early Daoists, particularly the elliptical Zhuangzi.

> The winds rise in the north, Blow west, blow east, And now again whirl high above. Who breathes them out, who breathes them in? Who is it sits with nothing to do and sweeps between and over them?*

The Daoist religion, on the other hand, is quite another kettle of fish. Going back to the beginning of the Christian era when Buddhism began to take root in Chinese soil, it met with a movement calling itself Daoist, but which was essentially a potpourri of popular ideas and practices current in Han Dynasty times, much of it concerned with the attainment of material immortality. The belief in immortals, elixirs of eternal life, and the practices of divination, faith healing and suchlike, amalgamated into a movement with priest-magicians who by the first century AD came to be known as *dao shi*, practitioners of the Way. The word *dao* had by this time strayed from its impeccable origins to acquire hierophantic layers and unclassical significances, a magical meaning.

Alas, practising taiji as 'an alternative life-style' may be a part of this kettleful. Ancient Chinese preoccupation with the preservation of life gave forth a plethora of concentration practices, breathing exercises, dietary injunctions, all kinds of bathing methods, sexual techniques and alchemical procedures. This search for longevity has surely lived a long life. Fuelled by – and fuelling – our fear of old age, sickness and death, it has jumped oceans and cultures; rejuvenated in new age garb, it provides a jazzy counterpart to the more austere aspects of taiji practice.

And Zhuangzi, wild Zhuangzi of the Lacquer Grove, what did he say? For him, "to pant, to puff, to hail, to sip, to cast out the old breath and induct the new, bear-hangings and bird-stretchings, with no aim but long life", these are the preoccupations of the Inducer, the nurturer of the bodily frame, *yang xing*. The wise, on the other hand, would nurture life, *yang sheng*, in quietness, stillness, emptiness, not-having; these are the "balancers of Heaven and Earth, the very substance of the Way and its Power".*

> The True Men of old did not know how to be pleased that they were alive, did not know how to hate death, were neither glad to come forth nor reluctant to go in; they were content to leave as briskly as they came. They did not forget the source where they began, did not seek out the destination where they would end. They were pleased with the gift that they received, but forgot it as they gave it back.*

> Death and life are destined; that they have the constancy of morning and evening is of Heaven ... That he [the sage] finds it good to die young and good to grow old, good to begin and good to end, is enough for men to take him as their model...*

> Tzu-lai fell ill. He was already at the last gasp; his wife and children stood weeping and wailing round his bed. "Pst," said Tzu-li, who had come to call, "Stand back! A great Change is at work; let us not disturb it." Then, leaning against the door, he said to Tzu-lai,

> "Mighty are the works of the Changer! What is he about to make of you, to what use will he put you? Perhaps a rat's liver, perhaps a beetle's claw?" "A child," said Tzu-lai, "at its parents' bidding must go north and south, east or west; how much the more when those parents of all Nature, the great powers Yin and Yang command him, must he needs go where they will … These great forces housed me in my bodily frame, spent me in youth's toil, gave me repose when I was old, will give me rest at my death … If the bronze in the founder's crucible were suddenly to jump up and say, 'I don't want to be a tripod, a ploughshare or a bell. I must be the sword *Without Flaw*,' the caster would think it was indeed unmannerly metal that had got into his stock."*

Twenty-four centuries later Zhuangzi calls us freshly to attention. We are brother and sister to the ancients.

Ebb and Flow

There may be times when practice by yourself loses momentum. You get bored with yourself. You begin to wonder if effort is worth the while. Perhaps it is not the right kind of taiji? Not the right teacher? Should you do aerobics instead, or—any kind of a great number of options on offer.

Pytt, after she saw the old man at his morning routine by the Yangtze estuary in 1949, looked in vain for someone to teach her the movements she had seen him perform, which she was told were called Shadow Boxing. Acquaintances responded to her interest and she was taken to a gathering of martial artists. To her it looked more like a bout between heaving men than the glimpse of mystery that she had been granted that early morning in Shanghai. As she went on searching, Mao's revolution swamped the country. She and her family together with other foreigners were confined to their compound for a year. When they were allowed to leave, they went down to Hong Kong.

Pytt had not forgotten her old man by the water; she went on with her enquiries. A friend who taught at the university practised T'aiChi, but to her request that he teach her, he said that he was only a practitioner, and that he would find her a real teacher. True to his word, one day two gentlemen were brought to Pytt's and David's house in Hong Kong. They were dressed traditionally, in long robes with skull caps on their heads. The younger was Choy HakPang, student of Yang ChengFu who was the grandson of Yang LuChan, the man who had lived and studied with the Chen family in his youth – but this is quite another story.

Pytt was most intrigued by the older gentleman. They both played their T'aiChi for her, and in the older man, she saw how she wanted to grow old. His body had a transparency. He was very much present before her, but he appeared to be breathing in another air.

They asked her to play for them her art, which was modern dance. She recounted that there were many regretful shakings of their heads as she bent this way and that, one move being no good for the liver, another no good for the kidneys, yet another very bad for the heart.

In those days more than half a century ago, there were very few outsiders in the T'aiChi community. But Choy HakPang was a refugee from the revolution; this was the beginning of T'aiChiCh'uan's arrival in the outside world. Pytt was accepted as a pupil, taught first by Choy HakPang, later by his son Choy KamMan.

After her return to England in 1958 she went on practising religiously. To her disappointment, no one in England was interested in T'aiChi! Practising alone, with no further input from a teacher, it became a routine that weighed her down. She said that it dried up on her. As it can happen, illness gave her an eye to see into darkness. She began to read books about China, early travellers' accounts and those of later explorers into the Chinese psyche. It was during this time that she discovered LaoTzu, ChuangTzu, Confucius, Mencius, the *I Ching*. The translations and writings of Arthur Waley were treasures in themselves, and the volumes of Joseph Needham's mighty work *Science and Civilisation in China** just then starting to appear were for a lifetime's study.

Amongst the books in her fast-growing library were works on Chinese poetry and art – painting and calligraphy, sculpture and ceramics. The names of certain T'aiChi moves which had sounded quirky were now given background and sense. She returned to her practice.

So it is natural for interest to ebb and flow. When you get tired of Twining Silk, do some form. When form appears too daunting, return to the Standing Pole. If your body or your mind is lagging, read a poem or two.

An Inner Sense

If one is able to enjoy being on one's own with the taiji, a curiosity about the practice begins to sprout. How are we in our bodies, as we do the taiji? Are we lugging the body about, is this what we do in daily life? Do we listen to what the body tells us? When I began taiji, I found myself fascinated to meet this person who had been me for some twenty years.

In chapter 1, I mentioned the power of the taiji to deconstruct the practitioner; this is what happened to me. After having learnt the Yang Style long form with Pytt, it became my daily companion. Practising it on my own was like looking into a mirror, much of the time disconcerting. It was not all psychological. I noticed that in recurring places, I was most uncomfortable; the position of the body in that moment contained a spot of misery. In order to continue to the next move, I would somehow circumvent that spot. In my old form, in those days, I could cheat and skirt around it; no one else seemed to notice.

Here is such a moment in 1989, from a film taken at Kramhúsið in Reykjavík.

Actually, now that I look at this picture properly, I see it is more curious than I thought. The left hip and leg are in order; this is the weaker side and I am surprised to see it functioning properly. The pronounced turn of the upper torso leftwards would be tenable, if the right hip and leg had been integrated. The right being lax, the support that it could give the centre has been wasted. There is some sense of centre, but the right side's waywardness threatens whatever balance I am managing somehow to maintain. With such contradictions in the posture, no wonder I so often came across those spots of misery!

Many of us do taiji in this fashion. We hang on by hook or by crook; by the effort of muscular strength, we are able to get from one movement to the next. The centre is partial or lacking. This way of doing taiji is costly to the body's parts and to one's store of energy.

In my case, it caught up with me, as soon as I began ZhanZhuang. By then, I had already learned the Chen long form, I could remember the sequence of moves and could do LaoJia on my own. This is actually the starting point; the exploration of taiji commences once the form is memorized. Observing ourselves as we practise, we may begin to understand the gap between how we are and how we wish to be.

The years of living with my old Yang form, doing it in all states of mind, whatever the circumstances of my life, gave me the strength to face the physical difficulties that had been waiting just beneath the surface. It was as if ZhanZhuang and Chansigong were the *jingang*, the temple guardians whose pounding of giant mortars the first movement of LaoJia evokes; it was as if they were standing over me. Under their merciless gaze, I finally got down to serious practice.

CHAPTER 3

Help Cook ~ Taiji as a culinary art

MY PRACTICE was guided by a gradually awakening sensing of the body's internal connections. Little by little, after the initial phase of being quite overwhelmed by the excellence of Chen XiaoWang's TaijiQuan, I began to be able to see where the power was coming from. The ability to discern to some degree what is happening inside the teacher's body, comes from sensing certain connections in one's own body. These connections, when strengthened and brought under conscious control, underlie a completely different way of moving, aptly called 'moving from centre'. Through exquisitely detailed guidance of the student's movement, and precise indications of the alignments which need to change, the teacher can elicit in the student a rudimentary sense of these connections. The most direct and effective way for the teacher to communicate this is through his hands. Chen XiaoWang calls this way of teaching, 'hands language'.

First comes 'body language'; Master Chen shows us with his body a different way to move. Then there is the language of words; he explains to us how he is moving, and explains how we can try to do the same. Then there is 'hands language'; through his guiding touch, feather light yet focused and insistent, he directs the student's movement along courses which cannot easily be discovered.

Seminars with Master Chen involve long sessions of learning – watching, doing, watching again, trying again. During these periods, when we are being taught without words to refine our capacity to observe, he does not allow questions to be asked. Then, after we have taken in as much information as we can, he will say brightly, "Question time!"

Perhaps a student will step forward, with a query about a part of the form. Chen XiaoWang will have her do it as best she can, and if he is in the mood, he may himself show the section again. Or he may pause the student in mid move, and say "Correction!" Then the group becomes alert, for we know that there is going to be a demonstration of 'hands language'.

Many of his students have experienced this method of teaching, some despite themselves. They may have come up with some particular question, but found themselves being given an answer to another question, one which they did not know they had. The posture which they present moves Chen XiaoWang to respond to this most urgent of questions.

Being answered in this way, a few never step forward with a question again!

Listening

When one is intensely involved in trying to carry out a movement, one might not even hear what the teacher is saying, let alone feel the touch of his hands. Having the idea that a stance is challenging, that it is big and deep, we dive into the imagined deep end. The mind is fixed on an idea, the muscles are tensed in trying to carry out that idea. Awareness is often not present. The surprising lightness of the teacher's touch, if by good fortune one chances to become aware of it, can act as an antidote to one's rigidity. One softens and begins to listen.

The advantage some students may have is often due not to previous experience in taiji, but simply to being able to relax and not worry about how one appears. Previous experience is often a hindrance. Early in my training with him I was complimented by Master Chen who said, "Kinthissa very easy to correct." The person sharing the lesson with me said, "Of course she is, she has been doing taiji for nineteen years!" To this, Master Chen replied, "But this very difficult to correct."

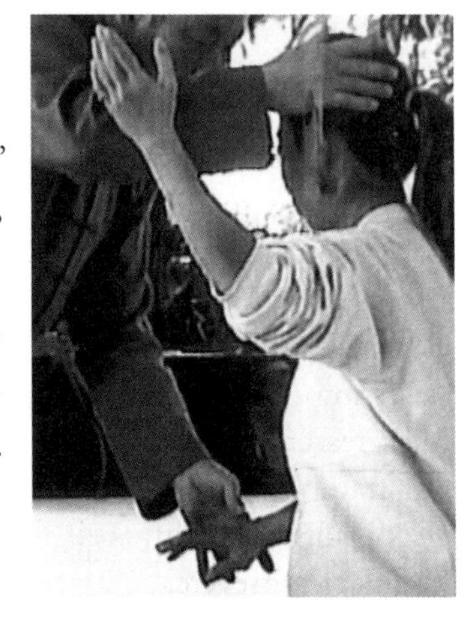

I was not particularly laid back, and by nature I try hard at things I want to do. Yet from the start I was receptive to the language of his hands; they spoke to me clearly, and affected me deeply.

Depending on one's sensitivity, his touch can be light, hardly there and yet clearly guiding. Often the message is straightforward – let go here in the shoulder, turn the left palm before shifting weight to the right, allow the head to follow the leaning spine. But even with such an apparently simple direction as, "relax this spot on the top of the left shoulder", a direction given without a word being spoken – if one listens to its prompting, one might be fortunate enough to catch an unmistakable linking running all the way from left shoulder to opposite hand as one starts to shift weight to the right.

Led by his hands, I moved along an unknown path. There was no need of knowing, the way was clear, seen in a wordless light. The breathing became very subdued. I think this was the result of how keenly the body was listening. For those moments, I was charged from a source that lay within me, a source I would slowly come to appreciate.

But the way is long, and those moments that I experienced in my first year of training under Chen Xiao-Wang were glimpses of an unimaginable terrain within the body. To travel further in Qi-scape, I would need years of practice. Indeed I am a novice on the way trodden by masters such as Chen XiaoWang.

Having lived with the taiji for some years already by the time I came to this technique, I realized the value of those glimpses, and dedicated my resources to further understanding. Many who are new to taiji may find such experiences extraordinary, but as novel sensations, they disappear; what remains is the memory of a possibility. Master Chen says that the mind is more important than the body in taiji training. The greater part of what the student brings to the training is their mental capacity and keenness of discernment, their desire to learn, and ability to persevere.

Chen and the Art of Cooking

Chen XiaoWang sometimes draws an analogy between eating and learning: breakfast must be digested before you can eat lunch, likewise the morning's seminar; no use being greedy and stuffing in too many forms too quickly, etc.

But another matter more interesting, and challenging to try to put into words, is the art—not of eating—but of cooking, in Chentaiji. In the next chapter, about the standing practice *ZhanZhuang*, we shall see the kinds of changes that occur while one is apparently motionless. Bringing about such changes, and recognizing what is happening both physically and energetically, is a skill that I have acquired through being 'cooked' by Master Chen.

We – Ben and I, and a few of our taiji friends – call it 'cooking', because of the intensity of the experience in these close encounters with a truer alignment, 'correct' structurally and energetically, and perhaps the latter beyond the confines of structure.

Fortuitously, one of my first experiences of this kind of intensity was captured in a rather fuzzy video during a lesson in Switzerland, in 1996; the pictures earlier in this chapter show the beginning of the sequence, the gentler part of the experience! They lead up to something rather different, as we shall see.

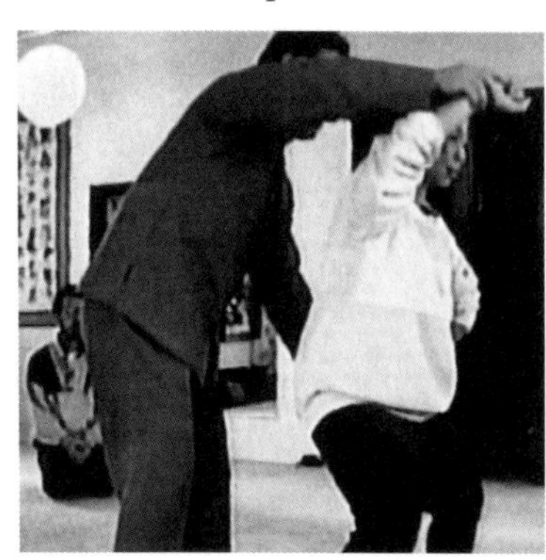

The stance, *bei zhe kao* 'Lean with Back', is one of the more demanding positions of Chen Style, occurring in both LaoJia and XinJia. The legs are wide with the feet level, the right foot a little turned out with this leg bearing the weight, and left leg stretched out to the side, foot placed straight. Both hands are fisted, the right arm twined out to its end position with the fist palm out above the head over the right shoulder; the left arm is folded in with the knuckles of the fisted hand pressed into the soft part of the waist on that side, palm facing down.

People really groove into this big Chen move more or less like this: first they take an enormous step out to the right, and throw themselves to that side; then they thrash about, left and right, and by the time they are in the final position, over the right leg, they have lost all points of reference. The finishing touch to the scene is a wrung neck atop a twisted torso.

I imagine I did it in a similar fashion. The stance is full of drama, and one sees Chen XiaoWang breathing like a dragon astride a storm cloud, or like a god emerging from some watery realm. We do not know, or we do not remember in such moments, that he has worked on this stance for half a century. When it appears to be such effortless skill, we forget that it has taken hours of practice daily for much of a lifetime. He acquired his cooking skills over decades and knows his own body so well that he can see into ours.

Ben once asked Master Chen what he sees when he looks at us. As Master Chen was mulling it over, Ben produced a picture book. It was a science fiction story where a man has been stripped down to a network of nerves. Master Chen laughingly said, yes, I see you a little bit like this!

A Chen XiaoWang correction happens more or less along these lines: he first tackles the hands and arms, making you less tense in them, the position less extreme than the tight spot you got yourself into. His touch is so sure, so light, that you trust him and begin to relax; you may even have the thought, that perhaps it's not so difficult after all. This is Master Chen setting up the stage for beginning the real work. In order to commence the deeper adjustments, which are to pelvis and torso, the more relaxed and willing you are to go with it, the easier it is for him to carry out his masterly task.

Many people in seminars ask to be adjusted in the huge dramatic stances of Chentaiji. When it is someone who is not familiar with the technique, it can be a pointless undertaking. I know from feeling under my own hands the body of a person who is not 'ripe' yet for correction; there is very little substance to work with. After all, since there is a body, perhaps a strong one, standing there asking to be worked on, why is there a remarkable difference between a trained body and an untrained one, or one not yet trained enough, or not trained in this technique? How much does mind, the awareness, the understanding, play a part in the whole affair?

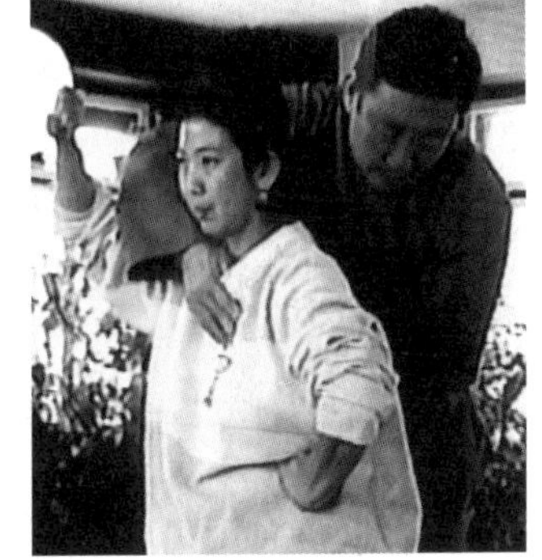

I remember from that first big correction – for that is what it is, and we say 'adjustment' to be politically correct – the immense effort involved in taking the correction. First, we stand and take up a stance in a way that is skewed to our particular misalignment. Then, when parts of the frame begin to be moved towards a better relationship with other parts, sensations may arise of such ferocity that we easily label them as 'pain'. One needs to be able to take a back seat and observe what is happening, rather than be freaked out immediately and jump out of the stance. The feeling in one way or another is of qi being nudged and shifted, caused to flow in a hitherto unknown way. Tension is qi, and flow is qi. One is tight and unyielding, bottled up qi; the other is light and carefree qi.

I think that it is not the correction which stresses us; the correction puts us face to face with the deep underlying holdings. The sensations can be indescribably intense, sometimes a burning in the upper thighs and a searing through the legs which takes away all their strength to remain useful, as limbs that support your weight. Many a big muscular man has collapsed under the impact of Master Chen's 'hands language'.

On this occasion he began slowly, making little changes to my fisted hands, already somehow affecting with these alterations the shoulders and chest. The adjustments during Zhan-Zhuang the standing practice are also like this. He takes, with his two hands, your hands which are up before your chest. His hands sense your reluctances; your hands inform him where you are holding back. With a few very slight movements he can set off a kind of flushing through your arms, which you feel all the way to your chest.

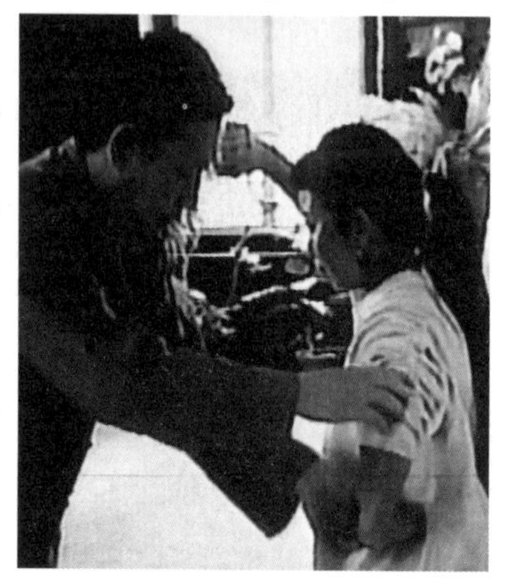

Then it was time to tackle the core posture. After making a couple of further small adjustments to my fisted hands at their respective positions, he stood behind me and placed his hands, one on each joint, where the femur comes into the hip socket. I think it was with the four fingers of each hand that he was sensing out, minutely, the orientation within the inguinal fold. His thumbs bracketed my hips, and between applications of varying pressure between thumb and fingers on both sides of my pelvis, he was altering the way my legs were sitting within the hip joints. Then holding the alignments together, he sat me down deeper into the now more correct posture.

Next to be tackled was the sacral spine. Still standing behind me, he put his right arm over my right shoulder to place his hand on the sternum; the palm of his left hand held the top of the sacrum, the heel of the hand placed to exert pressure from behind. Now it was prime time: the two hands probed and felt their way inside the structure of my body. I cannot say that there was pain, as there seemed to have been during the adjustments to the hips. There was something like a storm raging within my chest. My eyes were tightly closed, all my attention entirely focused interiorly.

A whirlwind of sensations is sweeping through me. Every now and then, there is quiet, as if parts at odds with one another have joined up, giving me relief. Then I am taken further, to another juncture along the way to reconciliation. Master Chen is looking for that conjunction, that only he knows of. We are drawing closer to it, but by now my body is protesting strongly. Urgently he tells me not to move. I allow myself a second's reprieve, but I want to go through this experience; I return to the task at hand.

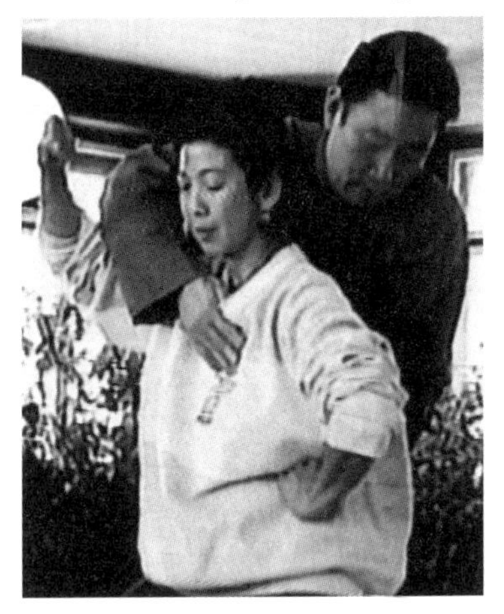

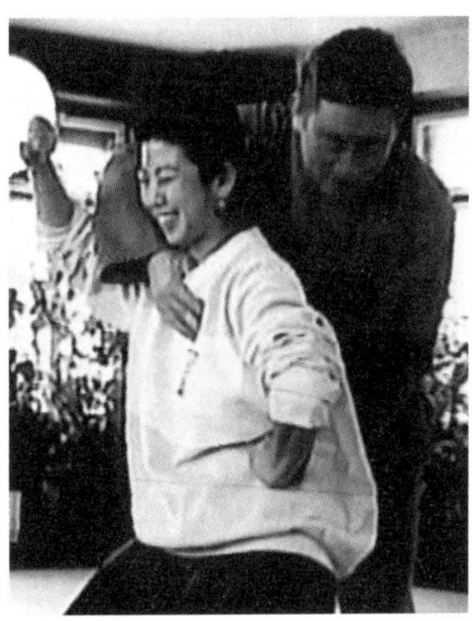

There were moments when I nearly said, "Please, enough, Master Chen." But no words were spoken. Then there came a scene which I saw and felt at the same time. My body, its outer frame, was standing, and falling inside its walls was rubble and dust in a slow descent from all sides; in slow motion an inner world was crumbling. All this happened within me, I do not know what was visible on the outside. It was utterly vivid, and completely still and mute.

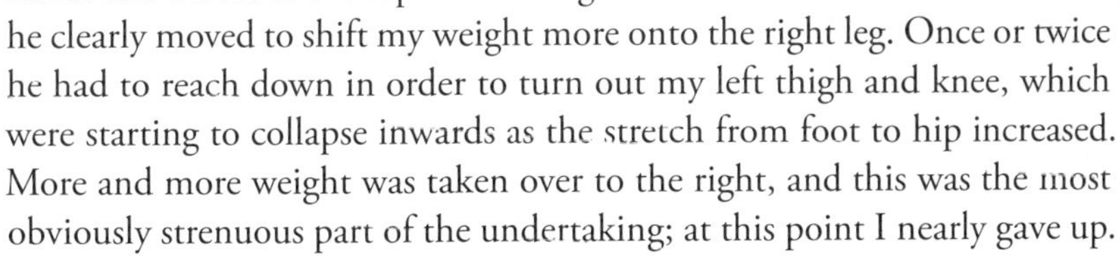

Watching the video now, I can see that there is a sudden giving way to rightness; I recognize the place, although I have never been there before.

Then Master Chen returned to the hips, placing his hands like before at the tops of the thighs. This time he clearly moved to shift my weight more onto the right leg. Once or twice he had to reach down in order to turn out my left thigh and knee, which were starting to collapse inwards as the stretch from foot to hip increased. More and more weight was taken over to the right, and this was the most obviously strenuous part of the undertaking; at this point I nearly gave up.

He came around to the front to cast his eyes over the situation. Not yet ready. Legs shaking and on fire, torso somewhere unknown, I remained in 'Lean with Back' while he returned to put the final touches (for this occasion) to the work.

In the years since then, I have experienced this kind of correction many times. Every time, however prepared I may think I am when Master Chen approaches to alter my stance, the ensuing assault on my fixities takes me by surprise. It may fairly be described as shocking.

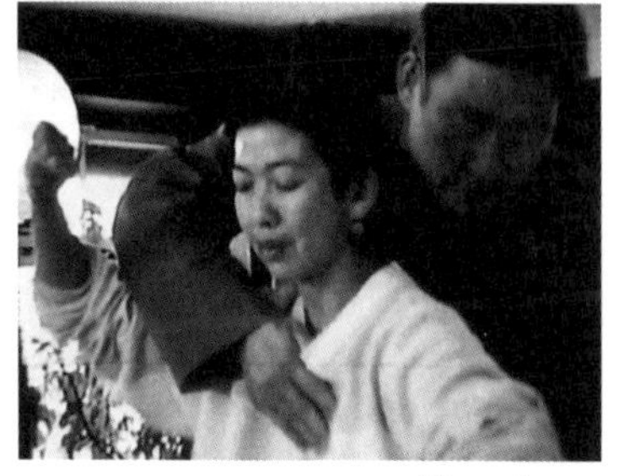

The correction often begins gently. Having worked some years already towards improvement, I may even allow myself to think, "Ah, this adjustment I could not have taken so easily last year; now I am stronger!" Even while I am having this thought, perhaps I unexpectedly relax somewhere critical, for suddenly he is able to take me further and deeper than ever before, or so it feels, from the blast of heat that passes through me like a desert wind. Inside those walls where an interior world crumbled in 1996, there are piles of old leaves that catch fire; I watch the conflagration, and feel thankful to clear one more dead pile.

Here is something I wrote a while ago, about this experience of Chen XiaoWang corrections:

> It may take him time to change your weight distribution: the stance requires the weight committed to the right side, the left leg stretched and dramatically twined all the way through … the burning is unbearable in the right thigh, the left leg shakes uncontrollably. You may panic as your entire body is gripped by overwhelming sensations.

> Then all of a sudden you stop resisting, you yield in your chest. Your mind clears … *"If you can fill the unforgiving minute with sixty seconds' worth of distance run"** … you stay. The body is in tatters but you are calm. He returns to your hands. A tiny touch here and a tweak there at the periphery result in a flooding of qi throughout your torso. Zoom down into dantian … out to heraldic arms.
>
> You are happier than you have ever felt. Chen XiaoWang steps back, satisfied. He announces, "This now TaijiQuan."*

Zhuangzi wrote of Cook Ding whose chopper remained as fresh as it had come off the grindstone although he had taken apart several thousand oxen. The cook explains his art, to "insert what has no thickness where there is an interval," so that "at one stroke the tangle has been unravelled. ... I stand chopper in hand, look proudly round...".*

Help Cook

The phrase is one of Chen XiaoWang's favourites. When he is a guest in somebody's house and he sees that there is a small amount of food remaining in the pot at the end of the meal, he will gleefully serve out the food to anyone still able to eat it, announcing "Help Cook!" (meaning, "Help the Washer-Up!").

At one of our bi-annual gatherings in the Bienne dojo, we announced to Master Chen that we were trying to learn to correct ourselves, instead of waiting until the next time we saw him. He said, "Yes, not wait!" So, how to Help Cook?

The experiences of being repeatedly adjusted in ZhanZhuang and Chansi-gong gave me a storehouse of internal references to work from on my own. Chapter 1 touched on learning to recognize the feeling of qi flowing. It is a process of exploration that starts with examining the lack of that feeling, after the teacher's guiding hand leaves you.

When you begin regular standing practice on your own, say some twenty to thirty minutes daily, the guide to follow is the internal sensing. Outer details, such as where your arms were put by the teacher, are not really of much use. When he grasped your arms and put them in a particular position, it was in order to free you up, internally, as he found you on that day. Another day may well be different. Still, there are general guidelines which usually apply. For example, the enthusiastic apprentice will likely try holding her arms up too high at the beginning, before having learnt to relax the chest, and so the teacher will often lower them; in such a case, it is useful to be guided by memory. But beyond common sense details such as that, you want to look rather for the internal changes that the teacher brought about in you through external manipulation.

When I am receiving a correction from Chen XiaoWang, I tend to close my eyes. I notice that many people, when corrections are being made to their posture, often look down anxiously at the adjustments being made, hoping to remember the corrections from the appearance. I suggest, instead, close the eyes and listen with your whole body; try to feel and follow the internal shiftings. Each alteration that the teacher makes has an energetic effect; we want to experience this as fully as possible, to learn to distinguish, on a finer and finer level, the differing effects that outer changes can have. When one returns to practising on one's own, these internal signs will be the guide for 'self-cooking'.

Early on in the training, the changes that are made to the posture are usually big ones. The back may be so arched, the chest so lifted, that Master Chen has to move you around a lot in order to get you closer to something sensible. The aim of the student should be to Help Cook. At the next chance for a correction, if you can find for yourself some of the changes that were made, then the teacher can continue from where he left you last time. Slowly the adjustments become more and more fine, until they may be quite imperceptible to the onlooker, even though whole worlds of difference are being created inside the subject.

But the abundance of energy brought about by these changes, especially by the most imperceptible of adjustments, is there for all to see. A person is transformed. Every one becomes beautiful, full of an inner dignity. This is the meaning of *de*, virtue, the realization of potential. The power obtained from being in accord with the *dao*.

Self-cooking

In early days, whenever I asked Ben how his practice had been that day, he would say, "Like the small drumbeat of raindrops on a mountain." Water wears away the hardest rock. In time. It helps us to build technique when we take a long view of the process. Perhaps we should regard our bodies with a perspective similar to that of the potter, who works with materials that have passed through the ages.

> Knowing the secret ways of the winds and the rains, he penetrated deep among the slumbering rocks and learned their histories. He became intimate with cosmic affairs and was able to assist the divine process of decay and rebirth. He took the rocks and pounded them; using subtle mixtures, he formed the vessels and works of beauty from loaves of plastic clay. With precision he learned to blow upon the flames and transmuted his fragments of hillside into fragile bowls for the delight and use of man.*

With precision. An important skill which the taiji practitioner develops is the ability to tell the difference between good and bad pain. Bad pain is shrill and insistent, it makes you a more pinched person. Good pain increases your sense of substance, it leaves you feeling more grounded and balanced. Maybe the word 'pain' is not quite right for the second context. I will comment more on this later.

A danger in working on your own is that you may correct yourself too forcefully. You may easily fan the flames too enthusiastically and cook yourself to a crisp. So how to blow on the fire with precision, on one's own?

Suppose that you have had the experience of being adjusted in a particular stance by the teacher. Then, later on, you try to find that place again by yourself. You remember the strenuousness of it, the way the thighs burned and your insides screamed. Well, it would be a bad idea to go about trying to recreate that experience! A correct position, or to express it more correctly, a better positioning than the one you begin from, needs the delicate alignment of many parts. This you cannot find, by yourself, in a forceful manner.

The correction given by the teacher might have felt forceful, but what he was doing, the amount of effort that had to be exerted on you, was most probably due to your resistance, the resistance of your body set in its habitual manner. Resistance also from your mind, afraid of pain, afraid of failure. The situation is inherently confrontational in some ways; it is all too easy to take the correction as a bout with the teacher, an endurance test before a public. In the limited time that is available, the teacher may need to cut a quick and direct path towards the goal of improved stance. Part of the difficulty for both participants is this factor of time; it is a charged set-up. Alone, one has the time to sense the way. The deepest changes need to be made step by step, zigzagging towards the goal. And when there is time, the teacher also may work like this, circuitously. Sometimes in ZhanZhuang, he may place your arms asymmetrically, in order to allow one side of the body to clear itself before it can join up with the other. A skilled teacher such as Chen XiaoWang may, if there is time, give you many months of roundabout adjustments before homing in on the 'central problem'.

Watching Master Chen at work on his students, it becomes apparent that it is very hard for others to judge the effectiveness of the corrections being made. We can see only to a certain degree what is happening, what it means to the person being adjusted. Sometimes I have wondered why he has not changed the posture in a way that one would expect. It may be because it is not the time for that particular alteration. It may also be because he sees what we are unable to see, that the person is 'working inside'. The student is aware and is making shifts towards wholeness, on such a fine level that it is invisible to almost all eyes.

Ben once proposed to me the idea that perhaps we appear to Master Chen like a plate of spaghetti (a plate each). The body may be a tangled mass of pathways, very few of them travelling along an open route. The teacher must begin by pulling out a strand here and a strand there; sorting out a few unravels others, and eventually, there is some sense. The 'central problem' may not be apparent to begin with; a jungle may have grown around it.

It is a long time before one can understand one's predicament and how to go about changing it. It may be that one can change only to a certain extent, especially where problems arise from an old injury, and it may be more realistic to hope to gain an understanding of how other parts of the body can be recruited to help work around areas of weakness. Whatever the scenario, during the time that one is acquiring understanding and skill, it is the teacher who can take one to that charged place of confrontation with one's difficulties. Progress can be set back by the attempt to recreate this intensity when practising alone.

In solitary practice, the best way to approach self-cooking may be as follows.

Go through the form continuously, noting the places where it feels uncomfortable. Do not pause, let the wave continue to the end of the form, or at least a whole section of the form. Preferably go through like this at least three times. Then, choose a stance and stay in it. Now comes the time to be delicate: sense your whole body, sweep your attention all the way through. At first, do nothing, make no change. Feel how you are, in the position you find yourself. See whether you are tense, anxious. Are you feeling cross with yourself? You know that when you are cross with someone, that person is unlikely to be receptive towards you. It is the same with your body. See if you can accept how you are in this taiji position, which you think is not very good. Your posture in actuality is almost certainly even worse than it feels! So be it.

Now, begin an experiment: relax, breathe deeply. However ineptly placed you are, this letting go of the mind's grip on the body will initiate a good process.

With a relaxed attitude, you can now begin a slow simmering.

CHAPTER 4

Reasons to Stand

How is it that in order to move, I must first stand still? Ever since ZhanZhuang, the practice of standing, was introduced as part of my taiji training, my concept of movement has undergone moultings.

For nineteen years, I had understood taiji as a discipline that keeps the body fit and lithe, light and flexible. It had not been difficult to memorize the moves of the Yang Style 108 form, nor the state-sponsored 24 and 48 Forms. I learned them quickly and did them with the sense of satisfaction that one has doing something one can do. Learning the 48 and the Sword in the Beijing snow had been fun, and I very much appreciated the kindness of the man who taught me so generously every morning in the winter of 1986. I had found myself avoiding those who were keen to teach me Chen Style, although I had strong interest in the subject. I happily settled into a group in the park at Ritan, Temple of the Sun, in Beijing. It was an odd collection of men and women, the eldest being eighty-two years old, the next oldest seventy-four. The latter, very sprightly, had a gold tooth that was of significance to my practice that winter. We began the lesson in pitch darkness, and when the first sunray lit that gold tooth and hit my sword's tip, I knew I would soon be able to see what the teacher was teaching. Full of zest I woke up before 5am and walked to Ritan, past the man standing still by the tree (hey!), the woman circling another tree, another woman singing her head off by the wall, every morning for nearly three months with the temperatures plummeting. Then, at seventeen degrees below zero, I headed for Yunnan, 'south of the clouds'.*

The Beijing experience, and the Kunming experience, were confluent with what I understood as T'aiChiCh'uan (both spellings).

What was it that changed, in 1995 when I met Chen XiaoWang, and in 1996 when Ben and I followed him to Australia? Mulling over it all now, I realize it was ZhanZhuang that brought the dawn.

ZhanZhuang, 'Standing Pole' – the pole that connects Heaven and Earth – is a practice in its own right. One could have it as the only practice that one did. It is sometimes referred to as *Wuji ZhanZhuang* – merging with the void.

When T'aiChiCh'uan was introduced into Europe and America in the 1950s and 60s, it was quite unapparent that ZhanZhuang was a major part of the traditional curriculum. It was not until the 1980s, or even to some extent the 1990s, that a fuller picture became generally available. Descriptions of a traditional training, such as the following from Feng ZhiQiang, would have been met with incredulity by most of the early European and American practitioners. Here he describes his training with Chen FaKe in Beijing between 1951 and 1957:

> When I was studying under him, I had to train very hard. Every morning I had to get up at 4:30 and train until 11:30, a total of seven hours a day. The training started with two hours of Wuji Zhan Zhuang, Xinyi Qigong, followed by practising the form; after the form each individual posture and eventually push-hand.*

When we arrived in Sydney and went to pay our first visit to Master Chen at his house, we caught glimpses of the lesson he was giving to two pupils in the garden. Peeping out from the window, I saw them standing still with their arms up, in the shady practice area beneath the trees. Surprised, I said to Ben, "They are standing!" Fifteen minutes later when I took another peep, I heard myself saying, "Ben, look! They are still standing!" And so did we, when our lessons began.

Staying at the Chen house in Sydney, we would see our teacher standing in the garden first thing every morning. Later, when we or others having lessons were in ZhanZhuang, he would stand again with us, after twenty minutes or so of giving adjustments to our postures, a few tweaks at a time, with pauses in between while he contemplated his life and we tried to accept our present. Ben and I had jumped into the deep end, and we started off our ZhanZhuang life with half-hour standings. As challenging as this was, we soon got used to it and before the year was out, we were into one-hour standings as part of our daily practice.

One of the surprises in store for the person who takes to regular standing practice is the ease with which the raised arms may be maintained. When one is first introduced to ZhanZhuang, it is natural to worry that standing unmoving for a stretch of time will be uncomfortable; the additional thought, that the arms are to be held raised up for the whole time, can be quite alarming. Of course there will be aches and fatigue to begin with, but much of the difficulty is simply the result of tension.

We are used to holding ourselves up by our chests, necks and shoulders. There is tremendous effort involved in this daily practice that we all do unwittingly! When we decide we want to live differently, we can begin to change our habits. The mind can learn to let go of the body. There is no need to hang on to our arms. We may find that standing with arms up is easier than standing with the arms down. The arms can support the stance, they provide an ample surround for the body. These days, when my shoulders or neck feel tired, I stand, and this cures me of aches and pains. It is a great relief to earth the body.

When you see someone stock-still with the eyes closed, apparently oblivious of their surroundings, it looks kind of strange. When Ben's sister comes in upon one or both of us in ZhanZhuang, she says, "Oh, you're standing like a tree!" Even though she is an acupuncturist of thirty years' experience she is a little surprised.

There are myriad things on the move. Standing still makes one keenly aware of them. The whole body is a mass of buzzings. Some are collected in bunches, while others are like fireflies flashing in the night. It is not dark inside. In a sense, the eye is looking and seeing what is going on, it has learned "to look more closely, not at things but at a world closer to myself, looking from an inner place to one further within".*

One also hears, with which sense I could not say. The entire body is listening to itself. The calmer the mind is, the deeper the sensing.

My favourite time of the year for ZhanZhuang practice is winter. Here in the valley, the silence can fall so thickly that it absorbs all disturbances. Attachments to other places loosen and I feel myself adrift on the surface of a vast stillness.

It is good to be cold when starting practice. Our house has no central heating, and the winters are old-fashioned ones, the heat coming from the cooking stove in the kitchen, and the wood stove in the den. When I begin ZhanZhuang in this season, I can follow better the flow of qi as it quickens in the cold body. First there is the sensation of tiny tricklings, like water oozing out of crevices in the body here and there. It is usually a warm

sensation, but it can also be a delicious fresh tingling which is almost cool. As isolated areas link up, a tracery of pathways begins to appear; I call them pathways, for they have direction and continuity. Once the standing gets under way, the acute stirrings against the background of chill in the body become generalized, and I can feel as warm as toast.

Now we are enjoying some mild February days. I have come to appreciate this month's place in the scheme of things; there is much afoot in this period. I have been taking the chance to be outside. Here follow accounts of standing practice on seven consecutive days. The first two days, I wrote down an account immediately after the event. On the third day I decided to try an experiment: I hung a tiny recorder that I have for my music study from a string around my neck, and on the remaining five days, during the hour or so of ZhanZhuang, it recorded my whisperings along with the bamboo's rustlings and sounds of the valley. There are long pauses during which I was too absorbed internally to say a word, witnessing changes too fine to be easily described. Now, a week later, I am going through the recordings, and I will see where I can let the words stand starkly, with many dot dot dots in between, and where there is need to fill in, for the sake of some sense. Italicized passages signify memorable internal shifts. I regret that this book cannot include the sound of the birds calling, and the swishing of the wind.

Zi

A lively easterly stills the mind. I am standing in the bamboos, looking out through them and down onto an open field in strong winter light. The wind stokes up fiercely every now and then, making the great high culms throw themselves about in sudden abandon. The green leaves have a wet sound, a whooshing, while the bone-coloured bamboo that have died knock drily against one another, a comforting hollow sound.

My feet are resting on old leaves that have accumulated in the grove, forming a soft bed not firmly level, but level enough for this morning's standing. The give in them is useful today, making me articulate my feet and legs as they search for the rooting.

I go straight inside, for the pull-push wind has cocooned me.

Without thought, the arms have already taken their resting position, palms before the diaphragm. My mind immediately scans the body, once over, lightly. I begin to settle down into a 'sitting' position, as though in a harness. I notice that as I lower my centre of gravity, from the chest to the belly, the weight slides forwards off the right thigh and knee, rather than straight downwards to the foot. The right hip joint is tensed, making the leg brace itself against the ground. The effect of this is a tightness on the right side of my upper spine, and a waywardness of my right shoulder.

This is the general pattern that I often find, when I first look inside. It comes from early years of weakness on the left side of the body. The right side took on the task of keeping the body upright, bracing through the right leg; the left side, weaker but gentler, prefers to slumber.

I hear Bill Williams' directions from long ago: "Once again, we can safely assume, we have been stiffening our necks, we have been pulling our heads backwards and down, we have been shortening and narrowing our backs, and now we have a chance to stop."

The beauty of ZhanZhuang practice is first and foremost the stopping, coming to a standstill, time to look and see what is happening in my mind and my body.

"There's no hurry, there's no one to please, the less I know and the less I care, all those wrong pulls that I've been unknowingly generating can start to unravel…".

The wind does the unravelling. So many sounds, so varied, wash over me. I open my eyes for a brief moment and gaze up at the tossing heads of bamboo, and am carried back to China, more than twenty years ago: I had lain in a bamboo grove where the dappled light had warmed me on a winter's day in

the far southwest of Yunnan. Today, here in this singing valley in Lunigiana, the wind has a bite. I note that I am still a little cold, and immediately realize that my chest is holding itself aloft. I breathe easier, and feel the shoulders sink further; the arms begin to let go of the shape they have been holding. They now find a gentle twining; I feel it from the upper back and along the arms, the merest rotation through to the hands, and the fingers immediately begin to warm.

Z2

I head for the bamboos once again, today with the winter sun just past its highest point. I remember yesterday's twinge in the left knee as I came up the terraces to the house and remind myself that I must not push myself too much, as I am only now getting back into serious practice after last year's 'mishap'.

The clump I am heading for is the one planted to hide a little garage built by the previous owner; I objected to its corrugated-iron appearance and fancied a screen of bamboo. We planted bamboos out of pots from the local nursery, three each on two sides of it, having painted the outside of the garage a rich golden yellow. In Maggie Keswick's wonderful book, *The Chinese Garden*, there is a picture of bamboos before a wall painted such a colour, in an old garden somewhere in China.* In the nearly two decades since we have lived in this valley, the bamboo has become a grove, and the house which is called *I Prati Sereni* we now should call *I Prati Perduti*, the lost fields, although they are more serene than ever. Among the bamboo is a black kind which disappears at dusk, leaving only green leaves floating.

It is quiet in here today. Birds flit about in the trees below; I spot the robin. As I look for the place where I stood yesterday, I think how funny it is that we like to go back to the same spot, just like animals. The thick pile of leaves provides an adjustable surface, and I settle down.

Immediately a breeze picks up, but today it is light and only makes the leaves rustle and whisper. The light dances against my closed eyelids, silver with gold flashes.

The first thing I note is the feeling of my chest hanging forwards on the right. Ah, the overhanging cliff sensation! There is not so much a bracing in the leg, yesterday's standing was of help. Today I notice a swivel of my torso towards the right, which makes me sag forwards in this direction. I trace it back down to the left hip; I can feel the ilium rotated clockwise, and see in my mind's eye the way a person looks when they swivel to one side as they walk, swinging the hip around.

My attention goes down to the feet. The sole of the left foot is uneven in its placement. Rather than the feel of contact through heel, the ball of the foot and all five toes, the pressure is inwards to the big toe: it feels as though it's falling into a hole! Now, could I have chosen a bad spot to stand on? Something tells me it is not the fault of the spot.

My left sacroiliac. The bane of my life (at least, one of them). When this joint, which is not like other joints, is out of true, it wonks that entire side. Depending on the degree of misalignment, there can be pain. Today, I would only have noticed it at moments, for example in the slight tendency to approach the kitchen sink at an angle, rather than square on.

Now I look for a pegging down on the back corner of the left heel.

Mindful that I need to relax, I let go of the effort. I hear dry twigs of bamboo breaking off in the wind which has got up. Ah, if only I could break off bits of myself. I hear Master Chen say, "No body perfect!"

Z3

As I step out, the Red Admiral greets me, out from its hibernation on a sunny and calm day. While putting on my shoes I even glance at Fedele's slit in the stone wall, from where he peeped out daily last summer, though it must be way too early for the snakes to wake up. I wonder how deep into the hillside their tunnels go.

The weeping willows are showing a tender green, the basal leaves of the leaf buds already curling open. Bamboos welcome me. Yesterday I cleared a lot of dead culms, some twenty feet high; once it has died back, and has let go of the underground rhizome network

that is spread horizontally some six inches below the surface, the dry bamboo stock becomes light and all twenty feet of it come up with a small tug. This little spot facing south is becoming a room of my own.

The far edge of the field below, and the north facing slope of the hills opposite where the valley floor rises, still bear last night's frost. A woodpecker across the valley calls me to attention.

Today I have a voice recorder hanging on a string around my neck, an experiment.

Distant cow bells.

Arms warming… leaves rustling… silver flash……

Elbows to waist… weight to feet… soften right pressing… chest sinking.

Arms slowly up……

Let whole body breathe… calm down.

Wayward left ilium… big toe, left, down a slope.

Head up, listening behind……

The way down the back… its left bank all clogged up.

Left thigh falling in… left arm, lower arm… characteristic drooping.

Rustling qi down the back.

Left shoulder blade, lower edge, hooked up…debris.

Qi flowing down the back.

Baihui [One Hundred Joinings, crown of head] up, open… Qi road, big road, down the back.

Little bits of debris being pulled into mid-stream.

Left side of pelvis… drawing in to mid-line. Left arm begins to join up.

Chest sinking……

Mauves against my eyelids… shot with light.

Big toe lightening, left side.

Lower thigh, a little rotating out.

A moment of full sun on the face, then cloudy mauves.

Left side of abdomen… less pressure, more parallel, not curving in, not so much.

Clinging to right bank, down the back.

Looking for parallel hips. Still too much weight on left foot, outer edge.

Drop down the back. Left side of harness coming into play. Let go right hip joint, let go its grabbing. Sit down.

More debris down the back, flowing along.

Pressure on the outside of the left thigh, near the knee… pushing outwards; that's where the pain was last year. Ilium out of true, thigh the same… pushed out and trying to pull in towards the inside of the left knee, so the pain there, yesterday. Left side of stomach, also twinges.

Left shoulder now opening. Left arm opening. Pressure lessening on left side of neck.

Left arm still a little caught on a branch.

Flashes on the face, against the eyes.

Meandering stream down the back.

Stomach easing out.

Looking for a pegging down, outside of left heel… sit down.

Arms now wandered up to chest height, from waist height. Lower them, level to the bottom of the rib cage.

Open the lower back! Not tucking under. Looking for the back left corner of the pelvic girdle. Thigh opening, weight in the heel, outer left.

Each adjustment needs time, to be absorbed into the whole picture. One change affects all parts.

Head up, qi down the back.

Qi from chest to palms. Upper back filling, back of the lungs.

Rounding, filling: back – arms – palms: one ball. Peng.

Easy breathing.

Two sides of body, two hands, arms, like two different babies. Right side plump legs, open smile. Left side… decrepit baby. *Poverina.*

Eyes open. Silvery light in the valley. No more frost on the north-facing slope of the southern hills. Shrub bamboo in the lower field… horizontal slivers of silver.

Arms slowly slowly down.

Woodpecker… attention.

As much as I can… letting go of the debris.

Flowing down into the earth, healing earth, accepting all.

Z4

This morning upon waking up from a deep and long sleep, I immediately noticed the absence of pain around the left iliac crest. Yesterday, as I was walking down to the bamboos, I had been thinking ruefully, 'Ilium Irk'.

Today's standing is indoors, at my old ZhanZhuang spot by the long window of our bedroom, looking down the terraces and over to the other side of the valley. The weeping willows' spring green is fuller today. In the winter, the bare branches hang in glinting cords, which the wild easterlies whip into an electric frenzy.

I see that the notes on the standings so far give no indication of the long stretches in between the objects of attention, the out-of-time spans of 'working inside'. I wonder if I will slowly be able to give more of a picture of "spontaneous dynamic patterns in a perpetual dance".*

Chimes sound on the balcony outside my window.

The parting of feet. The breath.

Left toes tense. Left side of pelvis… hooked up. Weight too much on right side – I'm centred over the right, head on the right side. Left side of lower lumbar spine is lifted up, throwing me onto my right.

Sheep bells.

Looking for centre line down the back… let go this hanging onto the right pillar.

Relax stomach, sink the stomach. Shoulders rounding, chest sinking.

Pain on inside of left wrist, alongside the lower arm.

Head fallen over on the right side, bring it back… head a little more up.

Still no feeling of centre line, head too much on right.

Left side not in pain at the moment. Top of dorsal spine, that hump, pushing forwards and rightwards. Come back to it, lean back into it.

Face upwards for a little bit… connect neck, cervical spine, come back over dorsal spine. Now head more straight, open the eyes, gaze forwards. Down on the willows. Woodpecker just now calling me back. (7 minutes 40)

Left toes still scrunched, relax *yongquan* [Bubbling Spring, slightly inward from the transverse metatarsal arch].

Lower back, pelvis, left ilium area, still lifted up. Sit down left side, look for back corner of harness… relax the diaphragm, sink the stomach. Relax the right hip joint.

Looking for *mingmen* [Gate of Life, between the kidneys]. *Mingmen*, and kidneys parallel!

Left side of rib cage… needs to peg down on the outside… through sitting down in left hip, through the left thigh rotating outwards, away from falling towards the inside of the knee. Relax right hip, sit down left side.

Bring head back to top of spine. Two sides of the waist, two sides of the torso, looking to be parallel. Chest, upper body… over lower body.

Two hands come up… elbows sink, hands rise, whole body breathing. (12m16)

Listen! The cow bells. Deep breaths.

Hands come to rest, diaphragm height. Rosy reds behind my eyelids.

Drawing left thigh in, tucking it back into hip socket… opens left chest and left arm… less drooping.

Weight now in left foot moving more to the outside, not pressing in on the big toe.

Left shoulder girdle feels quite nice, unusually!

Right arm, upper arm… twining through lower arm… let the wrist join, not banked! Flowing to fingers… fourth finger not joining. Relax upper arm, the outer top of the arm. Twining, let it wind through.

Relax right thumb… the web between thumb and forefinger, like the web between upper arm and breast. Inside of right lower arm aching.

Yield back in the neck, that hump, lean back into it. Relax left side of chest, sit down left, thighs parallel. Let go right thigh, hip joint.

Relax dantian. Whole body breathing.

Still the right arm is a little caught. Pain in the wrist… relax chest. Sit down into harness, head up. Aching top of upper arm, right side. Relax rib cage, let go the breathing.

Chimes calling, carrying me away.

Bill Williams: "two shoulders sailing away, off the spine, off the edge of the table". Let myself lie on the table.

Crown of the head up, qi flowing down the back.

Searching out Heaven's Pole through *baihui*… flow on down through the body. Two sides equal, looking to be equal. Two parallel banks each side of the spine… flow down the middle. Two sides join. Flowing towards the middle. Got caught on left side, left shoulder blade.

Again, left ilium looking for its lowest point in the harness.

Chimes reminding me to let myself be carried. Equalizing the pressure in the feet, today standing on wooden floor. As I sit down, lowering myself, weight goes into the left heel, outer edge… pressure in the foot lessens.

Hands have now come up, breast height.

Relax inside the shoulders, two parallel lines down the front: inside of shoulder to breast, down over the rib cage, both sides.

Now feeling caught on the left side of neck, hooked onto the left bank. Let go left breast: right side of rib cage balloons out. (24m)

Something soft and stretchy… elastic… very soft fibres arising from, or attached to, the under-side of the rib cage, its lower rim. It rises slightly up under the sternum, inside the chest. I look for its lower attachments. Something like a parachute, elongated, attached along its upper rim, and its lower edge. The left ilium is too hoiked up, let it sink back. Like a parachute sinking down. As soon as I sink down, the top billows more fully, more evenly.

Now I feel the sacroiliac, left side.

The upper part of the parachute… billowing out through the arms, attaching to the lower edge of each hand.

Left hand a little drooping, come more close, fingers closer to chest.

Qi from chest flowing along the arms. Settle back.

Now, lower part of parachute is stretching… not oval, more rectangular. Rectilinear. Jade water.*

Lower part now finding its attachments, in the pelvic basin. Wonky basin. Sit down left side, let go right side. Lean back against the Pole. (29m)

Tally the four corners.

I open eyes and see my two hands more like each other, two friendly babies, chubby fingers, thumbs attentive. Fourth finger of left hand a little forlorn. Lean back, close the eyes.

Relax the chest, soften the rib cage. Relax sternum. Left shoulder blade, lower edge, joining the current down the middle. Two sides… lower rims of shoulder blades… come together, flow down the back.

Orangy reds to purply reds. Palms move closer, towards lower rib cage.

Forgetting, losing……

Woodpecker.

Now more womb-like. Cocooned.

Left thigh is still working, rotating out from the hip joint, freeing left side of abdomen, easing the stomach.

Chimes carry me on the breezes. (32m)

Open lower back! Open chest. Lean back against the Pole.

Left ilium working. Left corner of pelvic basin… lowering, drawing in.

Right side of rib cage sinking.

Now move ilium.

The feet, two feet, each in its own harness. Outer edges more parallel. Inside the inner arch, it is free: empty of rubble.

Right side quite even, from heel, outer ridge, across to the ball of the foot, all five toes: equal feeling. And the left side? Not too bad.

Left side of neck, too much pressure inwards – better not to insist.

Arms down. (38m12)

Z5

At the long window, looking out across the valley on yet another clear day.

No wind. Sheep bells sparkling like a gamelan.

I look down to see if the insides of my thighs are framing the front part of my two feet symmetrically. Not too bad. Left inner thigh is falling in a bit.

Head up, and I see the willows, greener still. Three days and they have changed into spring dress.

I can feel the inner edge of my hip bone falling in, just like the thigh when I look down at my feet. Head up. Qi flowing from crown of head, back of neck… the centre line is down the left side!

The inside of my left hip, inside of the bones, left side of the pelvic girdle… let it incline, slowly… move in towards the centre… relaxing stomach, sinking stomach. *Yongquan*, left side, spreading, letting off the pressure in the big toe.

Let go of bracing in right hip. Relax waist.

Attention flowing from chest, down hips, down the legs, both sides. Attention passing down the back of the body. *Baihui* still too much veering to the left. Let the stream be more centred.

Relax both hip joints. Upper body is a little bit too open at the moment. It's okay. Looking for *baihui* and its connection up to Heaven. Qi from above flowing down into the body… warm current.

Whole left side, on the outer side, kind of lifted.

This is where I find myself after yesterday evening's bout of nerve pain. No pain at the moment. Relax stomach.

Whole body breathing… breathing in all the stirrings outside. Little lamb calling. Sheep bells floating past.

Two hands up (8m55). Now chest sinks.

Just the sensation of the hands coming up, how can it be described?

It is easy to speak of the persisting, insistent sensations like the tightness at the back of the neck. How do I describe sensations of flow, now, even with the left shoulder still hoiked? Enough qi from dantian… making the arms rise.

A little blue behind my lids… cloudy rose.

When the hands/arms lift slowly, I notice places of stickiness, in the shoulder, in the upper arm, elbow, lower edge of the forearm, its outer side. The rising hands pause. By now it's instinct to sense where the reluctance is coming from.

Little lamb calling.

A holding back in the arm somewhere along the pathway, or in the chest, rib cage, or in the back of the neck, or in the breathing.

I cannot say there is an adjustment. But there's an altering, a shifting… then qi flows more fully through that place. It goes a little further along the arm, till the next sticky spot.

Leaning back into the universe. Its fullness becomes my fullness. It would all be impossible without the breath. Breath calling Qi, wild sister.

Rooting the Spirit, whole body… to be a welcome abode for Spirit to visit, to inhabit. (18m)

I can see the unevennesses, but at the moment the body is gently finding its balance. Being left to sort things out, by itself. Instinct feels lack, deficit; instinct releases from where there is too much, whooshing it over, filling the lack. The whole body… there is something on the move… like clouds, amorphous, a vapour. Reaching into dark corners… all pervasive, enveloping.

My left thigh that was rolled in, I notice it opening outwards. And now more even is the flow, straight down the left bank. The centre line – I can begin to sense.

This change below is affecting the left side of my neck, its insistence. It aches.

Upper chest, waftings inside the upper chest cavity. I feel the left side of the rib cage, of its clockwise twisting to 1 o'clock, 12 being centre; now more to 11 o'clock. Two sides of rib cage being levelled. This causes more pain, brings out the pain along the left side of the neck.

It is instinct to let the vapours sink down into the left hip... and now, coming into the abode of Qi, dantian.

Lower rib cage a bit sticky. *Mingmen*, two sides of gate not level. (27m)

More wafting of the vapours. The corner of the pelvic girdle, back left, I now find. The back wall of the abode, ilia... sliding into place. Which lifts the insistent neck back, letting it rest back against the Pole.

I notice the left arm is cooler. Relax sternum. Rest the head back. *Dumai* [major qi road down the back]. Shoulders looking for hips. Top of left thigh, move back into the hip joint. Head up. Whole back open, big road.

Woodpecker. Empty chest.

A ballooning out on the left side, backwards, down and backwards into the pelvic basin, and upwards into the left rib cage, chest, letting off the pressure on left side of the neck. Now left arm billowing. Feeling a fullness on the inside, under the shoulder, right side; upper chest, the chest cavity... parachute opens.

Cool breeze coming into the room. Clouds over the valley. (34m)

Now feeling both sides of parachute filling. Now quite equal, the two sides of the neck. Chimes carry me.

Arms – feel the palms come closer towards the breasts.

Now the heart can breathe, take its correct place. Centrally, not pulled this way and that.

Eyes open.

The green curtains are forming, willows in springtime.

Across, the oaks with their old leaves. Bare hornbeam. Bare chestnut.

Poplars with peachy leaf buds, just there, betokening summer, and the arrival of the Golden orioles! If we are so blessed.

Who said, resting in imperfection?*

Hands down.

Z6

Again at the window. Sunny day, but frisky breezes. Quite chilly. Powdery white winter's light in the valley. The light of northern Italy. Venetian light.

Chimes.

I find my head over the right side of my chest. Like that photograph of me when I was two.* Maybe I came out crooked, the birth was a face presentation.

A little sliding and… rounding forwards of left shoulder. Still over the right. I feel my left hip lifted, causing a pressure all the way around the outside of the left, then in towards the left side of the neck; from the lower body's instability, left side of body curves out. And then in the neck, it tries to come back in, taking the head over to the right side.

Chimes. Very soft.

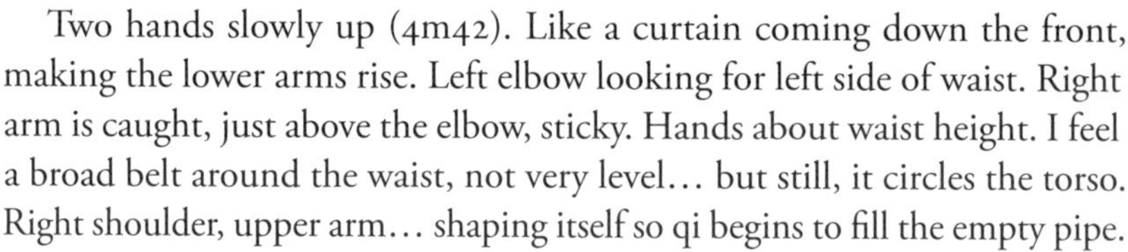

Two hands slowly up (4m42). Like a curtain coming down the front, making the lower arms rise. Left elbow looking for left side of waist. Right arm is caught, just above the elbow, sticky. Hands about waist height. I feel a broad belt around the waist, not very level… but still, it circles the torso. Right shoulder, upper arm… shaping itself so qi begins to fill the empty pipe.

Head is looking for centre. Its central place. Blue in the centre, between my eyes. Now purply rose.

Left side colder, a bit like a broken wing, particularly lax in fourth finger, even in the middle finger today. Like a bird's foot, claws curled in, dead chicken's foot.

Breathing. Chimes, come inside!

Wafting about under the diaphragm. Left arm fills a little. Left wrist is high, hand drooping. Middle finger fourth finger little finger, no flow. Not filling yet from dantian.

Head up. Dropping back into the void.

Stomach relaxing and opening. Little trickles in the chest. A frozen stream, and underneath, it begins to trickle. From chest, it goes down the outside of the rib cage, left side, warming; it goes around outside of left hip; now the hip is more at ease, it sits down a little… this opens the small of the back, making hip more comfortable, more warm. From the top of the thigh it comes in; instead of curving out, it's now coming in. Stomach sinking.

Open eyes: I see my left arm, left hand, quite a bit lower, about two inches lower than my right. Hand is still cold. I'll leave it there, draining. Sometimes with Master Chen, I think he's put the two hands asymmetrically, it feels like that. When I then look, he has put them asymmetrically. Draining one side that needs to be drained. (15m)

Now I feel the left side of the rib cage coming in, warming left side of chest, elbow, left side of pelvis. Now the head, neck, more centre. Right hip has let go of the bracing by itself. Now that the left is more stable, right side can stop grabbing.

Just the breath doing its work... ease stomach and diaphragm. The jaw is relaxing. The bite letting go. Saliva beginning to flow. Lips closed more tenderly.

Sometimes one opens one's eyes and sees Master Chen standing with his head right back. I find myself doing it the last few days, putting the head right back, so that it's more the forehead up, rather than crown of the head up. Not till the neck cricks. Shoulders can then relax. Kind of draining down the back. *Dumai*. My shoulder blades hang.

Little movements... now there's a swelling and settling of an inner tube, its top the diaphragm. Head has returned to being more upright. Waist area filling, tiny movements... filling.

Left hand is still cold, particularly from the middle finger outwards. Just breathe in, let breath waft about... tiny shifts: one place changing, drawing in another part. Like a mist that curls, covering, uncovering.

Chest begins to merge with the lower body. Left side, shoulder... still left out in the cold.

I can hear the wind through the willow... and the pines, the Umbrella pines, they are whispering.

Left foot now coming into its harness, its thousand-toed grounding. Sideways motion, a little bit the heel coming in, as if the ridge stretches out the line along the outer edge. Feeling of *yongquan* as the big toe lightens, inner arch freer.

Right thigh has come in parallel; left side is tempted in by the right side's rightness. Not warm yet, the left, but less cold.

Wafting about the solar plexus. Right arm is relaxing, upper arm. Pain at the left side of the neck, where there's too much pressure pushing into the right; as it relaxes, a little more pain. Again I put my head back.

Just standing and draining, dredging the left side. Chest hangs forwards a little. With the eyes closed, I can feel the asymmetry of the two arms. Right side not so perfect either... letting go......

Crown of the head up. *Baihui* to *huiyin* [crown of head to perineum], looking for a clear drop, perpendicular.

Stirrings in the lower belly… a kind of slow unwinding, unravelling on the left side of belly: from the middle, around the left side, around the back. Same thing needs to happen at the neck, unravel, undo this binding onto the right. Letting go of that.

Left hand not so chilly. Quite a lot of pain on the left side of the neck. Odd that there's pain as it starts to free itself from being yoked.

I see that the two sides of the rib cage are looking for balance, like a weighing scale. Left arm begins to let go. More unwinding now on the left side of the pelvis. Left arm fills, the pipe fills. I turn my neck, too painful. I see my left hand not so drooped, not so broken at the wrist. Outer fingers have uncurled.

Now the web between thumb and forefinger… I feel both sides, both hands. Left side tied up in the shoulder a bit, but decent. Gentle curves in the right arm. Fingers slightly going up: the spiral from below, continues through the arm to fingers. Left side, left behind.

Light of attention shining atop the dorsal spine, this place where there's a break… not so much life there. Tiny waftings. Somehow it's being interfered with. (38m)

Looking to sit down through both sitting bones. As much as I can involve the left side in sitting down, the left side of my spine can unravel; it brings the head back, more upright, more centred. Now some feeling of fullness… so that beneath what is frozen, there's the barest trickle. Trickling through to thumb and forefinger, filling those two fingers. I'll sit it out and see what happens.

Chest sinking. More of a long line straight down the back on the left side. Pain in the left side of the neck.

Now I do something, which is to try and articulate the left side of the pelvis; let it kind of square itself, so that there's more of a feeling of ninety degrees outside of thigh and under the buttock. And now a lot of heat, in left chest, left upper arm, reaching the hand.

I notice the right side is a little stuck. Now left wrist is unbroken, connected up, left hand warm. Fingers – middle finger, two outer ones – still a bit curled, but warm. I wanted to be careful with the left sacroiliac and ilium because of the pain two nights ago, night before last. Now left shoulder blade… unsticking itself from the back of the rib cage. Arms filling nicely, both sides now. Master Chen says it takes one hour for him to fill – and that is really filling! "To feel full", he says.

Peng! Filling from inside. Big, wide belt around the waist, and out to the arms. (46m)

What a relief on the left. Uncluttered heart.

Breeze picking up. Willow curtains being moved. The Umbrella pines look like young teenagers. Strong. Dancing.

I look down at my two feet. More or less equal view of the front part of each foot.

I look down at my two hands. Two sisters growing not in each other's shade.

Hands slowly down.

Z7

Breeze picking up. Seventh day. Bamboos.

Pole of Heaven. Two sides of the body looking to embrace it. Chest sinking. Shoulders gentle, containing.

This cock crows at all times of the day. The sound often takes me to the hills that lie between China and Burma.

Two arms hanging down, left side of the chest a little forwards. Pulled forwards by the neck. Rest back. Listen! Stirrings all around. Whole body breathing.

Stirrings outside. Stirrings inside. Mind calm… heavenly heart.

It's chilly inside the bamboos today. Little cold slivers of light flashing through the grove.

Arms up (6m). Left arm colder, but more open than when I started yesterday; the shoulder and hip are together. Opening out and sinking down, then coming in towards the centre. Left thigh working to open out; lower thigh fans out, and upper thigh… finding its insertion into the hip joint.

Shoulder blade still floating freer. This began towards the end of yesterday's standing. How encouraging, I keep thinking I have to start all over again.

Woodpecker! Where is it?

Most encouraging… left wrist not broken, fingers inclining upwards.

Dry twigs of bamboo, being nudged by the breeze that's gathering strength.

Bits to be broken off, and shed, turning into the nice soft bed inside the grove.

Tummy gurgling, feeling quite at home.

Much motion inside the bamboos. Breeze is becoming the wind.

Cocks across the valley all calling. (14m)

Little bird in the pear tree, the old pear tree with its hard fruit.

Crow flying overhead, cawing.

Shoulders began to flow towards hips. Left foot is quite open… heel, outer ridge, bearing the weight.

Looking for 'sit down chair'.

Constantly working between the two sides – now between the two thighs, two sides of the pelvis – a little lowering, a little drawing in, a little loosening: tent pegs.

And this harness, what does it feel like? It is stretchy, from a nice substance, eco-friendly; not like a sheet, because it has more substance, thicker. It takes your weight, it is strong enough to bear it, you can trust and sit into it……

Is it a form that you make? Does it have its own shape?

First thing is to find this harness for the torso to sit in. Look for its lowest point, which is below dantian. Dantian's hollow.

I notice how the rustling of this tall bamboo here has a wet sound. The shrub bamboo that grows only ten feet or so, with its flat broad leaves, makes a dry brushing sound. (24m) Now I hear the top fronds, thirty feet tall, or taller? Tossing their heads. Their hair! The earth's wild symphony.*

The left leg has been working nicely all this time.

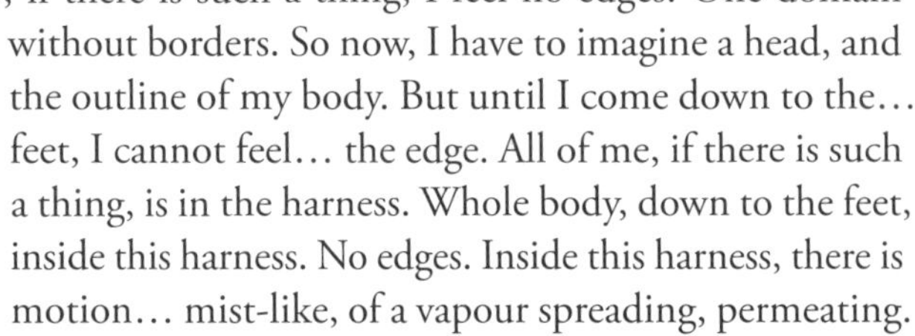

Inside the body, if there is such a thing, I feel no edges. One domain without borders. So now, I have to imagine a head, and the outline of my body. But until I come down to the… feet, I cannot feel… the edge. All of me, if there is such a thing, is in the harness. Whole body, down to the feet, inside this harness. No edges. Inside this harness, there is motion… mist-like, of a vapour spreading, permeating.

I open my eyes and see my two hands. So they exist. I am not sure if I am glad, or sad.

The left fourth finger is a tiny bit drooped, I guess all four fingers are a little drooped. Very little, that's a nice change. And fingertip to fingertip, from one hand to the other, corresponding fingers – there's a connection maintaining the circuit. (32m)

Qi-girt, encompassing, rooting. *Ben shen*, rooting the Spirit.*

Arms slowly down… all the way down. Relax shoulders, relax elbows, relax the hands. Whole body breathing.

Two hands slowly cover dantian. Women right hand first, then left hand over; men the reverse. Two hands overlap well, so that the outer hand holds the wrist of the inner hand. Two *laogong* [Palace of Toil, in the palm of the hand], together. *Laogong* and *laogong*, left and right, on dantian: three points, one line. Relax the elbows, relax the breathing. Chest qi, dantian qi… flowing. Upper body, lower body, joining. Arms melting, merging into torso. No part holds away from centre. Gently contain centre. Whole body relaxed, flowing towards dantian. Now, this relaxed business… has its bounce. Arms not hanging limp and heavy, pulling down, depressing. Vibrant legs, give full support to dantian.

Relax deep inside dantian, soft and strong. From dantian, qi flows over the whole body, oozing into every part. Sit down nicely in the harness. Head up. Back channel open, open the neck. Front channel open: open the throat. *Baihui* to Heaven, *huiyin* [Meeting of *Yin*], deepest place of *yin*, to Earth, sit down. Pelvic girdle contains dantian's abode.* The hands, the arms, gathering, encompassing… gently protect this abode. Inside dantian, at home. Inside dantian… vital spirits of the valley flow.

The big dantian outside, the world… bamboos flashing, dancing the light. Deep down dantian's hollow: listen, listen inside. Presence in the hands. At ease, and awake. See into the depths… feel the stirrings.

I hear the chimes from the balcony. (45m)

Dantian has its own pulsing life. That which happens from the body of its own accord. Go with this movement: small weight shift, from centre to the left, circling back through centre to right, like this back and forth. This circling, your arms follow: two hands come down the right side, by the lower rim of dantian, up the left side, across and over the umbilicus, and down the right again, along the lower basin, up the left, over and down the right……

Hands circling, weight shifting, whole body one with dantian.

It has been nearly an hour's standing, so the hands turn thirty-six times in this direction, and thirty-six times in the other.* When it comes time to change direction, slow down, and hands now travel up the right side, across, down the left, along the bottom fringe, up the right, over and down the left. Hips stay parallel. (60m) On a good day, when the structure is clear, the qi is strong, one is relaxed and at peace, dantian's stirrings may set the whole body spinning. A coiling, and uncoiling.

Two hands rest on dantian, return to stillness. Standing like a mountain.

Arms down.

In a Nutshell

Before writing this final entry to the Z section of this book, I went down once more to stand in the bamboos. It is cloudier and warmer today than on the days of the seven standings last week. Today's ZhanZhuang, without tape-recorder, proceeded so clearly that it gives a useful outline of how standing practice can develop.

The early part of the standing is a coming together at the core, and a return to centre, to dantian. With the calming down of heart and mind, errant qi from all over the body starts to wend its way towards dantian. Thus all the searching during my seven standings in this chapter, where I am looking for the pathway down the back, along *dumai*, the main posterior channel, with its banks, one to each side of the spine. And coming around from the back of the body, the pathway of the girdle encircling the waist, to dantian.

The breath prods the body all over, urging it to let go. This release is a clearing out. When it becomes continuous, a languid flowing melds the body; the two sides, normally at odds with one another and estranged from the core, unify. From the top of the spine, around and behind the shoulders, down the sides of the torso, winding around the waist, qi flows towards the reservoir deep inside the lower belly. There is a palpable thawing all over. The muscles behind the eyes soften, the jaw loosens, the tongue lies down in the bed of the mouth, and qi can flow along the spine, interiorly, towards dantian.

This phase involves letting go of the entire body while maintaining its frame – the upright stance – and meticulously balancing it in all directions: upper with lower, left with right, front and back, interior and exterior, core to periphery. The upper arms and shoulders drop their perpetual holding. The abdomen eases out, rising and falling naturally with the breathing. Muscles, ligaments and tendons are then able to draw bones together where they should come together, and to spread them apart where necessary. The hip bones in front move towards one another, creating a widening across the lower back, between the ilia. The two hips become parallel. They contain dantian. Flickers of movement all over fine-tune the stance, tallying all sides.

If the standing continues, there may come a different phase. After the initial letting go, with its sensations of sinking, softening, a homecoming, it can move towards a kind of tautening, a drawing together that is energetic. Once the rooting through the feet has been established, and there is a good contact with the ground – the weight falls perpendicular – one's experience of the body can alter: it may then feel weightless. The sensation is of the body becoming a dense sphere, oval. No more the feeling of impact with the ground, but a kind of suspension, the entire body in a harness. The legs are as if suspended from above, with freedom in the feet: they are able to choose the degree to which they grasp the ground, the way in which they hold the ground. Each foot nimble, in a kind of casing: well wrapped, girded, all round the ankle and a little way up the calf.

Then it can again change. The density begins to expand in all directions, there is plenitude. This is the stage when the qi begins to flow out from dantian, and in time fills every nook and cranny of the body, reaching to its edges. Chen XiaoWang says that the first stage, of finding the way back to dantian, is easier. He explains it simply, "Dantian is big!": it is easy from smaller places to find the large place. But from the large place, to reach into tiny places all over, this is more difficult, he says. It takes time; hence, about an hour's standing is required.

It is this filling from inside, from dantian, outwards through to arms and legs, through to the top of the head and down to the coccyx, amplifying the back and chest, which brings about the generous stance of an experienced practicant. Qi-filled posture, *peng*. Chen XiaoWang's way of ZhanZhuang is a 'tortoise' approach. Rather than begin by placing yourself in a wide and deep stance, with the arms held high and in shape, forcefully assuming a position, you begin gently, with patience. As Master Chen says, "Natural – first principle!" Daily, you look for a suitable stance and fine-tune your way, letting breath and qi work inside you, until one day your posture is impeccable.

The valley is springing in force now, the little wild tree that planted itself next to the kitchen is in its first flowering ever. We have been wondering what kind of tree it is. Now seeing the blossom, we think it may be mirabolano, *Prunus cerasifera* – perhaps the result of jam-making sessions, its mother-tree not very far away on the terraces below.

In ZhanZhuang, changes happen both of their own accord and because you make them happen. When you become an adept in the practice, these two ways are often one: your guidance of the process is so fine that there is no doing as such, it is 'Doing Nothing'.* This is not a distant goal if you practise regularly. You begin by observing things as they are; you notice tension here and there, pulls this way and that. There is a way to approach the matter where you leave distance between what you observe and yourself.

Much can be moved simply by breathing and awareness. Tension begins to dissolve around a joint, for example, giving more room for manoeuvring it into a better alignment. Such changes are guided not so much by effort as by intent. On the other hand there are moments, as we have seen in the foregoing accounts, when I try to alter the hip and leg alignment by specific and effortful moves. Each alteration like this needs to be given time. There is the action, then a phase of staying with what is happening, when you do nothing except observe; with care, you do not move. These phases are where you see qi at work. A certain adjustment, the tinier the more powerful when you become attuned to the practice, brings about shifts throughout your body. It is essential that you do not interfere with them. A joint is held together, for better or worse, by many connected threads, too many to separate out. Reorganizing a joint affects all these threads. Let one alteration sort itself out for a good while; this is the best way to proceed.

And what does it mean, this sorting out by itself? The qi, as delicate as it is, is an effective force. We cannot see it concretely, but given time and calm, its activity is discernible. When a habitual holding around a joint, for example, is momentarily released, the surrounding area absorbs the initial change. From here emanate shifts further and further afield. We can talk about this in terms of physical parts, these days more and more finely separated out, although most likely, we cannot feel them individually. But what we do experience is the spreading of warmth, a cool tingling, a sense of inward expansion, an aeration, the feelings of a pleasant flowing; or sometimes seemingly the opposite, an increase in density, even a startling shift, a kind of jolting into place. In any case, a lot of sensations hard to define but definitely on the move. These are some of the manifestations of qi. With further release of habitual tensions, longer and longer phases of allowing a stirring to waft about, a new body is slowly built. An energetic body.

I finish this account as the southwestern hills deepen into blue greys, the sky above them tinged apricot.

Bare attention, an incisive awareness, are the tools one needs for deepening ZhanZhuang practice. Attention moves through the body like the knife of Zhuangzi's Cook Ding. Breathing becomes very soft and barely there. A deep silence penetrates, even as one feels oneself being slowly kneaded and pulped.

> I now work with my spirit, not with my eyes. My senses stop functioning and my spirit takes over. I follow the natural grain, letting the knife find its way through the many hidden openings...*

If at the end no part of me were left, I imagine it would be a good way to go. But so far, when the period of standing draws to a close, parts remain, and I find myself at the end once again entire, reconstituted from what was not yet pulped in dantian's elliptical spinnings.

CHAPTER 5

LaoJia

TODAY IS the first day of March, and I think of the Lombardy poplars marching across the lower field. They had been planted as saplings, by a friend who happened to be a builder, one morning while I was out running errands. When I returned, I discovered that he had stretched a long piece of string taut, as though to lay the course of a new brick wall, and he had planted the young trees in fine military formation.

Now many years later, each tree has grown in its individual character, each one moulding itself in its particular spot, but they still march towards the eastern hills in a dipping swoop of heights.

This takes me back to the start of these notes on practice and training, begun a little over a month ago. I had just reentered my daily taiji routine that had been interrupted for many months, with the 'Wading Forwards' and 'Step Back Whirling' of *LaoJia*, the Chen Old Frame form.

I came to LaoJia in 1995 after nineteen years of practising and teaching the Yang Style 108 Form. The story goes that the Old Frame of the Chen family was taken away from Chenjiagou, the village of the Chen clan, by Yang LuChan, and in the course of a generation or two it acquired a different character to become Yang TaijiQuan.

When I began learning LaoJia, I certainly had difficulty in recognizing my mother-form. Following Chen XiaoWang in the first movement of lifting the arms, I sensed the unknown: there was something directing the arms that was not from breath and muscle as I was used to. And although I saw a difference, I could not copy his way of moving. This experience – of not being able to copy a movement until I begin to understand what powers it from inside – has been repeated time and again in my learning of all the Chen forms, especially in the 38, XinJia and Spear forms.

The ten-day London seminar on LaoJia in 1995 was an immersion in unfamiliar depths. The entire time, my conscious thinking was that I could not remember the moves (I am not especially slow in learning new forms). Yet somehow LaoJia took hold of me.

The year 1995 had been a momentous one. At its start we had visited friends in Kathmandu. I arrived with a high fever and to help me recuperate, I was taken up to Nagarkot, where on blessed days we would wake up and see the Himalaya. There is a video tape of me practising by the little shrine. As it happens, it is the last record of my Yang Style 108 Form, for we met Chen XiaoWang later that year and I have never practised my old form since.

Here in March 1995, with Tibet beckoning in the distance, I have just started lifting my arms, the first movement of my old form. Looking at it now, I see lack of internal cohesion in the stance, and nothing happening behind the lifting of the arms. Breathing out as the arms rise might help in relaxing the shoulders, but at best there is a floating up of the arms accompanied by a bending of the knees. There is no sense of the body moving as a woven unit.

In October of that year with Chen XiaoWang, I was aware that I could not copy the way he began the form. I, and others around me, were raising our arms, whereas he uncoiled his arms from within. Now I understand that the movement arises from *chansijin*, twining silk power; at the time, it just seemed mysterious and uncopyable.

Trying to imitate the external appearance, a deliberate rounding of the back, depression of the chest and contracting undulations in the spine – the result is generally ridiculous; it is what sometimes gives Chen Style a bad name.

In 1995, my body had not undergone the training of ZhanZhuang, nor had it had any experience of *chansijin*. Looking at the Nagarkot video, and another from an earlier time, I see taiji of not very much substance. Partly this is due to the style of movement, sparse and linear, despite all the supposed holdings of circles throughout the form. There is some upper and lower coordination, but it is very much on one side of the body at a time. The last years of practising Yang Style, it felt to me like brushing my teeth: obviously useful and good for me, but not very exciting.

The Value of "No..." Teaching

At the end of the October seminar I had a lesson with Master Chen which I asked Ben to record on video tape, because I was sure that I would need a record of the form, as I would not remember a thing afterwards. I see in this film someone I recognize, a person whom I know very well, like a sister. She is obviously into taiji. She has grace, but her movements are rather dream-like. I think the old Japanese might have said that she was too fine, too sensitive, a person of 'too much tea'. She gives me the impression that her depths have yet to be stirred, her power still lies dormant.

As I was about to lift my arms and begin the form, I heard him say, with his special long-drawn vowel, "No..." There were very many repetitions of this word, it appeared to be his favourite. Now in 2008, I understand how he could see even before the arms began to rise that the move would be fruitless.

Chen XiaoWang was utterly precise in his instruction to this novice in Chentaiji. Every time I view this tape, I am struck by the exacting care with which he corrected my every move at the start of the form. The first 'no' that I had the honour to receive, in the initial lifting of the arms, was elicited by my carefully practised Yang Style move: breathe out and let the arms float up, their lift coming from muscles deep down in the back. This obviously was not good enough.

Preparing Form

I went to sleep pondering on imponderables and was woken up just before sunrise by the wind chimes sounding like they were being ripped apart. March began its roaring more than twenty-four hours ago, our valley a giant tuba. Easterlies are furious winds, they can blow without ceasing for days on end. The bamboo grove

is a writhing sea at this very moment, with wild plum blossom flying and shreds of green willow curtain draping the bushes here and there. The pines are in their element. The Lombardy poplars glint in the early morning, majestic plumes against the southern hills.

That mysterious lift of the arms arises from the depths of dantian. It is preceded by a great unification of the posture. The upright stance which I had been taught previously to emulate was actually a trifle tilted back, the chest lifted and drawn away from the lower body. There was no way qi could sink naturally to dantian. The low stance was simply the knees bending, with no awareness in the *kua*, the inguinal folds. This kind of posture cannot produce the coiling and uncoiling of Chentaiji.

Master Chen's hands clearly indicated where to disperse, where to gather. The fundamental change which he had made to my preparation stance on the first evening of the seminar, the discombobulating one, was now being explained, all without words. The interior rearranges itself, there is accommodation of a new kind of life.

The rising of the hands is the first outward manifestation of an inner change: a subtle 'chest-waist change place', a tiny undulation of the core which ripples out along spine and limbs and brings about the lifting and sinking of the arms. The lifting and the sinking are not two movements; they are the visible part of a single rotational interiorization involving the whole body. The legs bend as an integral part of the movement; the palms sink as the body lowers itself into an invisible harness. With this compacting of the frame, the mind prepares itself for the unfolding of the form.

Here are some illustrative sequences from the video tape. I should explain that this lesson in 1995 took place on the day we were to drive back to Italy. I was dressed for the long journey, in a skirt and big cardigan. This did not seem to bother Chen XiaoWang; he could see my posture all the same. There have been amusing occasions when he has corrected people in full motorbike gear (except for their helmets). His fingers go straight to the spots on the body in need of restructuring, through thick leather jackets, trousers, scarves. If they had insisted on remaining on their bikes, he would have happily adjusted their seated postures too.

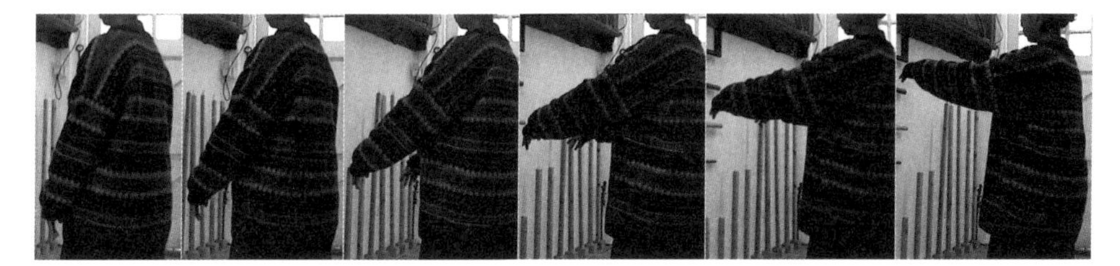

Does this look any different from the Nagarkot picture? Did it feel any different? Dantian becoming my true centre was a new experience. Where had it been, my centre? I think rather high in the body, in my head. I had thought, "Straighten up, crown of the head up! Suspend myself from above by a silken thread," etc. At times during those nineteen years, I might have gone in for circulating the ch'i around the body, micro and macro; but I cannot say that Qi, wild sister of Breath, ever bathed my interior.

First there was the bouleversemental alteration – from leaning back slightly I was brought forwards. The tiny change made me feel like I had been placed in a tilted position. Master Chen had made the same alteration at the start of each class during the seminar. Each time I had slipped back into my habitual posture without knowing. Now I felt him coaxing a new awareness in me. Could I accept that this new position which felt tilted was actually upright? Absorption in new sensations made my head drop forwards. He carefully made me aware of a spot in the crown of the head, *baihui*, One Hundred Joinings. His palm there alerted my attention, which was enough to bring my head back to rest on top of the spine.

Warmth began to tingle and spread through me. The arms were hanging in an unfamiliar way, with presence inside the upper arms. There was a sense of well-being, a coming to rest. Master Chen's three fingers on the top of my shoulder alternated their gentle and firm pressure, showing me three clear routes down my torso: straight down the middle, down the front over the chest, and behind the shoulder down the back. The presence of his other hand at the top of my head steadied a fine guiding thread running through me, and I felt a giving way of something that I had not known was gripped. A large area, middle earth, was coming into view, the waist spreading and encompassing a new realm.

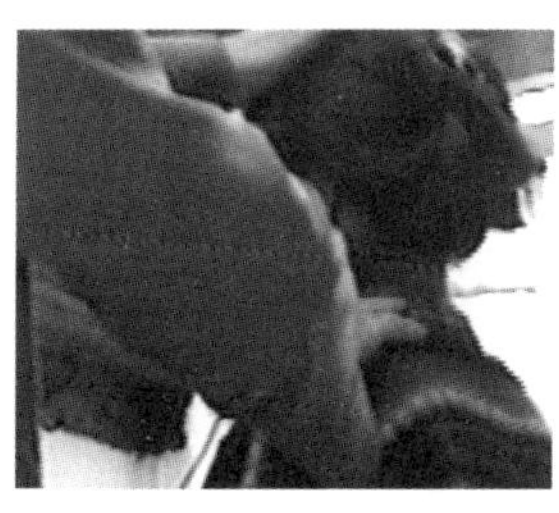

The arms began to rise from within. They got three-quarters, even four-fifths of the way, but then I ran out of core rotation. If I had been able to maintain the centre which Master Chen had established for me through such careful preparation, and if I had been versed in the art of coiling, then dantian continuing its rotation would have brought qi to the fingers, lifting them the last inch or so. Continuing further, it would have taken the arms down again, all the way back to dantian.

In this first lesson such details were unattainable. Master Chen waited until my arms were down, as best they could manage; then he stepped in to make two crucial adjustments.

The elbows! I had never really considered them. All my joints were very bendable when I appeared in Pytt Geddes' classes, they in fact had to be restrained to acquire what was considered the 'just right' beautiful hand, with only a slight articulation at the wrist. The elbows had been made use of in my Yang Style forms, but as for there being a vital connection between elbow and waist, I had not a notion.

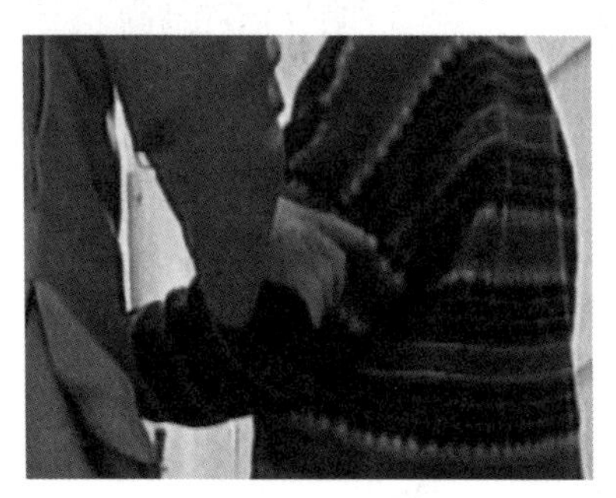

Between four fingers and thumb, Master Chen took a firm hold of my left arm just above the elbow. It felt as though each of his fingers was making a separate adjustment to the spiralling of my upper arm. With his other hand he drew my left hand inwards with unwavering precision. Then he went around to the other side and did the same thing, each of his fingers applying differing pressures in my upper arm. The result was startling: the elbows were suddenly responsive, poised. He returned to the left side and with the same unforgiving grip on hand and arm he drew my left hand in a little further.

Then he moved around to the front and took hold of both my hands, and with a pressure downwards and inwards, simultaneously slight and powerful, he elicited from them a springiness which seemed to come from the back, from *mingmen*. It excites me to remember all this, the opening of a new world.

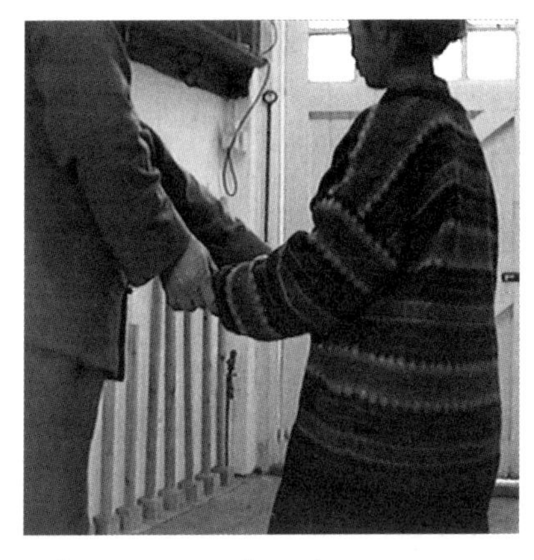

Sometimes when teaching a form, Chen XiaoWang gives this instruction: "Only think movement." Time is given during the lesson for thinking through the movements one is learning, for rehearsing them in the mind. Through this exercise, one can acquire the skill of feeling the movements without moving, of sensing the progression of internal mutations. While I was writing about elbows in the preceding paragraph, I instinctively practised 'only think movement'. That springiness which comes from *mingmen* appears, and this is exhilarating.

Well, here I am fifteen months later, in January of 1997. I see there has been some improvement, but there is still tension across the upper back. The hands reach a good height, and qi reaches the fingers. I can barely remember that pine tree looking so small; it was the first tree we planted when we moved to Italy.

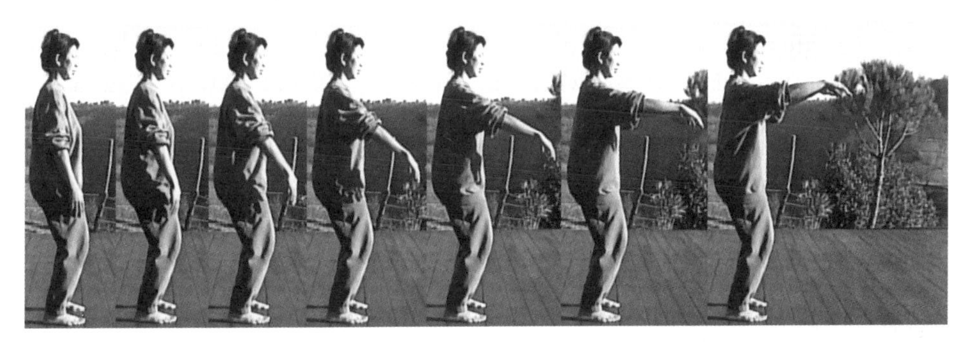

On the descent, the arms do not go down far enough. There is not enough core rotation to carry them all the way down. Externally, the arms stop short of the mark; internally, the circuit of qi is not completed. I can see myself trying to work it out – I see perplexed elbows.

Early Twinings

Now it is evening and the gale continues in the valley; the willows have taken to the sky. Snug indoors I hunker down to think about the almost imperceptible turning which evolves into an entire Taiji form.

The first movement of LaoJia is symmetrical. The arms rise to shoulder height and sink back down. Their rising and sinking are two aspects of one rotation, the result of a core undulation which affects both sides of the body equally. Without this initial coiling, not much of substance will follow. Done correctly, it generates the charge through which Wuji (one) differentiates into Taiji (two or many) and creates a momentous asymmetry, from which unfolds a complete sonata of some twenty minutes.

When the asymmetry becomes manifest for the first time as a turn of the body to the left, the crucial change has already occurred. The spark which ignites the drama is an almost imperceptible turning of the dantian to the right. Very relaxed, dantian rolls ever so slightly rightwards to initiate a rotation to the left, as the weight shifts very slightly right. This sets off spirallings through all four limbs. Each of these twinings follows its own route, with its own timing. The absorbing challenge of this first phrase of the form, 'Pounding the Mortar', lies in synchronizing the complex weaving which moves across, down and up, diagonally, back and front. There are not enough words in the ordinary vocabulary to describe the fine intertwinglings of the qi pathways which develop over time, through years of clearing snags and forging connections, *obrint i netejant.** And let us not think linearly or narrowly. In a well watered terrain, water runs not only in streams and rivers, gathers not only in lakes, but permeates the entire ground. Once the body is well linked physically and energetically, qi suffuses the body in flows and sweeps.

Now it is a little agonizing to see this turn to the left. My hips not yet anchored, the lower body could not accomplish its turning securely. The hands swing rather emptily and incompletely to the left. Master Chen sees that the right side of the body has been left behind, and steps in to bring the right hand back into contact with the left, tweaking the left middle finger (middle frame below) which somehow affects the whole hand.

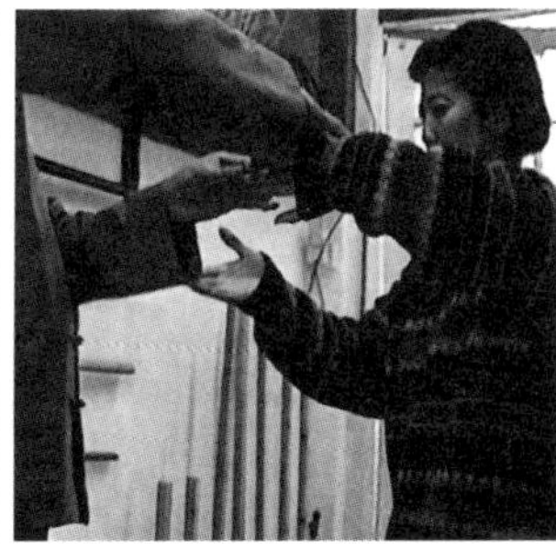

There will be many instances in this lesson when I am startled by the effect of little tweaks. I was a ten-day-old novice in Chen Style TaijiQuan; I had not yet been introduced to an understanding of *chansijin*, which would have shed light on Master Chen's meticulous instruction on that November day. We shall see in chapter 8 that what he is aiming for here is to bring the qi more fully to all the fingers of the left hand. He then shows with a gesture (right-hand frame above) the qi pathway from the right hand to dantian. As I was to discover in the coming months, this initial turn expresses the essence of Chen Style, where the movements evolve from interior loopings, invisible changes which manifest in a pervasive spiralling.

Anyway, with Master Chen's help I arrive (below left, 4m05) at the full extent of that turn leftwards. The next movement is going to be a turn to the right, which will take the body around to an approximate mirror-image position on the right-hand side. But as I try to start the turn I realize to my

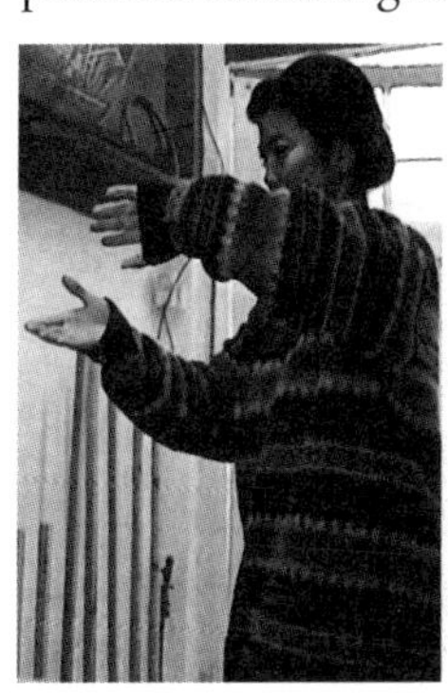

perplexity that I am unable to move! Or rather, that every way in which I try to start the movement feels wrong. This is a remarkable thing which tends to happen after one has been corrected into a new alignment. Qi is flowing, the body experiences an unfamiliar cohesiveness, and one feels that any tiny movement which one tries to make is a movement away from cohesion. It needs guidance and practice

to find the way of moving from such a position without losing the central connections. In the case illustrated here, the turn from left to right needs to be initiated by coordinated interior windings starting at *mingmen* in the small of the back, and at the side of the waist. More on this later, in chapter 8. For now, what is visible in the video is that I make an ineffectual wobble in trying to start the movement, whereupon Master Chen immediately steps in to guide me through the change.

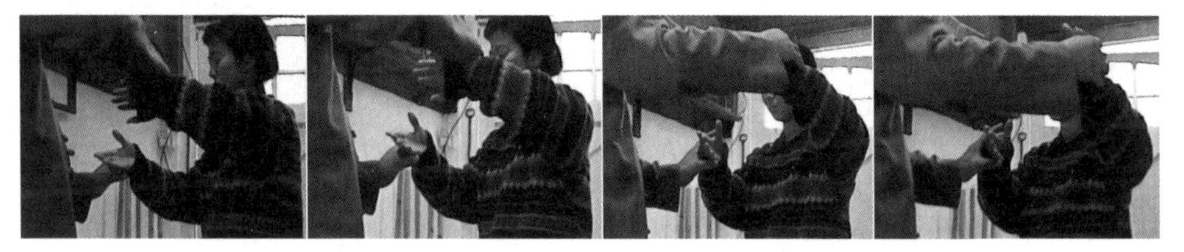

Every now and then I caught some of the few words that Chen Xiao-Wang uttered – *Qi to fingers*, or *Qi to waist*, or *First change inside, then change outside* – but the words were pretty much mumbo jumbo to me at the time. What was not mumbo jumbo was his 'hands language'. Without knowing anything of *qi* roads, I could feel that I was being guided to fill out each rotation of the arm, each turning of the hand. And doing this on both sides made a connection between the two arms so that they would loop around to the right together. This movement, so hard to initiate correctly, becomes perfectly easy once the correct internal connections are found. They are to be sought in a very delicate manner. The error lies in trying to move deliberately. One too easily does too much, too coarsely, and thereby misses the connections. As the arms moving further leftwards turn to go rightwards, there needs to be a kind of slipping into place, a soft and silky sensation along the torso on both sides. Interior linkings create a surface to travel on, a winding path to follow, and once the corner is turned, the way onwards is open.

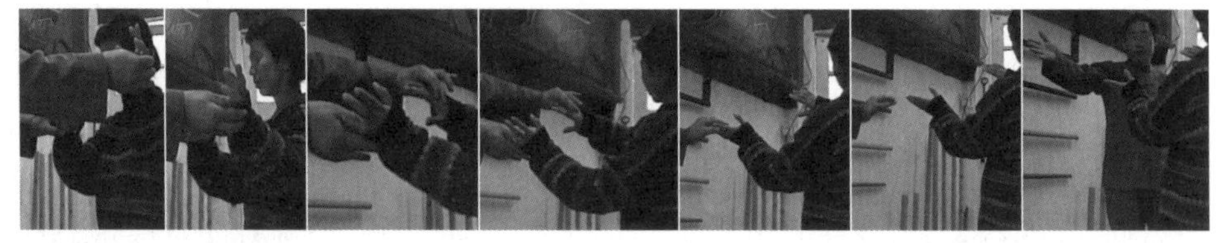

The turn completed, suddenly there is Master Chen on the other side of the room, gesturing to me as to where my gaze should be directed. Well, seeing this spawning of tiny twipoles, I am going to sleep on it, through the howling gale.

Coiling Power

This morning the wind is lying in wait, coiling behind the eastern hills. Every now and then it plunges into the valley with a startling ferocity. The plum tree hangs on to its blossom, and the Lombardy poplars are its sentinels.

The Chen twinings, which we see in the above sequence of the beginning moves of LaoJia, are progressive. They fold in one upon the other, reinforcing with each twining a build-up of power. At certain moments, when one feels the entire body knitted together and can sense the fullness, one can choose to direct the force outwards. This is *fa jin*. The character of *fa* in its ancient form meant to let fly like an arrow;* the sudden manifestation of a latent energy. *Jin* is the internal power that grows out of *chansi*, the action of twining. *Fajin* is a release of potency.

On that morning in 1995, the teacher's two hands guiding mine put me in touch with a palpable energy I had not been aware of in TaijiQuan. I had known quiet in the body, lessening of inner tension, enjoyment of moving, serenity. Now there was something of quite another order, *Ich fühle Luft von anderen Planeten.** It had viscosity, it moved into me.

After the turn to the right, the next thing is a difficult step forwards with the left foot. With the weight on the right leg, the foot pointing diagonally outwards, I am facing in the direction that I had been trained to – over the weighted foot, front right diagonal. And I would have stepped with my gaze in that same direction. But as I am getting ready, Master Chen indicates that I should turn my gaze to look in the direction that I will step, over the left shoulder as it were. A surprise for a Yang stylist! Nothing in Chen Style, not even the direction of the gaze, is as straight or as square as one is accustomed to.

The difference between the two styles affects every aspect of the stance, and most fundamentally the positioning and direction of the hips. For those of us with a Yang Style background, this can take a while to grasp. We are accustomed to turning the pelvis towards the front. In Nagarkot when I pushed with my two hands, the hips faced squarely in the direction of the push. The posture is much compromised in this position; it is a 'splittist' stance. The hips are being twisted in order to square themselves, and the back hip joint locks. The *kua* is not respected.

The Chen logic works along different lines. The form begins with a raising and lowering of the arms. Then the arms twine leftwards, then rightwards. All these are spiralling movements which involve the whole body, from feet to hands. The first step of the form, where the left foot steps diagonally forwards, comes out of this spiralling. At the moment of the step, the body is strongly spiralled to the right, with the right arm twined tautly through the elbow. The turning of the gaze in the direction of the step is integral to the *chansi*. When the weight then shifts forwards onto the left leg, the body advances in a diagonal orientation, remaining true in its postural alignment, its centre intact, with both legs twined to support dantian. The hip joints remain open.

In that first lesson I was far from understanding such subtleties. Master Chen had not yet tackled my hips. Anyway, without the entire frame being aligned, there can be no correct spiralling out of which a controlled step could happen. A core adjustment at this stage would quite likely have left me unable to step at all. Here he simply lets me step as best I can. In this little snapshot of that moment, my two feet speak volumes; they reveal the rigidity and discomfort of the right side, and how it compromises the left.

My next attempt to move, which involves twining both arms towards the left in preparation for shifting the weight, earns me a clear "No!" The awkward alignment of the hips is apparent in the left-hand frame below. With the arms not twined enough to the right, they cannot make the necessary spiralling change leftwards. Attempting to move from this uneasy position, my upper body dips. This elicits an immediate intervention from the Master. Then in affirmation of having understood his "No!" I dip again, as though to say, "No, I must not do this!" That really brings him close. We can see that he has made his point clear: in the right-hand frame I am as upright as my position will allow me to be.

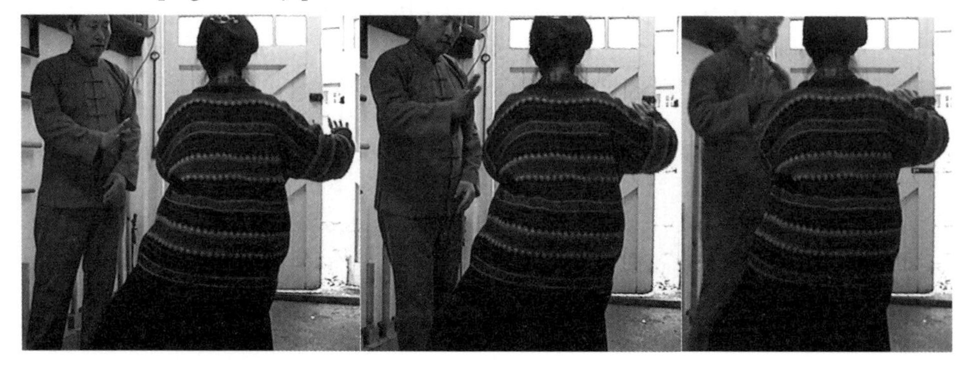

After indicating emphatically that I am not to dip in making the change, he lightly grasps my two hands. In the frames below, he guides my arms through a trajectory, apparently simple but deeply unobvious, which I would never have discovered unaided, and which opens the right side of my waist in preparation for the weight shift. Although I did not understand what he was doing, my previous training had developed a relaxed internal cohesion, in Chinese *song*, which allowed him with the lightest touch on my hands to affect the twining along the arms and sides of the body. The movement is initially rightwards (first two frames), continuing and completing the outward twining in that direction; then down and leftwards (third frame). Throughout, the weight must not shift at all, or the winding dissipates. Doing this movement well asks a great deal of the right leg. Finally, with three fingers on my right hip (just visible in the right-hand frame, 5m03) he allows me to transfer weight, although my stance here is a little too short for a proper weight shift.

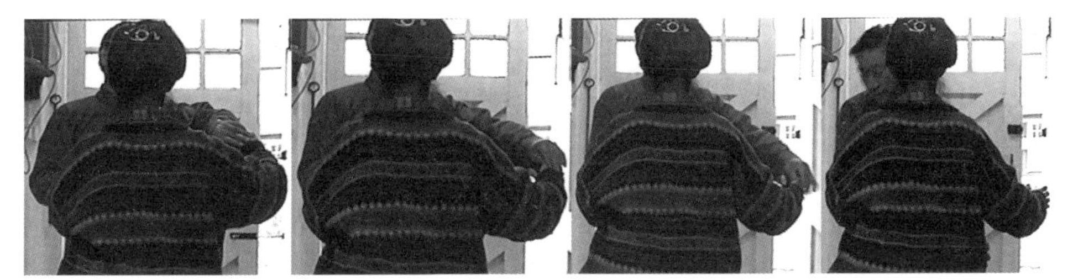

I think he is looking down to make sure that my left toes are pointing straight. If the left foot is turned in at this point, even slightly, it is like an obstacle, and as the weight shifts the body has to lift itself as though to clear a hurdle.

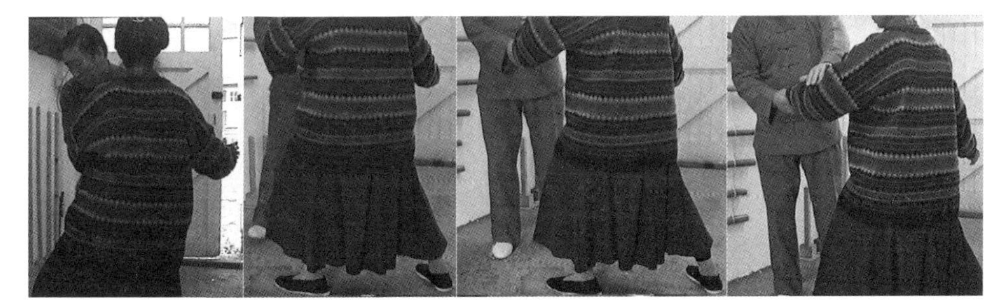

Then comes a moment in the form when there is a significant alteration – at least, that is how it is when Chen XiaoWang does it. There is a complex reorganization of the left side; only after that does the right foot step up. Here we see Master Chen giving me some feeling of this, in the lie of the upper arm. The elbow is critical. There is a release there, an airy disturbance which affects the left side, and then quickly gains momentum through the body. The two sides of the torso open and fold their wings; the right foot steps up with the closing. My hips here should have been more diagonal, coming around to the front only when the right foot steps up (second frame below).

At this juncture the way the two arms are placed in relation to each other appears very mysterious for quite a while. The right arm is rotated until the palm faces upwards, with the left hand's middle fingertips touching the right inner forearm. Master Chen always arranges this position meticulously. The elbows must be buoyant. When the position is just right, one can prepare properly for the pounding that follows.

Even more importantly, we have reached here a point where the teacher is able to make some crucial adjustments to the lower back – notwithstanding that in this position, the weight is being borne entirely by the left leg, with the right big toe just touching the ground.

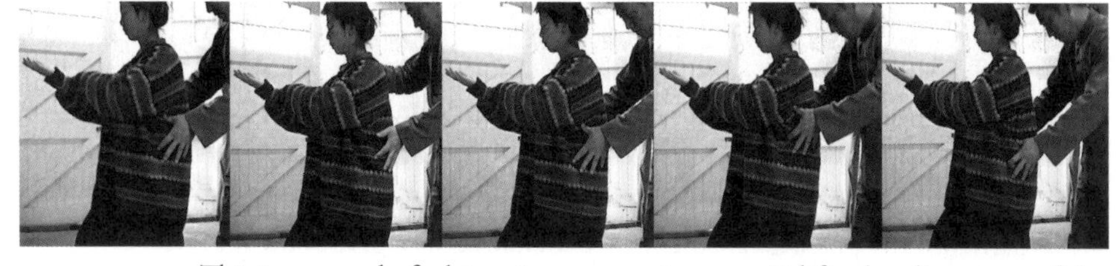

This is a record of a historic moment in my taiji life: the alignment of the ilia is being altered, the foundations are being laid for dantian's abode. The reason that I had not been able to complete the initial raising and lowering of the hands was due to the position of the lower back, which he did not adjust until now.

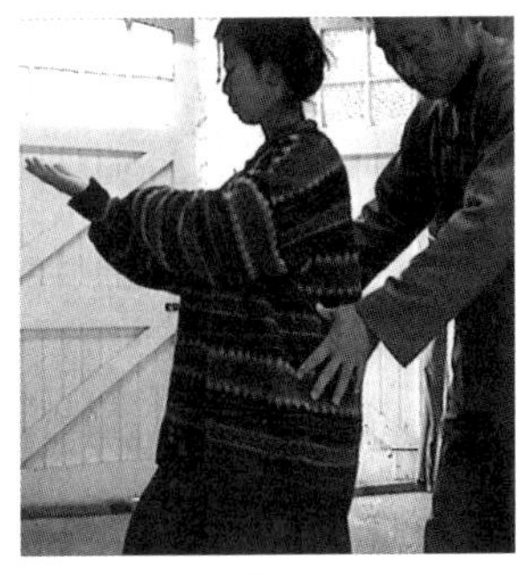

Well, this place is everyone's Waterloo! There are times when one thinks, Ah, it needs tucking under; and there are other times when the opposite action appears to be required. There is indeed a rotation. To begin with, the direction depends on the particular posture of a person; one person is too arched in the lower back, another is too slumped. In either case, the lower back needs both softening and strengthening. A slumped lower back is no more relaxed than an arched one.

At first, the corrections are on the gross level; the more out of true, the bigger the adjustment necessary. As training progresses over the months and years, the corrections become finer and finer. It takes time to understand the correct position of the hips, the pelvic basin, the lower vertebrae. The sitting down, as it were in a harness, is with the lower vertebrae poised, the spine very compact and articulate.

So finally, after all that adjustment, the actual *dao dui*, the pounding of the mortar.*

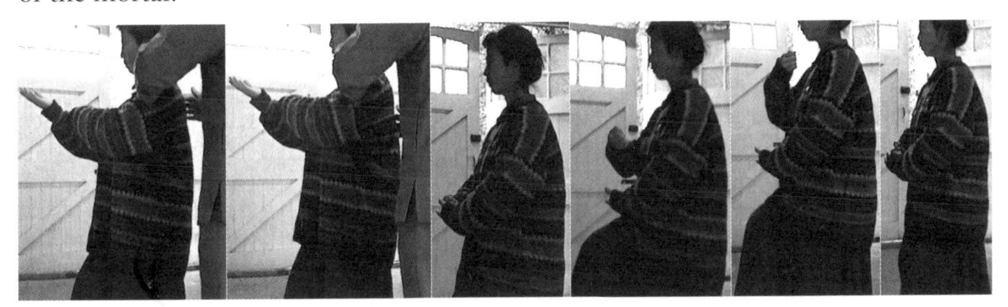

Three months later, I was to have the opportunity for going deeper into a re-ordering of my posture. ZhanZhuang then became a part of my life. As I slowly got myself together, I began to taste the changes of qi direction in *chansijin* and form practice. The opening moves of LaoJia began to absorb me totally. Now more than twelve years into Chentaiji, I continue to find the first phrases of the form up to the completion of *jingang dao dui*, 'Pounding the Mortar', a fascinating challenge. I watch with full attention this part

of the 1995 lesson with Master Chen; every time I am surprised to see new details. There are many forces at play in the position before the step up to Pound Mortar. You may remember the *jingang*, the temple guardians mentioned at the end of chapter 2. These formidable beings standing at either side of the gates to sacred enclosures are often depicted in this stance, with their robes swept up behind them by winds that passed an aeon ago. There is a fierceness, a gravity befitting this moment before one stamps, and the foot calls the earth to witness.

Having survived an easterly gale, this morning the blossom outside the kitchen has succumbed to a night of rain. It was a little wild tree's first flowering. A quiet rain now descends for some days, turning the valley into a bowl of mists.

CHAPTER 6

LaoJia 2 ~ realignments

Today is an indoors day. Some of the daffodils were rescued before more rain; the valley has disappeared.* Chapter 5 covered the first six minutes of a one-hour lesson. Having examined the intricate turnings that initiate the form, let us now skip ahead and look at some illustrative sequences from later on.

I mentioned that a fundamental difference between the Yang and Chen styles is in the positioning of the hips. Eleven minutes into the lesson at the second occurrence of *jingang dao dui*,* the matter is presented to me unmistakably.

In the frames below, I am getting ready to step; I am about to bring my right foot forward to join the left. Notice that my hips and shoulders are just about facing forwards, at an angle that I am used to from Yang Style. But before tackling the hips, Master Chen makes critical adjustments to my arms, first lying the left arm slightly down with a gentle rotation, and then softening the right arm to bring about a subtle twining through careful positioning of the elbow. I now feel a clear connection to the waist. This is how he usually proceeds; initial adjustments to the hands and arms have an easing effect on the student, who feels the rightness of the position starting to emerge.

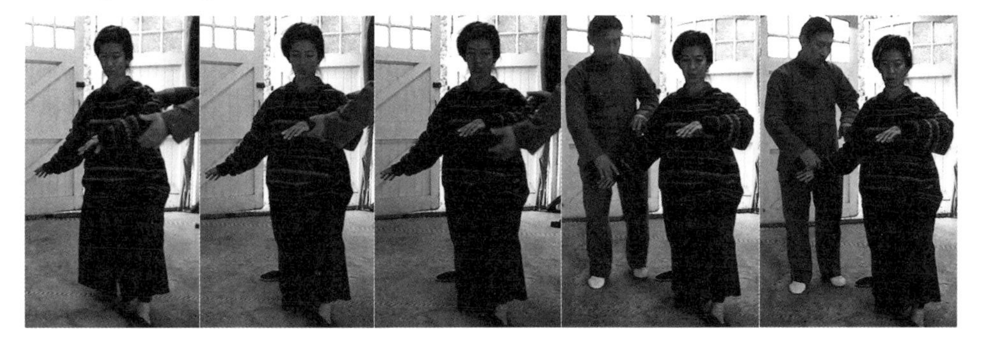

Then comes the most important change. The four pictures below can hardly capture it, so I will try to describe it. With a firm hold on either side of the ilia, Master Chen initiates a complex sequence of rotations and changes of alignment. The overall result is a change in the direction of pelvis and torso, markedly into the diagonal. But this is not a simple matter of moving from position A to position B. The change is made through repeated tiny adjustments, a succession of anterior and posterior tilts of the pelvis minutely tuned to the overall turn around the vertical axis.* It is as though there is a twisty invisible road which leads from A to B, and this road is the only way to get from A to B without losing the body's coiled strength along the way. As the road is invisible, the traveller follows it by listening and feeling, through careful attention to the contours and sound of its surface, adjusting the direction of progress with each tiny step. When the teacher guides the student along this road, he does so by feeling in each shift of the student's body the texture and gradient of the road surface, which communicate back to him through his listening and guiding hands.

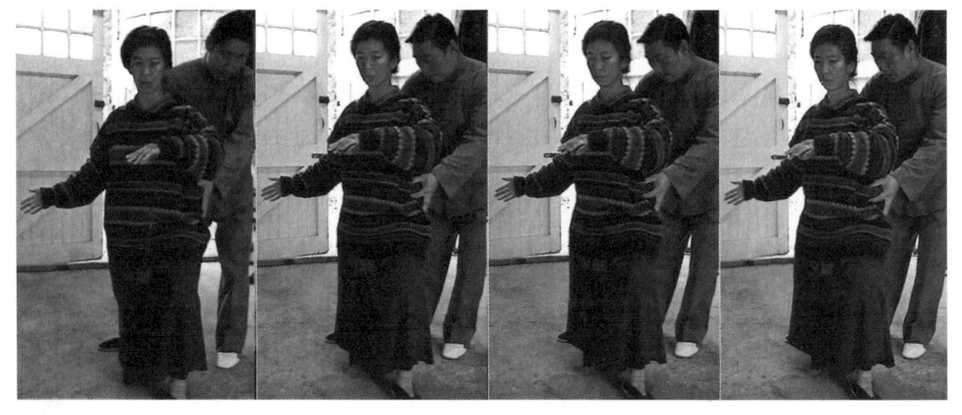

In the first two frames he is beginning the alteration. My arms are now in good connection with each other, each side flowing back to core. However, the forward-turned hips are visibly at odds with the ease of the upper body. He starts the delicate task of changing the alignment, listening to each side's differing relation to the mid-line, reorienting the pelvis into the diagonal.

Then in the second pair of frames he works to sit me down, a hand holding each ilium, thumb and forefinger feeling out the way while his other fingers support and restrain, all the time making tiny rotations forward and back, up and down. My centre of gravity is slowly being lowered – maybe half an inch. The two sides of the lower back are being drawn in towards the centre, the pelvic basin looking for its poised position. This is the next stage in the creation of dantian.

After all that careful balancing of my pelvis, when I actually step up in the second frame above I do not know how to keep the coiled centre intact. There is a feeling of hips going splat. The upper body unravels – the hips have turned to the front too early; they should stay diagonal until the two sides of the body snap closed as the right foot steps up.

Yet these initial experiences of pelvic reorientation affect me deeply. Half an inch is a long way when the alignment is correct. Adjusted thus, I feel for the first time in my taiji life what sitting down into the position means. After stepping up, I manage to gather myself back together in order to perform a decent lift of the right leg for the stamping of the foot. With the hips more unified, the foot will land in good connection with the centre.

Twenty-four minutes into the lesson comes my first experience of serious correction in one of the more demanding postures, known as 'Lean with Back'. In such positions it makes a big difference if you have got some of the internal winding already set up before you start. In the two left-hand frames below we see Master Chen tightening the guy-ropes a little; then I shift weight (24m09) and he prepares my right arm for the real work to begin.

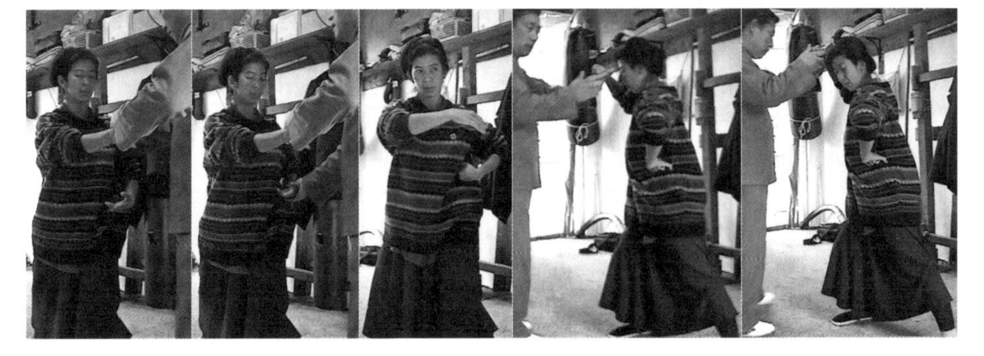

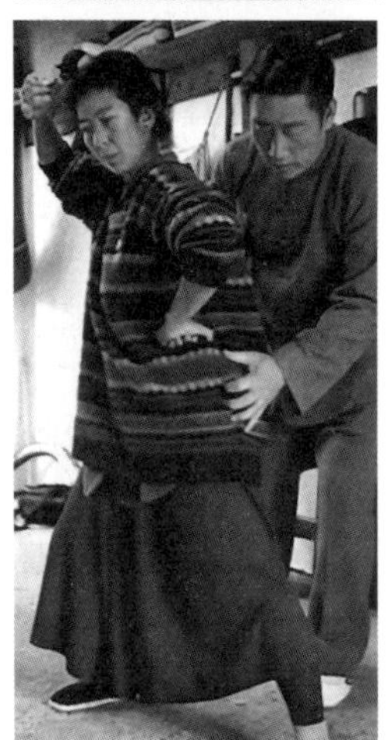

In these frames puzzlement spreads across my face as Master Chen unexpectedly coaxes my hips around to face forwards. You can see the progressive alteration of the pelvic direction, from swivelled to centred. This is one of the big Chen stances that people love to throw themselves into, imagining it to be how I must have imagined it: torso turned imperiously to the right, the left side of the pelvis hoiked around and locked into a twist. I show this sequence in the hope of clarifying this splendid Chen move, but in 1995 I was visibly puzzled. What is this novel position of the hips?

When Chen XiaoWang himself performs this sequence of movements it is a whirl of spirals. The weight surges right, upper body thrown at a dramatic slant. The sweeping arms redress the body, returning the weight to the left (where I am when we first view this sequence). Then the culmination of the drama as his gyrating arms wrap him into the final position, where he appears to twist his entire body into 'Lean with Back'. But actually it is not twisted at all. His whole body is so tightly spiralled that it gives the impression of being turned to the right, with the left side folded in towards the front. We copy the external appearance without the internal mastery, and end up in a nasty, squished, collapsed tangle.

At this moment (24m21) a coat becomes dislodged from its hanger on the wall behind Master Chen. He catches it and steps out of the picture to lay it aside. I am left alone, eyes rolling, adrift and uncomprehending in a position already difficult to maintain.

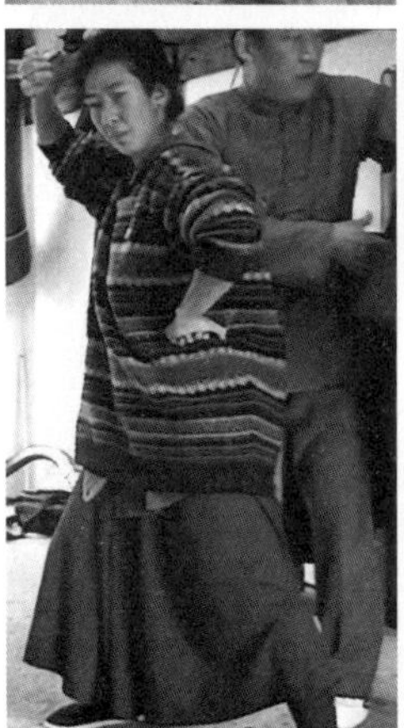

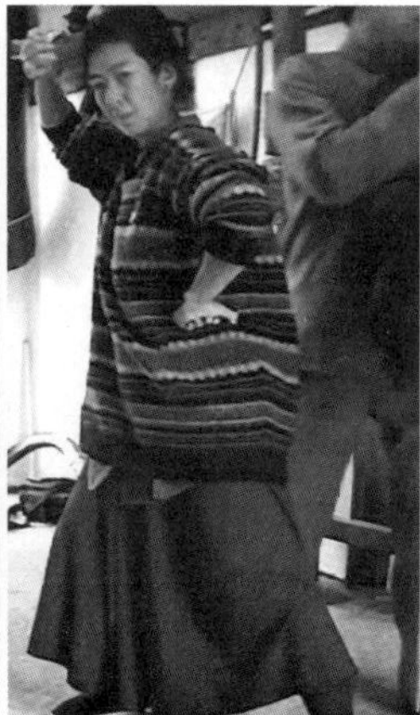

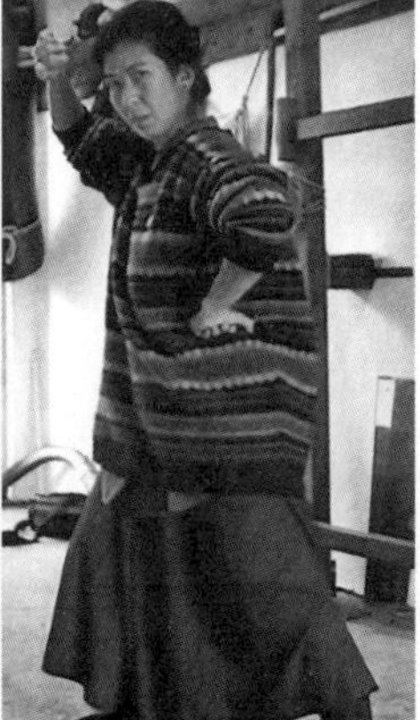

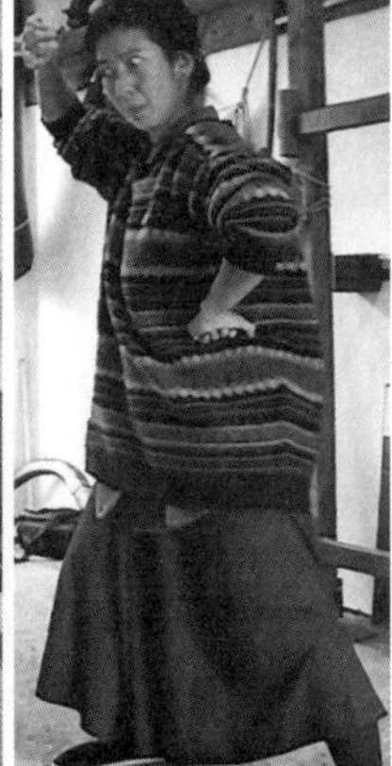

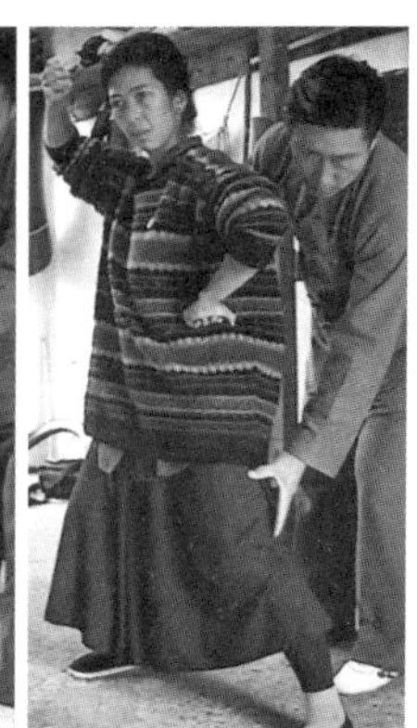

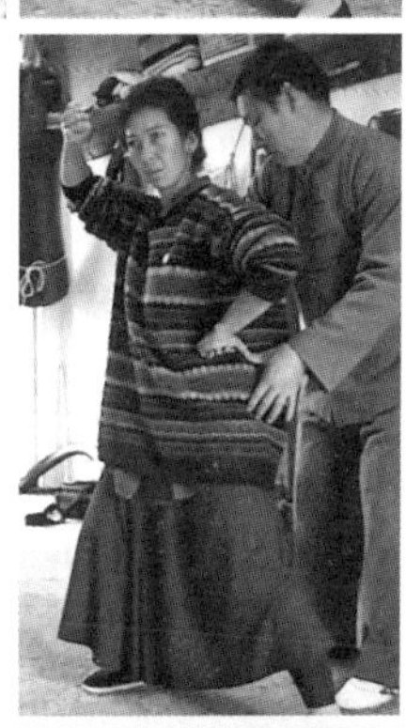

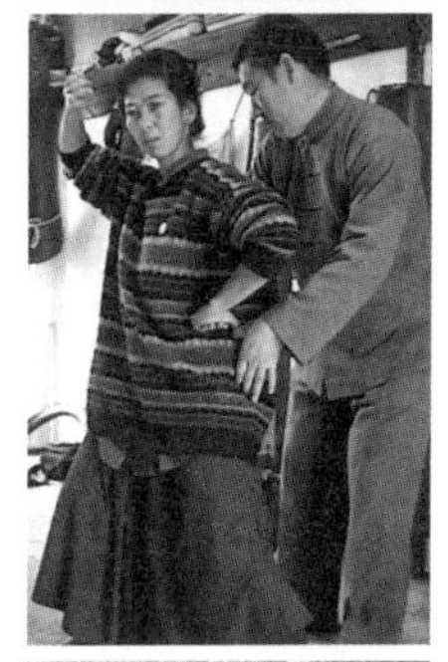

Master Chen returns to the rescue (24m27) and reminds me (right-hand frame above) to keep some softness in the left knee. As you can see, I am already wondering how long this is going to go on for. I was not aware of it then, but this is only the beginning of the real correction. The next 40 seconds are about to become burned into my memory.

It literally feels like burning. Now the tuning of right and left begins. Earlier in the lesson I had been corrected in the narrow, parallel, high stances of the initial movements of the form; and then in the wide and deep, diagonal and outward-moving preparation for Pound Mortar. Now I am to be corrected in a stance that is both wide and parallel, both dynamic and inward. In this position, fine adjustment of the two sides is enormously more taxing. As Master Chen begins to insert the right thigh into its hip joint, the entire leg starts to judder uncontrollably. I must simply try to endure, while I draw in the thighs and the two sides of the pelvis, and try to sit them back into the inguinal folds. Conflagration!

The move can be carried out decently only with very strong legs which know how to twine. Mine were strong, but I felt as though I was nearing the end of my tether. In the middle frames on the right Master Chen prepares to take me deeper into the now more correct positioning. My legs are already blazing. The fiercest sensations are in the thighs, hardly bearable. The frame at bottom right (24m40) is a major sitting down, clearly visible in motion. When the hips have been adjusted in correct alignment it is a severe task to sit down, a uniquely demanding application of the body. This is a moment in a correction when many people conk out.

And still it is not finished. The right shoulder must let go of its frantic clenching (left and middle frames above, 24m42 and 24m49) so that the arm can twine freely and qi can travel to the fisted hand. How to hang on to the body now? Master Chen makes me laugh, which gives me a few seconds longer, time for him to communicate (right frame above, 24m58) how the right fist and the left elbow relate, through a large stretch of the net in the upper back, which I was not to rediscover until six months later through further trial and tribulation.

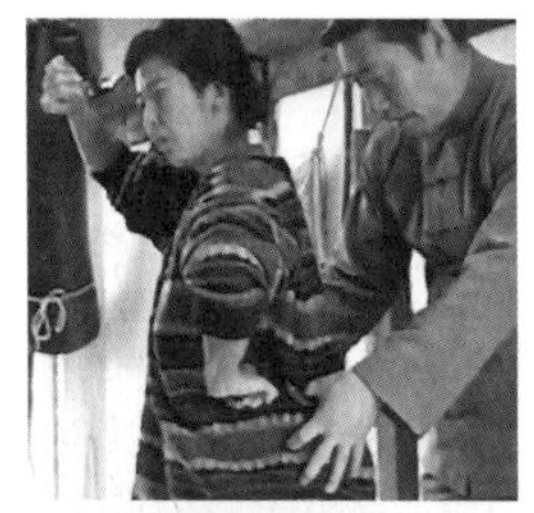

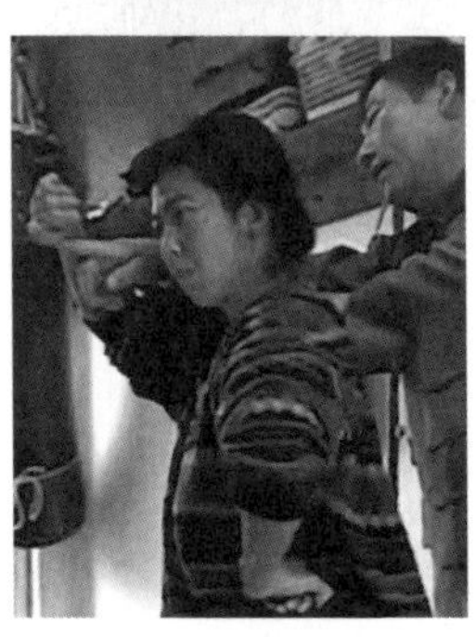

Having got me to relax momentarily in the most strenuous position that I had yet been put into, he goes once more to my hips, reconfirming their function in relation to the coiled arm. He chooses this moment (25m16) to point out with a long forefinger that my right hand's thumb has come slightly adrift from its fist. At least, that is what I wrote in the first draft of this chapter, what I guessed he was doing from watching the video. For the second draft I checked the soundtrack; what he is actually saying is, "Qi goes to this side [thumb side] of the hand." He also says, "Very hard movement, eh? Right movement, very hard." And then I have really had enough. I raise myself out of position for a moment's relief (middle frame below) and open my eyes for a quick look to see what on earth he is still doing to my right fist. Then with Master Chen saying, "One more second!" I try to refind the position.

A final moment of calm (right, 25m21) I had the good fortune to savour. One of the most remarkable things about hard corrections is that recovery after the ordeal is essentially immediate. Within mere seconds of liberation (below right, 25m26) I was looking reasonably back in circulation – but I have lost where I am in the form, unsurprisingly – and four minutes later in 'Step Back Whirling' (29m25 below) I was laughing merrily.

Deep corrections are enormously demanding physically. I have seen many strong people jump out of the position, startled by the sudden onset of what appears to be pain. But the intensity of sensation is the result of being put into proper alignment. If one can bear it, and remain in position, one is then flooded with sensations of another vibration. Then comes a rush of energy passing through the cleared pathways. But that also makes some people feel faint.

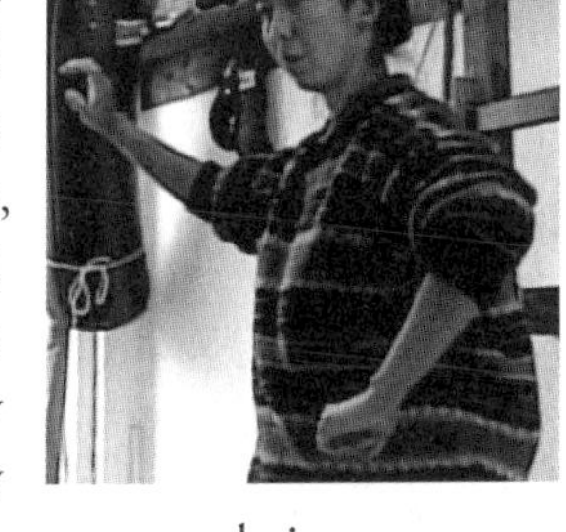

Having been through a lot of real, prolonged pain this past year, from the maladjustment I was given in a treatment by a health practitioner, I would say that what I have experienced of strong corrections under Master Chen's hands bears little relation to pain. The corrections bring about intense sensation, the least remarkable of which is the legs' protest in being used thoroughly. The realignment of misaligned parts brings forth energy fireworks from connections that are now suddenly working. As we are unused to flow, we can be frightened by it. Many people turn away from this experience, choosing a return to their accustomed stances. I think one needs to be unafraid of falling down, of looking powerless, of having little to show.

And as proof that what happens in deep correction is not really pain, there is no sense of having been hurt afterwards. All that is left is a kind of imprint on the body, a knowledge of having touched that true place, a body-memory of being bathed in pure energy. I find it highly addictive!

Part of the reason that I was laughing in 'Step Back Whirling' is that my hands kept going into Yang Style mode. To begin with, my familiar 'Fist under Elbow' from Yang Style had been greatly altered, bringing an entirely different view into sight. It really felt like 'Fist at Elbow's Bottom' now, left forearm so upright, right forearm from elbow to fist so emphatic in connection. The arms expressed the togetherness of a compact body; my insides felt different. And then as I began to step backwards, the previous nineteen years pulled me out of my Chen infancy.

In my old Yang form the lower hand draws back with the palm up as the weight shifts backwards. I could feel that this no longer made sense; it was too flat a move, quite unlike the feeling that one gets when the entire arm rotates (step back whirling!). The precise repositioning of the hips that I had been subjected to earlier, discussed at the start of this chapter, must have begun to affect my way of moving, for I found myself sitting into the diagonal rather than stepping back full frontal, so to speak. Together with the muddling of the hands, this was hilarious.

My mind was a riot with fresh feelings and old leanings, with all that I had learned of backward steps in taiji thrown into a swirling cauldron, from which joy was welling up, effervescent bubbles dancing through me. This part of the lesson with Master Chen came after the ordeal of 'Lean with Back'. I had made it through the most demanding series of adjustments I had ever had in my life. Strenuous use had been made of my capacities; every quarter of mind and body had been summoned to apply effort. This deep engagement brought forth joy. As Master Chen says, "Qi flowing – happy!"

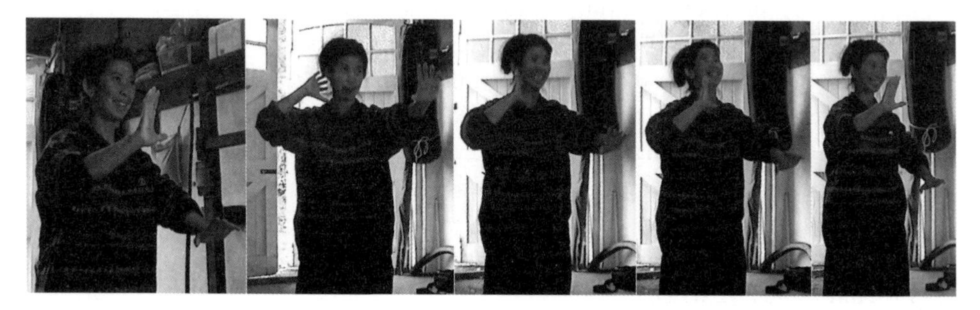

He also says, "Happy – qi flowing!" When we feel happy, we feel a lightness inside, a kind of togetherness with life; our energy feels in tune with the energy of the universe. Is there a difference between qi flowing from happiness, and qi flowing when the body has been brought into alignment? I cannot grade one kind of flowing above another, but I can say that the flowing which comes from clearing blockages in the posture is an intensely physical sensation, an awakening to the energetic charge lying dormant within the organism.

After the swirling backwards comes *bai e liang chi*, 'White Goose Wings Shimmering' (left frame below, 31m59) and Master Chen with sternly raised forefinger decides that it is time for another correction. When he wants to make adjustments to your position he says, "Not move!" and he means it; you had better freeze wherever you find yourself, or he gets rather cross. Listening now to the soundtrack I discover he actually says, "OK, good!"– I have managed to arrive by myself at a decent position in White Goose, and that gives him the chance to take me further.

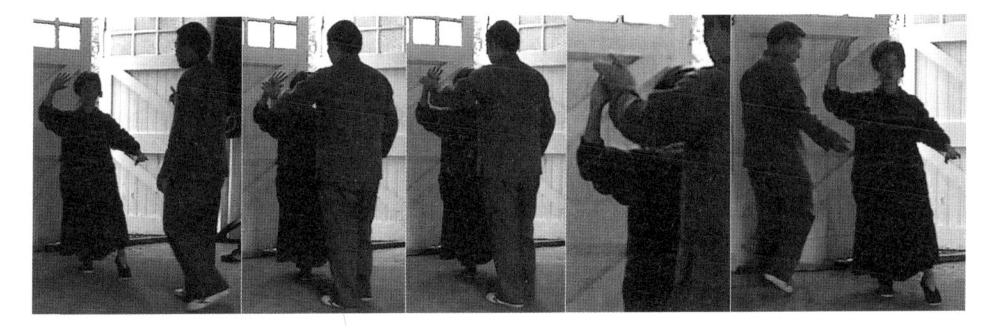

This is the second occurrence of White Goose in the form and my stance already looks quite unlike my old Yang form White Crane.* But the necessary internal reorganizations have barely begun. With the weight fully on one side, it is very difficult to sit down centred and not start using the other foot as an anchor. In the second frame above Master Chen begins by linking me up, somehow working on my chest and upper back through the manipulation of my arms. One of the remarkable experiences in this lesson is the strange way in which his adjustments to the arms affect me at my core, deep in the chest. He opens me up, turns me inside out; that is the feeling I have. In the third and fourth frames he is gently increasing the twining through the right fingers, while pressing a key spot at the top of the shoulder on the opposite side (obscured in the picture). Then, having shifted the internal landscape of my upper body, he goes around to the hips (right-hand frame, 32m12).

Master Chen concentrates on the right side of my pelvis, and on getting a truer alignment through the right half of the body. With the weighted side stabilized as it has never been – and to be truly in one leg with weight perpendicular, no ricocheting, is an extraordinary sensation – he brings about what will become more familiar to me over the coming months, a drawing together of the two sides of the body, upper back and shoulder, shoulder and hip, establishing crossways connections through the core (third and fourth frames above). There may be little to see from outside, but internally the effect is great indeed. Even though on this occasion he hardly tackled my left hip at all, he left me looking quite balanced (rightmost frame, 32m44) and ready for the next move. As he frequently says, "One number correct, next one also correct!"

Thirty-eight minutes into the lesson we reach the first of three occurrences in the form of *yun shou*, 'Cloud Hands'. I think it was in the Cloud Hands sequence that I was won over to LaoJia and Chen Style. In the old days, Cloud Hands was never cloud-like enough for me. For years during my Yang Style days, I had tried maybe five variations of Cloud Hands, all of them having a common factor of two-dimensionality. Some teachers had taught it high, some lower, but it had always felt to me that the hands were

drawing shapes in the air, not coming out of the body organically. It had been somewhat of a mental exercise, carefully turning and bringing the hands across the chest, the gaze locked into the rectangular shape which the arms were describing.

Now, finally, here was a way which made sense instinctively. The two arms express a complex of spirals spun out from within. They move along pathways that are inevitable; the hands are the visible ends of an invisible power. Learning these new movements in class, during the ten-day seminar that preceded this lesson, I had thought to myself, "Wow, this is really interesting stuff!" – even though I had barely tasted *chansijin* as yet, and thus could not give reasons for my feelings. Indeed, in that seminar I had merely learned the movements, without any contact with *jin*. Being guided was a hundred times better. I got a virtual ride on Master Chen's freeway. I fairly breezed along, enjoying lightness and oneness.

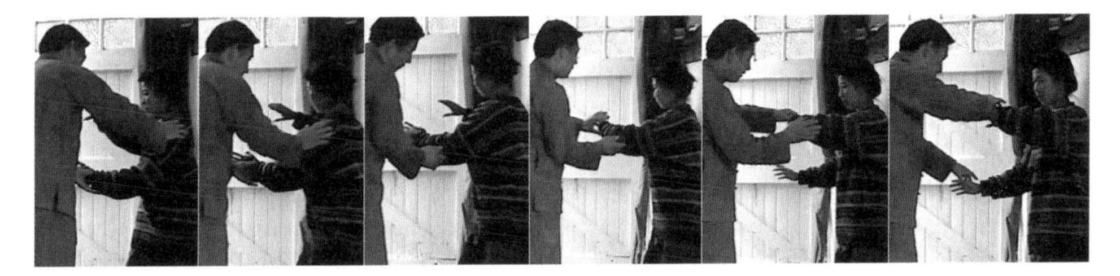

Chen XiaoWang's touch is *jin*. He spins it out of his core; watching him clean a swimming pool is a lesson in *jin* economy. On that bright November day in 1995, the Cloud Hands sparkle. There is no feeling of repeating the same moves, as it had felt when done in the old way. The arm emerges fresh from below each time, and travels its circuit fully, without being boxed into shapes. As free as it feels, it is ruled by an inner rhythm, manifested in the timing of the steps. The steps run the lower thread, while the arms loop in and out of the base line, in perpetual ever-changing changeless.

Gone, finally, was the methodical procession of two arms travelling in convoy across the chest. Ordering the arms to move in this fashion had been part of the 'nose-over-navel' approach. Pytt Geddes had loosened it up somewhat; she had emphasized the turning at the waist, allowing the upper body to swivel upon the hips fixed to face front. Now in Chen Style, I was discovering the waist to be a wide beltway, a concourse connecting chest and pelvis, a stretchy spirally core.

It was that, and at the same time it was a precise pivotal point low down in the back. But before I could appreciate subtleties, I needed to get used to another way of stepping sideways. Previously, I had been taught

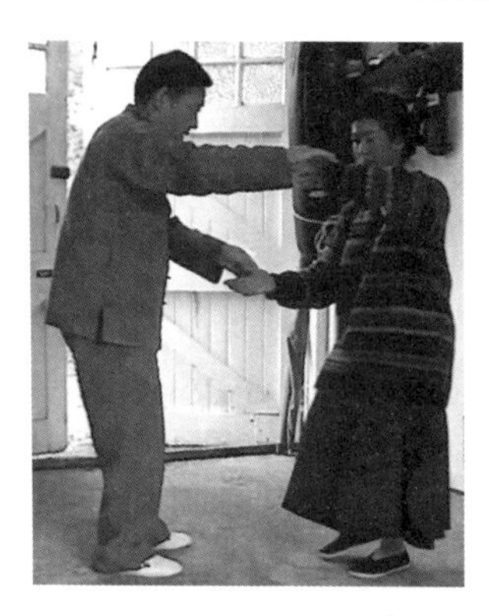

to step sideways in such a way that the inner front part of the foot gently caresses the ground first, and then the main bodyweight rolls onto the foot proper. We had been regaled with rumours that in Chen Taiji, the sideways stepping is such that the heel arrives at the ground first. This was viewed with great suspicion – it had seemed so crude and peasant-like. In reality, the heel-first sideways stepping is a matter of delicate strength and control. The leg extends from the centre, reaching out like a curvy tentacle, the foot sucking up the ground. Once it begins to develop, the inner twining that happens in the legs leads one to step heel first, and stepping in this way keeps the twining going.

Cloud Hands is a pure expression of the twining that is fundamental in Chen Style. As we shall see in chapter 8, its logic has been extracted to create exercise A of single hand Chansigong. In Cloud Hands the arms twine out of phase, qi flowing in opposite directions on either side of the body, from dantian through *mingmen* and up the back, out to the fingers; from there coiling back along the arm to the waist and to dantian.

With Master Chen arresting my weight shifts as he guides me, I begin to appreciate a little the logic of the timing. Before the weight starts to shift, the

upper arm has to sink as it spirals out sideways, an action linked through the core to the lower arm's rising. It feels like a complex change inside. The moments in time when one hand is rising while the other descends become slowed down. In this stretchy interval I feel little swivellings at the sides of the waist; only after these seem to move into place am I allowed to begin the weight shift. Then the transfer of weight feels deliberate and powerful. I am quite awed by the sensations of unknown mechanisms at work within.

Finally (left, 39m33)… try it by yourself! Not knowing yet any twining silk exercises, I have to trust beginner's mind. The arms feel wondrous, my posture just enough together to give support to the nebulous weaving motion.

Chen Style TaijiQuan is dramatic. Through being trained steadily in ZhanZhuang and Chansigong one comes to the practice of forms, such as LaoJia or XinJia, with an increasingly clear idea of the inner structure that makes the drama real and sustainable.

It is one thing to have a powerful experience after posture correction, and quite another to be able to move from A to B. Bombarded by qi blasts when we are adjusted in static stances, it is easy to forget that TaijiQuan is a technique of movement. It is a way of moving without losing centre. The adjustments that one receives from the teacher are for guiding one in learning how to move. A snapshot of the skilful taiji practicant taken at any moment should show a balanced and uncompromised frame. The initial challenge is to maintain the connections established in position A as one travels to position B, but the further aim is to transform position into continuity and thus to become free of position.

Chen XiaoWang's way of moving is both classical and free. The curious thing is that freedom may be found through hundreds of 'reps', rounds of practice of the same form, over years, with a calm heart and a detached mind. One must practise in humility for a very long time. The loneliness and solitude of solo practice give one resilience; facing one's difficulties makes one humble. It can be called a body training, but without the heart's perseverance and the mind's guiding light, it will not become art.

A neighbour calls from the other side of the ridge, and I go over to visit her. Their valley feels close but different, like a dissimilar twin. I walk back and see our settlement from the west, nestling gently into the side of a hill, clouds lowering in the east.

CHAPTER 7

LaoJia 3 ~ glimpses of a new way of moving

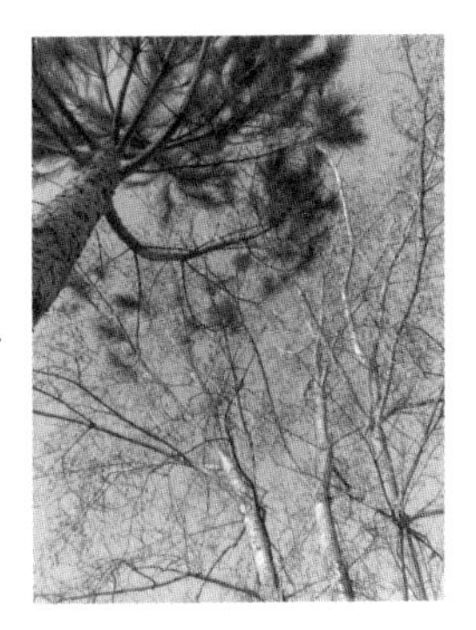

ON ONE of the misty wet evenings earlier this week I heard the Grey heron snark. It had come for night-fishing at the neighbour's pond. Today is cloudless, bringing out a pair of fresh Brimstones and the old Red Admiral now with a tattered wing. More plum trees scatter their petals, and the next ones to flower will be the old pear trees. Populus nigra waits for Pinus pinea to grow up.

Now I think the reason this lesson in London touched me deeply was not because it was my initiation in Chen Style TaijiQuan, but because it was my first encounter with a way of teaching hitherto unknown to me. I had been growing restless. At that time I was teaching both the older Yang Style long form and some of the composite short forms from mainland China. Undoubtedly I was looking for a new way of doing TaijiQuan. I had sought out a variety of teachers. Some of them brought attention to the function of the moves – here you block, there you deflect; this is a knee thrust, that is an elbow strike. Lessons like that were fun, enlivening the contact with others in the class. Pytt would remark sometimes on how I was getting into 'kicking and punching'. That had saddened one of her students, a man with a brave history as a conscientious objector in the warring 1940s. He had admired my serene form, and it was a disappointment to him that I would countenance the ruin of T'aiChi's harmony. But my martial artistic excursions were merely diverting, they had no profound influence on my life. I ask myself now what it was in 1995 that gave me an unerring sense of the direction to follow in the coming years. I think it was the experience of witnessing a step by step transformation of wonkiness into rightness. I was being urged to shed years of unclear motivation in the body. Every adjustment that Chen XiaoWang made had the effect of relating the arms and the legs back to the centre.

Sometimes even the briefest correction can touch the core of the posture. The four frames above cover a mere nine seconds. The first (45m37) is the crucial sterno-sacral realignment. It gives me the heebie-jeebies to look at this! With his left palm against the upper sacrum, his right thumb hooked inside the front of your shirt collar, his right fingers get you at the top of the sternum, and you feel the spine between those two points knit responsively. Because the pressure is at the upper end of the sternum, it does not make you collapse in the chest, rather it opens the upper back and brings about a sinking down through the spine. The sacral spine (the part that lies between the two sacroiliac joints) is reinforced from the top.

In the second frame above (45m40) Master Chen checks the resulting fullness in the waist area. Now, what is he doing in the third frame? Its effect I may not find the words to describe. The coat-hanger shoulders have been removed by the release of the spine downwards, and the shoulders have become as tender as spring leaves. Through varying gentle pressures at the top of the back and shoulders, rivulets open down the front, on the insides of the shoulders, flowing towards dantian. In the fourth frame above (45m46) and in the pictures below, he lightly guides my hand and arm. I sense momentarily an unfamiliar way of moving. Every inch of the way

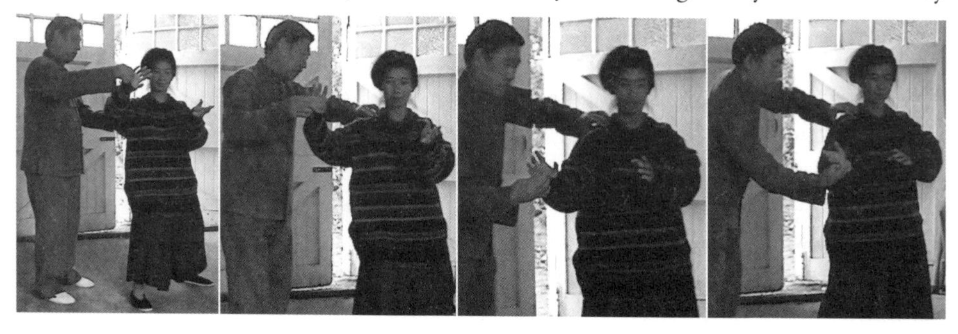

is felt out, the hand a link in a continuous looping from within, a process involving specific connections in the body – a precise place on the shoulder, in the elbow, the waist, the back. I find myself looking through a prism, amazed by the silent drama, the body like an underwater realm, pulsing with subtle motion.

This middle March morning has a strange feel to it. There is present the kind of beauty that an early summer morn can have, a fragility which makes the heart ache. The last gentle rain has induced the magnolia to show herself.

At times the feeling that I have during the lesson is of falling through trap-doors inside, and finding myself in a new arena. Here I am after the second Pound Mortar at *bai e liang chi* 'White Goose Wings Shimmering'. In this stance the arms are twined outwards to bring qi to the fingers of both hands.

In the first frame (13m08) Master Chen is working on me by holding the fingers of each hand (not visible in the picture), using them as a remote control device to prepare my centre. Through minute adjustments of orientation and changes of pressure in the fingers, he is able to translate a spreading of the extremities into an opening of the centre. The grasp of his hands on my fingers is remarkably strong. Often his touch is as delicate as can be, but this is different: it is as though his hands are using my fingers to poke around and shift my insides.

Then in the second frame he has gone around behind to work directly on my core posture. There is simultaneously a flowing outwards to my hands and a return through the arms back to centre. I balance the two flows moment by moment and experience for the first time the quiet power in being connected up.

Some months later, Master Chen was to explain how the body is linked by qi roads running in all directions. Some of these ways are big, some tiny like the cross-veins of a leaf. Here, I simply feel a melting in the back, little flurries of movement stirring and settling, like snowflakes. It is peaceful, listening with the entire body.

The neighbours' sheep keep interrupting my thoughts. They keep our grass short, but now they are under the poplars eating up the tiny lavendery violets. I know they have their eye on the succulent wild greens which are growing after all the rain, and which I intend to eat myself in an invigorating springtime pasta!

Here (14m21) I have come up after the first *xie xing*. This place that Master Chen touches very precisely, very often, right at the top of the shoulders, is a critical access point* along a main qi road. It is point 21 on the Gall Bladder meridian, *jianjing*, Shoulder Well.

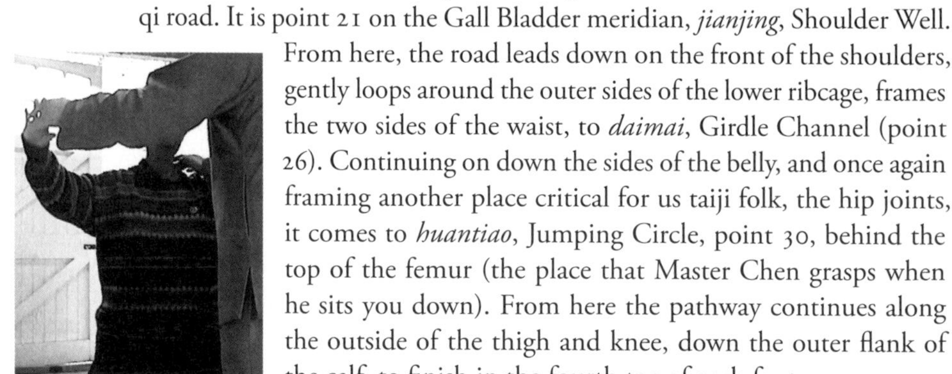

From here, the road leads down on the front of the shoulders, gently loops around the outer sides of the lower ribcage, frames the two sides of the waist, to *daimai*, Girdle Channel (point 26). Continuing on down the sides of the belly, and once again framing another place critical for us taiji folk, the hip joints, it comes to *huantiao*, Jumping Circle, point 30, behind the top of the femur (the place that Master Chen grasps when he sits you down). From here the pathway continues along the outside of the thigh and knee, down the outer flank of the calf, to finish in the fourth toe of each foot.

Without need of such information, I can feel the currents bathing my torso. There is a softening under the gentle pressure that he applies, an easing in the upper chest which makes my fingers tingle. Upper body merges into belly and legs.

From the point at the top of the shoulders the qi road curves up either side of the neck to the juncture with the skull at *fengchi*, Wind Pond (point 20), zigzagging around the sides of the head to its entry point *tongziliao*, Pupil Foramen (Gall Bladder 1) by the side of each eye at the temples. Small wonder that Master Chen's touch on this spot at the top of the shoulder would have such a calming, steadying effect on my entire system. Left and right (49m32 and 49m34) in *xiao qin da*, 'Small Hitting and Catching' we glimpse this precise touch.

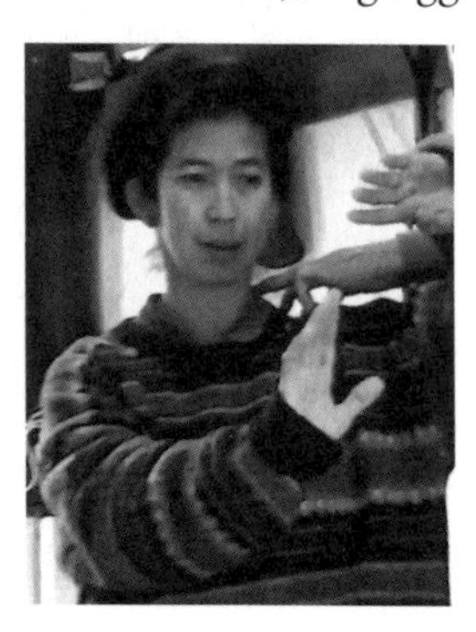

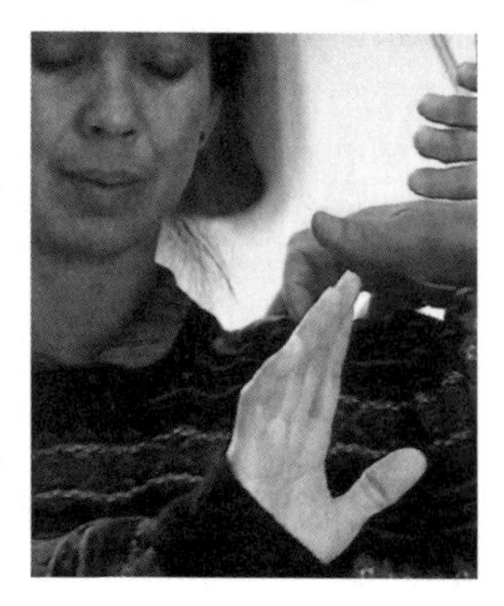

Yesterday as the sun was setting, the gathering clouds turned the eastern hills piebald in blue greys and powdery ochres. Recent days have been piebald too, one day light and one day dark. We are back in rain, and I have lit an early fire in the woodstove.

Now here (37m02) is the foxy preparation for Single Whip. Getting into the Yang Style version of this stance was always a bit of a do, and to me the position had felt somehow abrupt, truncated. In Chen Style, the right arm extends from centre in an intriguing way, taut and yielding at the same time. It is lightly coiled along its length, elbow poised, wrist strongly articulated but the joint open to make a soft closing of the fingers around the thumb. Here too, Master Chen touches the shoulder, but this time more towards the back, bringing about a settling of the shoulder blade, eliciting a feeling of downward and outward flowing. His left hand is holding my right wrist (obscured from view), giving it gentle tweaks as he eases out with his right fingers the place from where I should release the energy, which he monitors with his left. The correct placing of the left palm by dantian, which balances the right arm's extension, is essential in the preparation for Single Whip. Here my arm is too lax; the elbow should be more awake, the upper arm more pronounced in a slight outward rotation.

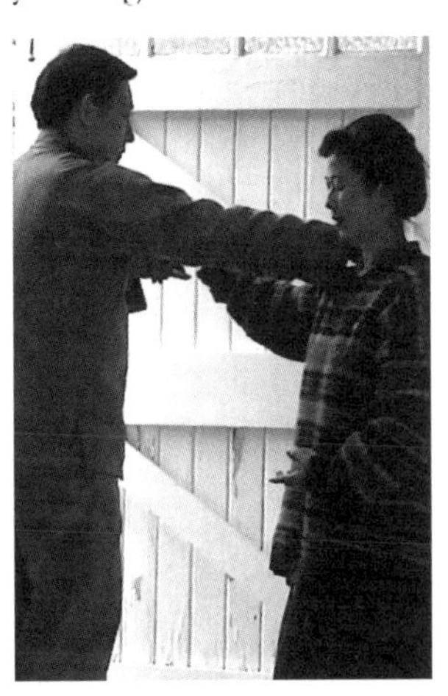

The laxness of the arm comes from slackness in the lower back. When Single Whip reoccurs later in the form, Master Chen goes straight for the core. On the right (51m52) he has lifted me into a high stance, drawing up the ilia so as to disallow any sagging of the lower spine. He is probing the area around the waist, getting some life into it now that the hip bones are better placed. He works on the right hip in particular, the side bearing all the weight, searching for a truer connection through the hip joint, at the same time drawing in the left hip so that it too joins in to support the lumbar spine. I can see that it is a new experience for me, a gradually forming awareness of bony supports, pressing close and true to the core.

With the lower portion of the spine functioning more properly, he shows me how the upper body can relax and depend on the lower (middle picture above). He goes about this very delicately, with just a small downward pressure at the top of the sternum, to make me aware of the way in which the upper spine and chest reinforce the lumbar and sacral spine. I realize later on in my training that this sterno-sacral connection is the crux of the posture.

Having eased together the upper and lower portions of the spine, Master Chen returns to the hips (right-hand picture) and really goes to work, shifting and rebalancing the ilia in relation to the lumbar spine as he lowers me into a deeper position. He brackets the ilia with his palms and fingers, urging me to feel what it is like when one sits down with the bones in alignment.

In the video I can see myself wincing. This time there is real pain, from years of misalignment in the lower back, due to the prolapsed disk between the fifth lumbar and first sacral vertebrae, which I think came about in that dance class in 1974—when the teacher had me doing pliés with a young man standing on my shoulders. This area of weakness in my spine will be uncovered as my 'central problem' in the coming year.

I try to stay in contact with Master Chen's hands, to work through the touchy place, but by this point in the lesson (circa 52m), I flake out. It is interesting to watch how this happens. My lower body holds; I do not want to miss this chance to find freedom, after all these years of knowing it was not quite right in the lower back. But the upper body gives way; my head slowly sinks until it drops. Master Chen knows this is as far as I can go, this time. He lets me carry on as best I can on my own, to enter Single Whip.

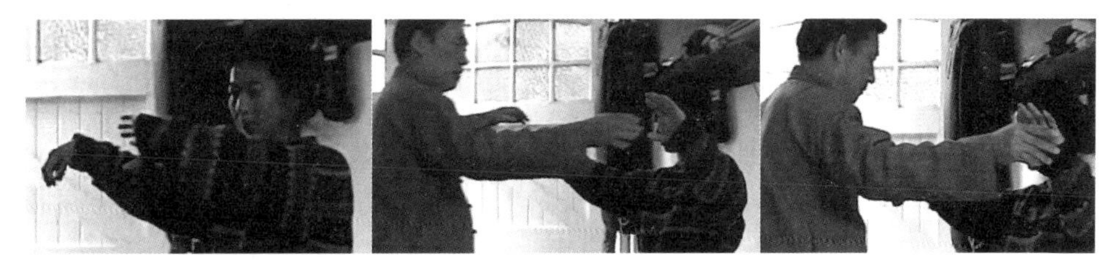

Once I am in position, he sets to work on the arms. First he lifts my left hand, and through the hand rotates and inserts my arm into the torso. Having found where I am holding, he touches me at the waist, first lightly, then sinking his fingers into my side; then the left shoulder; then taking the two hands, he listens again to the two sides of the body.

Watching the video now, years later, I can feel how he senses out the way, discovering the places of holding in the body and somehow urging them to flow a little more, all from the communication that passes between our hands. Slight alterations in the positioning of Single Whip dredge my insides. The teacher sees the ways clear a little. His two hands augment the charging of the circuit; the student's body is tuned between their span.

In the years since 1995, I too have learnt to listen a little through my hands. My eyes play a part in seeing as they are fit to do, but the hands also 'see', even better when my eyes are closed. I feel in my own body where the student is holding. The holding is a kind of lethargic opacity. To nudge it into motion, I simply listen empty-minded to my own body. There are stirrings and buzzings inside. They pass out of my hands. The rest is in the hands of the student.

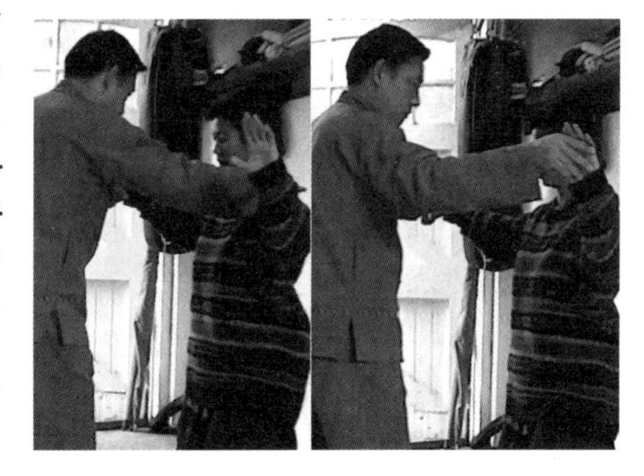

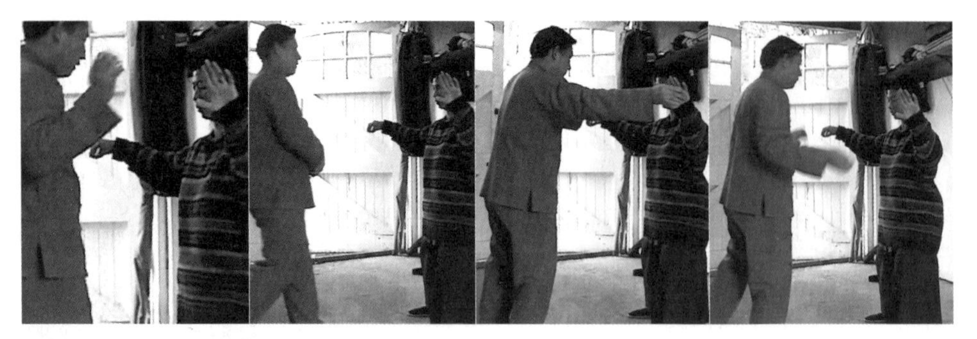

The listening and adjusting, now quite minute and hardly perceptible from the outside, continues for a while. Then he lets go, and steps back to have a look at the whole picture. He sees that just a little more can be nudged into place, and returns to give me a mysterious tweak or two, all of this leaving me quite incredulous. Only then does he step back (53m03) and allow me to carry on with the form.

Single Whip Chen Style feels completely different from the positions which I had known by that name. The joints are slotted into place like a jigsaw puzzle. From the middle the legs and arms route through intricate ways to hands and feet. The stance is commanding, open and balanced. That day twelve years ago it was a revelation to prepare for it so carefully. Every detail is a meaningful step in the alignment of energy.

I see in these pictures the good effect of Master Chen's hands on the gathering of my inner strength. He sounds me out, finding the key weakness in my back; through little adjustments, he shows that a supporting net may be woven around the fragility. He gives time for me to find a core strength which allows my system to absorb entirely new sensations of being and moving. Gradually I come to appreciate that the desirable aim is to find a way appropriate to one's own body, that the Chentaiji moves are to be found in our own making. In those early days, when he saw me taking enormous stances, he would say, "Small also beautiful!" His aim was to cultivate in me a sense of proportion, to know by experience that a strong stance is forged by energetic connections free of strain. In order to train correctly I had to be sensible.

I am not sure if the magnolia is being sensible. We are only halfway through March, and even though the clouds are lifting over the eastern hills in the late afternoon, the northern skies are darkening. It may be snowing up in the mountains.

The birds' chirping has woken me before dawn. There was a soft rain in the night. The valley skies are low, with a breeze stirring the chimes on the balcony. In amongst the yellow daffodils under the walnut is an ivory bloom with an orange centre. The bulbs had been under the sheeting that is over the new practice area, our 'stomping ground'; we are denuding it so that it will be bare beaten earth, the best surface for pounding the mortar. Entire plants had grown in the dark, I found them lying flat and whitened, and within a fortnight they have turned green and put forth several flowers.

Halfway through, the form leaps off the ground in a flying double kick. The real interest lies in the two or three seconds preceding the leap. The preparation involves a 180° turn of the body, a slow winding up internally, which begins at the completion of *ji di chui*, 'Punch the Ground'. The Yang Style version of this sequence is discussed in chapter 10; we shall see the similarity and the difference. The turn involves a spiralling within parallel lines, where those lines themselves coil, keeping a true relation between them; it is a complex move, unique in the form. From the low punch in a deep lunge, the turn begins like a wave rising within the core of the body. When the turn is completed, that wave is nearly cresting, its force still contained. The body is battening itself down in preparation for the leaping burst, *ti er qi*, 'Double Raise Foot'.

Immediately preceding the frame shown here, Master Chen has taken my two forearms in order to get them to settle a bit and connect properly to the back and to each other. Then he grasps my left forearm strongly with his left hand, while his right goes to the area around my left shoulder blade, coaxing it to rotate inwards a little. He is looking and feeling where I am, and whether I am receiving the information he intends me to have. The left side of the body, with the twined arm that Master Chen is grasping in a specific way, is the key in the preparation for the leap. He reinforces a subtle descending twist in the forearm, connecting it to the left upper back, where there should be a similar action. The body is coiled up like a multitude of springs, and the instant of release is a moment of pure exhilaration.

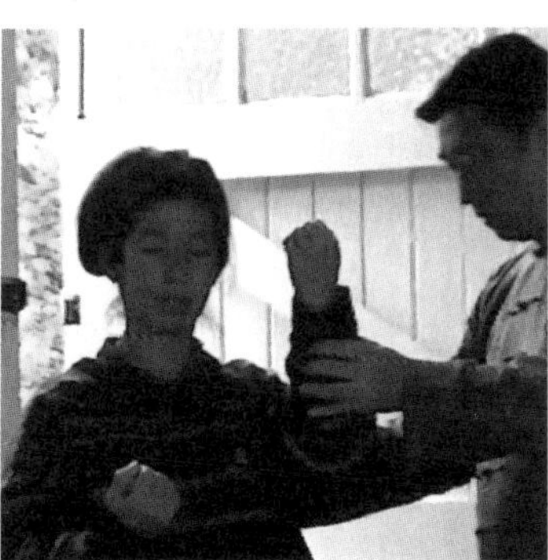

The morning is brightening. Bees are buzzing in the old pear tree; the even older pear on the upper terraces has put out a few blossoms.

The following sequence illustrates the great number of preliminary adjustments that may be needed in approaching a change at the core of the posture. Master Chen stops me in mid move and indicates (39m50) that I am not sitting down properly in my right hip. There are two aspects to the complex set of corrections shown here. First, it is necessary to unravel the extremities in order to access the misalignment at the core. From the teacher's point of view it can feel like clearing the way through the brambles to reach a hidden object. Secondly, setting up in advance the routing along the arms means that when the core is placed in correct alignment, the pathways will already be open for the posture to fill from inside outwards.

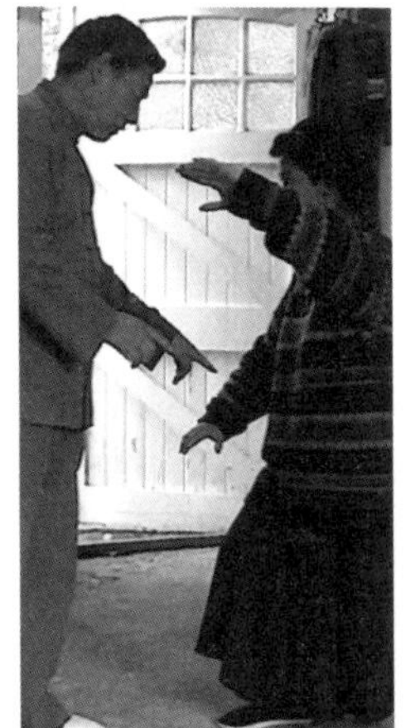

Frequently the way to the hip is through the opposite shoulder, and part of the problem here is that my left shoulder is blocked. To open the shoulder he takes hold of my left hand (below left) and sets off a strong winding, carefully working it all the way up my arm. The strange thing is that from this lifting, twisting, and tightening of the insertion of the arm into the shoulder joint, the shoulder becomes more free. His right forefinger, controlling the degree of rotation, is acting like a probe, finding the way along the now strongly spiralled arm, towards my core. With his other hand he adjusts the connections with a touch to the left shoulder, to the elbow, then to the right shoulder, then to the left elbow again (four frames below). Setting up the right degree of twine in the arm is a matter of extreme delicacy, like finding the right point of a wave on which to surf.

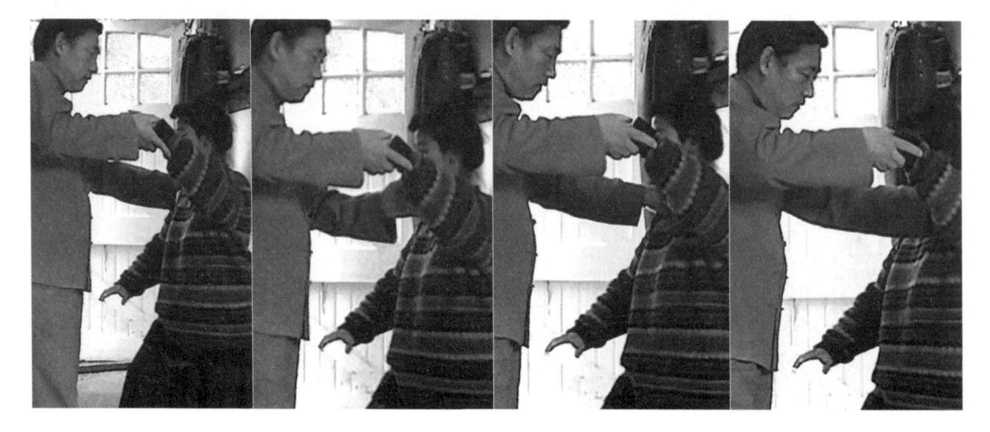

Then he sets about changing the orientation of the lower body. I had arrived in this position with my hips squared to the front. He subtly turns the pelvis towards the left diagonal; this affects the hip joints, opening them somewhat. That quick alteration of the pelvic direction, as it were away from the right, also frees the right arm; from being fixed and stuck in one direction, I now feel the manoeuvrability of my stance, with both arms spread actively from the middle.

Then (below) more work on the left shoulder and arm. A touch to the left side of the waist; yet more work on the left wrist and shoulder. I am struck by the easing effect of precisely executed exertion: the tautening and extension of the arm brings about release and flow. I think that my years of letting the posture hang loose had left a fair amount of tension trapped inside, and now it is being worked to the surface. But no amount of adjustment at the extremities would have freed me up if my pelvis had remained squarely fixed to the front. Minutely rotated now towards the

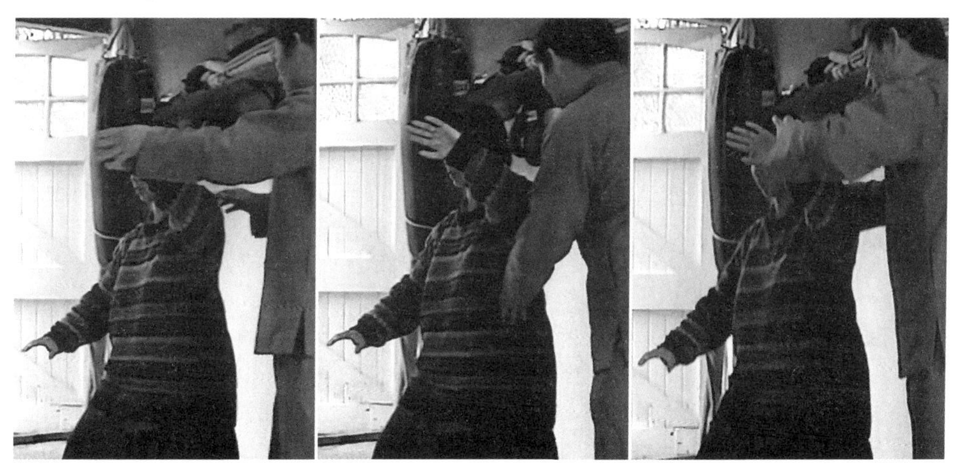

diagonal, the body enters the flow of a spiralling action that will eventually take me around 180° to the left.

Now the way through the brambles is cleared and the objective is within reach. Master Chen takes me down to the precise position for the right hip (left-hand pictures above, 40m27 and 40m36). This is a dicey move. If everything has been prepared correctly, and if the student can sustain the openings and is not too tired by the preliminary corrections – for they have already intensified one's experience of the body – then there is a chance that at this moment, qi will explode from dantian and fill the extremities in all directions. In this stance, that would likely be accompanied by a sploosh of red hot molten metal in the right thigh, and the student is liable to jump out of the position in alarm. There is not much time; that is is why he sets up the connections through the arms first, getting the framework prepared in advance before he sits me down in alignment and gives me a blast of qi. With the infrastructure set up before the core adjustment, I am given a chance to experience for a few seconds the sensation of being truly in the stance. This is the kind of learning experience that one treasures, and for which one continues the practice.

On this occasion there is just enough time for some final tweaks at key points of this stance in the upper body – my left hand and right shoulder (third picture above). With the right hip now in correct alignment, these minute touches can elicit a splendid drench in a waterfall of qi, from head to toes and fingers. Finally (above right, 40m44)… "OK!" A few moments longer, and I might have caved in. Master Chen gives just enough and not too much.

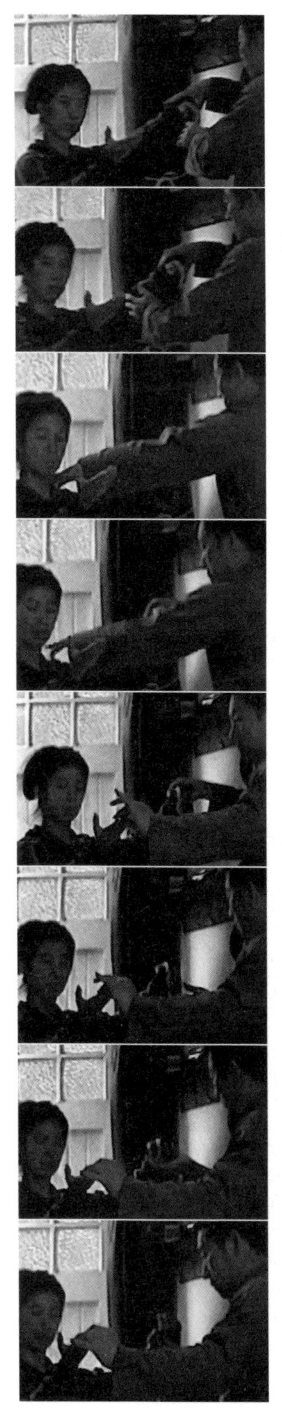

Here finally is a part of the lesson where Master Chen is only tweaking. It pleases me to imagine that by this stage my core posture had become so much in order that all it needed was a few tweaks.

There are actually an awful lot of tweaks. Here are 13 snapshots of 13 different delicate adjustments which Chen XiaoWang is making to my 13 fingers. What on earth is going on? Having had the experience of being corrected in this stance a number of times over the years I can feel the effect of each tweak on my insides.

This stance is in preparation for a glorious movement, a round kick in a 270° turn, *xuan feng jiao* 'Whirlwind Kick'. My arms, hands and fingers, that Master Chen is adjusting with great care, are hooks by which he pulls on the lines leading from each finger to a place deep within. He is coiling each line, finger by finger.

This is a very different kind of winding in the body from the preparation for 'Double Raise Foot', discussed just now, where the body explodes straight up into the air. Here, the coming action will be one of bursting open from centre, and closing with equal force. First there is a wrapping together of the two sides, the left folded inside the right. Then the left, inner layer will unwind with force as both arms wing out. The left hand thwacks the instep of the left foot as it swings open to shoulder height. Then the right side takes over for the second half of the turn, in a strong closing action which snaps shut the two sides of the body.

All these tweaks are preparing me for this coming drama. He begins by creating a potent undulation through my left arm which affects the entire left side, the side that will be wrapped in the interior of the bundled body. First he gets the necessary angle in the wrist and through the fingers, for they are the ends of the lines winding down my core, earthing me. Then he augments the curves in my left arm, filling out the elbow and further hooking the left wrist, making me aware of the singular path that runs through the curves. Then he connects the hooked wrist to its shoulder. In the fourth picture, he presses on *jianjing*, Shoulder Well (Gall Bladder 21), as he did earlier in this chapter, and again it has the same deep effect.

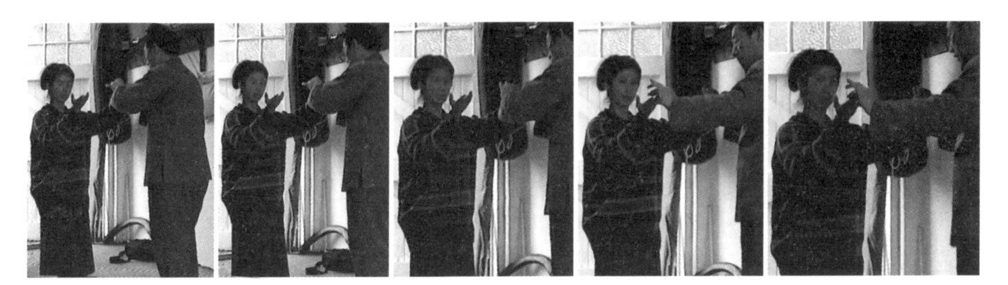

Now we see what fine-tuning means. He goes from hand to hand, sounding out their depths. Having been calmed down so deeply, I am able to listen and follow the effects of his varying touches, the lighter the clearer. The position of the two hands in this stance is unfamiliar. When I began to learn the other long Chen form, XinJia, I discovered that the way of winding the arms here is more typical of the technique in XinJia.

The first three pictures above show him concentrating on the left hand; this is the side that will take the lead in the coming action. Through the hand, Master Chen is increasing the diagonal and upwards undulation of the body's core. There is a gathering of the energy in the way the hands sweep from centre, with an asymmetrical coiling rise to the left. The still eye of the storm, and the whirling.

When he is satisfied with what he hears in my left hand, he returns in the two right-hand pictures above to give a final check to both sides of the body, softly sealing the experience so that I will never forget. I am surprised and pleased to see my posture so decent in this position. There is a clear plumb-line through the body, and somehow, by working only on my hands, Chen XiaoWang has put all of me in order.

The lesson draws to a close. Always when he teaches, Master Chen devotes a great deal of time to establish mental balance in his students. "Mind more than 50 per cent!" he says. Without the inner simplification, there cannot be profound learning. Working this deeply makes one feel well and contented. Turning to the camera, Master Chen says "Legs very strong, not fall down!" The last movement of the form is the same as the first, *jingang dao dui*, and

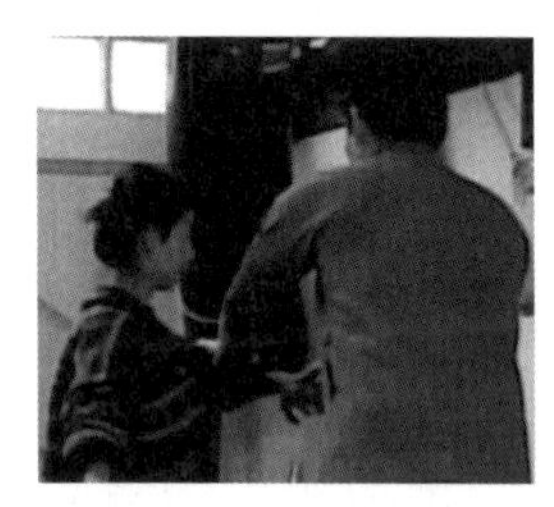

here Master Chen makes the same adjustment to my leading arm that he had made the first time around. The elbows must be buoyant. When this position is just right, one can prepare properly for what follows, *dao dui*, the pounding of the mortar.

As profoundly as this first lesson in London affected me, he in fact tackled only lightly the changes that would be necessary if I were to start doing TaijiQuan. The corrections he gave me that day were absolutely right in their timing; fundamental shifts were indicated, and enough information for me to take away and digest on my own. In order to train myself clearly in a new way, I gave up my old Yang Style form.

CHAPTER 8

Loopy Chansijin

THE TWINING silk exercises are like the musical scales which pianists practise first thing in the morning. Or in my case today, last thing before sunset. The long-tailed tits with their shallow dipping flight were swooping southwards as I came up the terraces to the deck, my old *chansijin* spot. The Apennines stretch like a great wall to the north, still bearing a fine ridge of snow. Spring arrives late up there. Shadows lengthen in the valley below me. I am here to mull over *chansijin*; this deck reminds me of the early days when I had just learnt Chansigong, and I used to practise the exercises often up on the hill.

Chan is the action of twining, something turning around itself. *Si* means silk. *Gong* means trained skill, and *jin* means something like power – according to Chen XiaoWang, "like power, but refined power". Chansigong is the exercise or skill of twining silk; *chansijin* is the spiralling power that is led out of the *chansi* action.

On our first visit to Australia to study with Chen XiaoWang in 1996, we were introduced to Chansigong as an integral part of Chentaiji, together with ZhanZhuang, the standing qigong. ZhanZhuang forms the backbone of the practice, and is in different ways common to many martial arts traditions. Chansigong expresses and trains the essence of specifically Chen TaijiQuan technique. On each of our subsequent visits to Sydney, standing and twining silk were the foundation practices which we were eager to deepen.

The adjustments that Chen XiaoWang had so carefully made to my LaoJia in that first lesson in the Streatham garage, discussed in chapters 5, 6 and 7, began to make sense with the input of Chansigong instruction and practice. What begins as a bewildering array of information in the early stages of learning – for example, a palm or a wrist to be turned at a specific angle here but not there – is slowly pared down to changes deep inside the body.

The purpose of each detail specified by the teacher is to help set up a particular twining action. The student copies the appearance, before having learnt the feeling from the inside; in chapter 2, the reasons for copying as closely as possible are touched on. Over time one cultivates the delicate motions within the core which create spirals spontaneously in the integrated body. Once one learns to twine, then one simply twines, and there is no more a profusion of detail. Centre changes, and the entire body manifests it.

Reeling and Writhing

Chansigong is sometimes called 'Reeling Silk'. Today I prefer not to use this name, because 'reeling' suggests the winding of something onto a reel. At one time, however, I thought of it so. Mentions of silk in my old T'aiChi days were usually linked to that idea, of how to reel silk.

The way of moving in T'aiChi, I was told, should be like the action of drawing silk out of the cocoon: slow, smooth, steady. If you do not pull firmly enough, nothing will happen; if you pull too sharply the thread will break. Cool, gentle and firm was the way to wind the fine thread onto a reel; this was for many years the image which I understood.

So when I heard Chen XiaoWang's explanation of the name, I was startled. He likened the internal movements of *chansijin* to the writhings of the silkworm as it creates silk from within itself. The taiji body wreathes and writhes in an ever-changing pattern of connected turnings. It was not the silk, it was the worm!

The penultimate exercise in Chen XiaoWang's Chansigong series, usually not taught in the beginning years, evokes an instinctive impulse in the body. I will describe that part of it which brings out the core action. The stance is the same as for starting the form – the feet at shoulder-width distance, the head up, weight falling perpendicular, knees unlocked but legs nearly straight. The palms of the hands are placed one on each side of the lower abdomen, fingers pointing in towards dantian, elbows relaxed, the breathing natural.

A wave-like motion begins in the torso. The mid back rises slightly, with a tiny arching pushing through the lower spine. The shoulders and arms minimally follow the motion, while the palms remain in the same position for the time being. The movement up the back continues and completes its circuit by a rounding and sinking down the front of the torso, the chest giving way. As the rippling through the body is repeated over and over, the entire spine becomes involved in the motion, from the lower body up through the back and down the front, and rising up the back again. It passes through the whole body, including the legs. There is a rising and sinking with each undulation, while the feet stay in full contact with the ground. The neck is relaxed and the head follows the spine's motion.

This 'chest-waist change place' exercise evokes wonderment in passersby, even in people who have some familiarity with Taiji. Those who have heard of strange Qigong practices from China may think that it is an Induction exercise, such as the ones mentioned by Zhuangzi, the 'bear-hangings' and 'bird-stretchings'. But at the centre of this exercise is one of the keys to Chentaiji. In one way or another it directs every move of the forms. It is the invisible beginning of the very first movement, when you simply lift your arms.

Simply lift… but if your posture has been finely tuned, then this starting movement of TaijiQuan can initiate a great journey. Once in a while we catch a glimpse beneath the surface. Chen XiaoWang will occasionally skip the first movement of LaoJia entirely, showing instead a magnified but still barely perceptible version of the hidden impulse which underlies it, a slight turning of the dantian which changes everything.

How does one learn to twine, so that these subtle turnings of dantian bring forth entire forms of TaijiQuan?

A, B, C

A tiny breeze lifting the chimes wakes me up, with first light glancing off the shutters. Stretching my spine against the bed, I find the pillow under my head; I normally sleep flat with no pillow, better for the neck; I must have dropped off quickly last night.

We had some of our lessons in a park in suburban Sydney; usually twining silk and then form, but always first of all, standing. After adjusting our postures Master Chen would settle down to stand with us, and at this point in the lesson he would be facing towards us. On one occasion a couple of Meadowbank boys passed by, aged about 9 and 7. They stopped and stared; we heard the elder one say to the younger, "Tie-chee-chwan!" We were impressed that they knew what we were up to, standing stock-still, eyes closed. When the time came for us to follow Master Chen in Chansigong, he turned around to face away from us. We saw on the back of his t-shirt, 'Tai Chi Chuan', in big letters.

Strangers wonder why on earth some people stand still for ages; they are no less perplexed by the absorption of a lone practitioner waving one hand in the air, or sometimes two. Let us now enter the Chansigong arena.

There are three single hand exercises, which I will refer to as exercises A, B and C. There is also a double hand exercise, a leg twining exercise, and the torso-with-wrist-and-arm exercise which I described above. Viewed casually, they seem transparent. When Chen XiaoWang introduces them in a seminar he says, "Very easy to learn, one morning. To go deep, one lifetime not enough." At the heart of all these exercises is the serpentine action which I described above. The body's core undulates. Master Chen says simply, "Move like snake!" However, it is not easy to explain movement with words alone. "Move like snake" is evocative, but we are not required to slither on our bellies.

If we were now standing in a room together with our teacher, we would have three 'languages' for communication. There is the language of words. Then the language of demonstration: one gains some understanding from seeing what the teacher means by 'moving like snake'. There is also what Chen XiaoWang calls 'hands language': one can feel from the teacher's touch and guiding hands something impossible to communicate in any other way. Until I met Master Chen, I knew only the first two languages.

We begin learning by looking and copying, and trying to follow the teacher's directions. Chansigong's apparent simplicity in itself presents a challenge. For a good length of time, one cannot understand why these exercises are interesting. You will hear descriptions of qi flow, qi direction, qi stations, but you cannot feel them perhaps for a long while. The exercises appear merely to consist of very simple arm movements and the shifting of weight, eventually including repetitive stepping.

I think I was lucky that my keen sensitivity to discomfort alerted me to the value of these exercises; I soon realized that they would help me to understand niggling things in my posture that I had tried to ignore for years.

Under the silent teaching of Master Chen's hands, I was at last facing a weakness in my body that I had been aware of in my Yang Style days, but had not needed to sort out. Somehow it had been possible to do my 108 and 24 and 48 Forms bearably, even with satisfaction, and to give the impression of ease and flow.

Now, however, it felt as though I could hardly take a step! Or stand. Let alone move like a snake. Finally, it was no longer bearable. This is a crucial moment in one's training. When postural problems become unsupportable, development of technique can truly begin. Master Chen has a good way of putting it. Each person must come to know what he calls their 'central problem'. It cannot be changed overnight; but to not recognize it, "This very terrible."

It became imperative that I worked out my posture. The first single hand exercise gave me a chance to observe as if in a mirror the working of the hips, the way the pelvis's placement affects the legs, and how the arms and hands are tied to the lower body.

That is the logical and pragmatic explanation of my interest. But beyond that, I was motivated by something less physical and more inexplicable. I became absorbed in the challenge of doing the movements over long stretches of time, intrigued by the experience every now and then of a charged flowing, a linking up of the body. I noticed that this flow was different from what I had felt before. There was now a palpable 'stuff' inside my arms; experiencing this in the legs came much later. I hardly realized in the first couple of years of Chentaiji practice that the new sensations I was experiencing had to do with the establishment of dantian as centre, 'your true centre', as Master Chen says. The twining silk exercises, along with ZhanZhuang, were constructing dantian.

Forging

If we were able to view the aware body performing its daily mindful training, we would see a kernel forming in the lower belly. Over time, myriad pathways will become evident. They run along the torso, down the legs, through the arms, linking the kernel to the rest of the body. Some paths are more distinct than others; many will be fine like the tiny veins of leaves. Large and small, they bind the upper body to the lower, one side to the other, the limbs to the core. The paths crisscross, too numerous to separate, along axes at all angles.

Chansigong practice forges these pathways. Daily you are weaving your frame together. Your body comes alive from the inside outwards, there is a sweetness flowering within, a liquid on the move.

Usually this can only be found through some tough work, but the toughness has not to do with pounding sweaty effort. Master Chen reminds students in his seminars that "learning taiji is not like road work", or hard labour. It is a delicate business, best done with gentle attentiveness and persistence. Especially when it comes to qi-matters.

So, little dipping swoops into the practice of Chansigong. We start with four numbers. Let us consider exercise A, the first of the three single hand Chansigong. Like B and C, it is performed standing with the legs open in a wide stance ('horse riding stance', but more astride a water buffalo), with the two feet level and parallel. The arm cycles through four positions:

1. slightly gathered, the arm out sideways but not outstretched, rotated smoothly
2. fully gathered, the upper arm completely relaxed and the forearm slightly lifted, palm up, in front of the body
3. slightly expressed, the whole arm turned and lifted, palm down, still in front of the body
4. fully expressed, the arm fully rotated away from the body and out to the side, palm out

And so on, 4...1...2...3...4...

Dantian is main terminus; qi roads connect all parts of the body to it. The connections run somewhat deep inside the body, but first we shall describe their surface aspect, which is generally where the qi will initially be felt by the exploring novice. And to simplify, we are here concerned only with the road map of the upper body, and with only one main concurrence of flow. From dantian, deep in the lower abdomen, the road goes behind to the small of the back, then up the mid-line of the back, to the top of the dorsal spine. From there it branches across the back of the shoulder and along the arm, following a gently winding path to the fingers. That is half the circuit – from dantian up the back to the fingers. Returning, the road winds back along the arm to the elbow, along the inner upper arm and down the side of the torso, to the side of the waist, then back to dantian. Thus the circuit is completed.

The routes for all three single hand exercises pass through these four stations: the side of the waist, dantian, upper back and fingers. For the *chansi* action to happen throughout the body, the core must be spiralling freely. To train the core to spiral, there is an exacting procedure to follow. Referring to the four stages of the arm's rotation,

1. qi comes to the side of the waist
2. qi from waist to dantian
3. qi up the back
4. qi to shoulder, then elbow, then fingers

the arm's spiralling motion is precisely coordinated with the weight shift. It takes months to appreciate what this means, but the directions are:

1. no weight shift
2. shift weight
3. no weight shift
4. shift weight

Moments arise when a flash of insight startles me. I recall such moments *in situ*, I remember the place where each occurred. For example, Master Chen's continual "Qi to waist-side" had passed me by for months, without raising the slightest glimmer of understanding. Then one day when it was raining, we had the lesson indoors, in the dining room of an apartment in Strathfield. He corrected my single hand stance at position 1. When I then shifted my weight to position 2, it felt as though a heavy table had moved sideways into me. I had arrived in dantian. And I have just been talking about qi's delicacy!

It is difficult to achieve a 'centred' weight shift. Much of the preparation for this is in *lo Standing*, as the Italians call ZhanZhuang. Qi is first gathered and refreshed in dantian. Then in the twining silk exercises, you learn how to move while maintaining balance in the centre. After these fundamentals have been sorted out, you can begin to feel your movements evoke and guide qi according to intent.

The day has passed with practice and writing; it is already nearly bedtime. The sunshine was back this morning and I took the chance to go down to the bamboos for ZhanZhuang. All these years I have tended to do my standing practice indoors, but somehow I took to the grove when I began writing the ZhanZhuang section of this book. In February I found myself going daily, weather permitting, to the same south-facing spot in the bamboos, where my feet made two nice hollows. I enjoyed arriving in the grove and stepping into my 'stirrups' – that was all it took, and off I would be, on a ZhanZhuang adventure. After a week or so it occurred to me that standing in the very same spot was in fact not a good idea, because of the malleability of a surface composed of dry bamboo leaves. My two sides had probably made different impressions in the leaves, and even with fresh attempts to level them, it was likely that I was working on a surface that had been made compatible to my imbalance. So the March standings, when I have been down in the bamboos, have been moveable feasts.

With all the recent rain, the terraces are already lush with new growth, attracting the sheep. Ah, now I remember, the excitement of the day! *Funghi*! For some years I have been looking out for morels, though none of our neighbours admitted to finding them (we are all rather secretive with our mushrooming finds, we *fungaioli*). Once many years ago, before I knew of the delights of mushrooming in this valley, I thought I had seen something like morels on the path by the elder. And today, as I was approaching the bamboo grove from below, there they were, at the bottom of the arbour. But I have to admit, they look quite different from the true morel, *Morchella esculenta* or *elata*. And neither are they the False Morel, *Gyromitra esculenta*. They may belong to the *Helvella* family, but resemble none of the ones in any of the books. I will not eat them.

Then late this afternoon, as I was in the middle of a XinJia rep on the pottery roof, I caught sight of something stark white on the hill, standing out against the green on the other side of the fence. It could only be a mushroom; I had to go fetch the binoculars and have a look. Now, I have been waiting to find out if St George's Mushroom *Tricholoma gambosum* grows here, calculating that it would be a month earlier here in Italy than in England, the good saint's day being on April 23rd. Tomorrow first thing, I will dash up the hill and go under the neighbour's fence, to check if it is what I hope it is.

A Confounding

In the night, I did not dream of earthly things, like mushrooms, but of wind and wide spaces; it must be the preoccupation of these recent days with *chansijin*.

I have just woken up with a dream. I am on a high spur in the mountains. About level with me, but in the vastness before me, there are birds flying. Of no special colour, and not very big. They are travelling fast, from my right to the left; I watch them, mesmerized.

As one after another flies past, I see clearly how they are manoeuvring their way through the air. Their bodies roll, back and forth, a little left, a little right, with tiny risings and sinkings, all of which appear to maintain their buoyancy and onward direction.

I almost never have to tell new students that Chansigong is harder than it looks. They discover this for themselves in the very first lesson. But why, for such a simple exercise – the arm drawing a circle before you on a count of four, with two weight shifts – why is it so confoundingly complex?

To begin with, it can feel perplexingly uncomfortable. The discomfort seems to arise for no discernible reason. In contrast, the discomfort that one might feel in the walking exercise, which I discussed in chapter 1, is easier to understand. In the walking forwards and backwards, the challenges are more apparent: the coordination between upper and lower body is more obviously complex, and stepping slowly often makes people wobble. But in single hand exercise A there is only a sideways shifting of weight, no stepping to begin with, and it really seems as though it should be easy. However, I have yet to see one person, new to the technique, who looks right immediately upon starting Chansigong.

Those students who most immediately feel awkward are on track for starting to learn Chentaiji. After a couple of months it begins not to feel so terrible, and then challenges of a deeper nature surface and you find yourself struggling again.

It may then come to the point where one feels oneself in what appears to be a downward spiral (without *jin*!). One feels worse and worse while practising. Master Chen reassures us, saying that this can be the experience of deepening understanding. And better this way, he says, than to be one of those people who sail along feeling OK, even very good, without their technique ever improving. To me, it was encouraging to consider that I might actually be moving along the right path, when so often I felt worse than ever before in my taiji life.

Once, after observing me struggling in a seminar about a year after I began Chentaiji, he said, "I see you, you looking for qi. I know this. Before, I also like this, we travel same road." And he indicated with his hands where I was on this road, and where he was, not too far beyond sight!

It is a conundrum that I have pondered for some time, and discussed with anyone who is interested, that it appears to be possible to do tolerable taiji in other styles with intermittent practice, whereas in Chentaiji, unless you dedicate yourself to regular practice under good guidance, you cannot feel at ease. I imagine there will be people disagreeing with me on this point.

Some might feel that Chen Style is easy, or that I hold this view because I am not so aware of other styles' rigours as I am of Chentaiji's demands. Nevertheless, having practised a Yang style for some twenty years and then a Chen style for some ten years, this is how I feel.

A Closer Look

I have just been up the hill and under the fence, to see if the glimpse of white yesterday was mushroom or rock. It is a *fungo*, not St George's but a local saint's; there are a score of them scattered on the hill, hidden in a fold of the slope. I would have needed a basket were I gathering them. I did bring a couple back for identification; the one that has begun to open weighs just under 500 grams. Strangely, they are of the same kind as the ones that come mid-autumn, high up the hill near the deck, always on the other side of the fence. I think it is unusual, a kind of mushroom that comes in spring and in autumn. Types that fruit both in summer and autumn are common, but the spring ones, I thought, are only of the spring. Identification is not straightforward, there appear to be many local variations, as with the moths. The nearest I can get is *Amanita vittadinii* (not for eating!). It is rather early in the year for me to get *funghi* fever.

Observing closely the inner workings in standing practice for this little book, I have been more alert to the day-by-day transformation of winter into spring. Stepping out under the stars last night, I tasted a bubbling valley. Good for pondering on *chansi* and *jin*.

Performing the single hand Chansigong satisfactorily requires

(i) enough strength in the legs to support dantian, enabling one to execute
(ii) a clear and controlled weight shift while staying intact in dantian, so that
(iii) the body becomes linked as the snake's is linked, relaxed not only in the main joints but in the many small articulations; and it requires
(iv) understanding of the internal changes at counts 1 and 3 of the exercise, and
(v) continual calibration of one's level of energy through sensitivity to qi flow.

With regard to the first point, 'strong' does not mean merely having developed leg muscles. These may be a help or a hindrance. Built up muscles which are impacted, inelastic, knotted and unyielding are, literally, stumbling blocks. It may often be to a person's advantage to start from 'weak' legs, if there is enough commitment to work on strengthening them. Without going to this extreme, and with some perseverance, a person with reasonably sound legs will not take too long to develop the kind of strength we need for Chansigong.

Having just come from ZhanZhuang in the bamboo grove, I have a suggestion, something to explore step by step. If you begin by standing on fairly straight legs, knees unlocked but legs hardly bent, you will be able to test this out. The sensation that you will probably have is of standing on the legs: you are centred in the chest and standing atop the legs, they are stiff and more or less braced against the ground.

Now look for a slight 'seated' position, what Master Chen calls, 'sit down chair'. You lower your centre of gravity a little, with some softening in the chest so that you do not merely bend the knees; look for an integrated alteration, the chest also sinking a little towards the ground, without any collapsing. If you can bring about this change, from standing atop the legs to a slight sitting down into them, feeling somewhat relaxed, the process of 'sinking the qi' has begun.

Sitting down in your standing stance, body upright and alert in the upper spine; the central point of the crown of the head, *baihui* – One Hundred Joinings – sky-wards; the body's weight dropping plumb earth-wards; within this frame relaxing every part you can sense out, maintaining the frame, neither sagging nor collapsing in the relaxation; this is the beginning of *song*.

You will feel your body's weight arrive in the soles of the feet. Any gripping in the feet can be released. The weight should be even, from the heels down the outer edge of each foot, wide across to the ball of the foot, the toes spread nicely. The transverse arch* of the foot around *yongquan* – Bubbling Spring – is articulated, and the big arch between heel and ball of the foot has breathing space. The little toe has a friendly contact with the ground.

These conscious articulations of the feet require varying alterations in the way you sit-stand in the legs. The ankles come into play importantly. There is more liveliness around the ankle joint, perhaps an unfamiliar awareness on each side of the Achilles tendon and along the outer ridge of the foot. The feet are slowly placing themselves on the ground like a pair of articulate hands; you could now sensibly tackle climbing a toddy palm tree, in search of the nectar at the top.

Standing stationary, breathing fully and quietly, at ease in the chest and abdomen, you are developing the kind of strength you need to Twine Silk.

The slow building of power in the legs involving muscles, tendons and ligaments, is a task running back and forth between the pelvic girdle and the feet. You are constantly adjusting upwards from the ground and downwards to the ground. In order to maintain the rounded arch formed by the two thighs with the pelvis in between, while the pelvis itself sits in a kind of sling or harness, the legs need to twine along their length, turning around the long axis of the bone. The upper leg rotates outwards while the lower leg including the foot rotates inwards. There is active articulation in the foot, no collapse inwards flat footed, nor rolling outwards. The rotation in the thigh is to be found without causing pressure in the kneecap; the rotation in the lower leg must not throw the weight askew. The calf muscles must not grip in the effort to find the twining action in the lower leg. The rotations are fluid, continually searching for the twining action with little loosenings and tightenings, miniature rotations happening in the opposite direction to the overall direction of twine. There is play, a fine tuning, an elasticity.

This is the stationary training for strengthening the legs. Legs trained in this way (and they become quite stocky; farewell to designer jeans!) can support dantian.

2 Shift Weight

Point 2, to shift weight clearly without losing centre – what we call a centred weight shift – now becomes a real possibility. As the weight is fed from one leg to the other, the leg you are moving away from twines outwards in the thigh, working to support dantian in the weight shift while maintaining the inguinal crease, *kua*. At the same time the lower part of the leg twines inwards, with a strong articulation through the ankle joint, thus grounding the twining actions of the entire leg. The sole of the foot must be rooted in the heel, arching slightly along the outer ridge and across to the ball of the foot, rooting again through all the toes. The wider the stance, the greater is the looseness required in the ankle joints and surrounding ligaments and tendons, in order for the feet to maintain a good contact with the ground.

The hip joints should be relaxed, *song kua*: relax the inguinal folds with the hips loose, unlocked, as you sit down with the weight falling perpendicular.

The shifting of weight is a play between the two legs, each side relaxed in the hip joints and the many articulations.

It is obvious that the leg supporting most of the weight of the body has to be strong. What is not so obvious is that the leg bearing less weight also has to have a subtle strength, the capacity to maintain an active twining from its join with the hip to the knee in strong torsion, and upwards from the foot and ankle. To achieve here a relaxed *kua* is no mean feat.

This is especially the case in the most difficult part of the circuit, the transition from counts 2 to 3, where qi from dantian rises up the back. The rising arm must not be lifted by the upper arm muscles; there should be no feeling of force or tension in the shoulder, no striving in the chest. The turning in the spine has to be accomplished without turning the hips and thus locking the *kua*, which would take one out of dantian and separate the upper body from the lower.

The impetus for shifting weight must come from underneath, low down in the back. This point not mastered shows immediately when one looks around a roomful of practicants: a heaving and shoving, action from high up in the body, that mars the execution of all the movements, through all the forms. It may be a lack of resilient strength in the legs that makes people press from their upper bodies when they shift weight, or it may simply be that they have a wrong idea of what is involved in these exercises. In those early days of Chen practice when I spent a great deal of time up on the deck on the hill, immersed in Chansigong and LaoJia, I would hear Manuele, our neighbour in the next valley, giving riding lessons. When the wind is in the right direction his powerful voice fills the sky. "Gambe! Avete le gambe! Usarle!" *Legs! You've got legs! Use them!*

People sometimes ask if the turn is in the waist, the waist in the conventional sense. Do the hips face front, while the upper body turns? That would mean twisting the chest against the lower body, which would be wrong. The movement that one is looking for is not an obvious manoeuvre that the untrained body can do. The correct turning is one that takes place within the integrated core. As you turn, you remain centred in dantian. There is no twisted reaching from the upper body, no pitching over from side to side. You sit, unwavering, unmoving.

3 Like Snake

The third requirement is to link the body through relaxing not only its main joints but all the tiny joints. This comes about through long hours of practice in Chansigong. When centre stays centre, dantian a fulcrum, with legs acting as springy arches, the core is empowered to spiral and articulate through the many little joints of the torso and limbs. This is a lifetime's training. Master Chen studies the creatures of the animal kingdom; he can watch nature films for hours, scrutinizing some scenes over and over. The search for a harmony of all parts refines continually his ability to create an extraordinary impression of balance and stillness, however fast he is moving. From apparent languor, he may explode into the air like a jungle cat, the frame of the body intact in suspension, the centre unruffled.

4 Rolling Up Our Sleeves

Stormy first light on *Venerdì Santo*. The old pear is in bloom. Once in a while this tree gives forth little fruits with a delicious fragrance. The ash of its wood may yield a stoneware glaze of the finest softest blue, when fired in reduction.

The fourth requirement is to understand the internal changes which occur at counts 1 and 3 of the single hand exercises. These delicate and critical manoeuvres need careful examination. They are turning points in the flow of qi along particular routes around the body.

Dantian is main terminus, ample home, qi hub. Imperceptible changes at the core affect the direction of qi flow. In order to cultivate a sensitivity for feeling tiny internal changes, it is necessary to pare down the movements of arm and weight shift.

First we shall look at the change at count 1. When count 4 completes, qi is fully expressed to the fingers ("turn switch on" says Master Chen, which often baffles new people). As count 1 begins, qi turns back towards dantian ("turn switch off" says he, and people realize he is using the on-off light switch as metaphor). Exercise A has a preparatory set of moves which bring you to this point. The circling arm is fully rotated away from the body, the palm turned out; qi arrives in the fingers; you are ready to begin the exercise. On count 1 the palm that was turned away from dantian starts to rotate inwards, and with this turning of the hand the direction of qi flow changes from outwards to

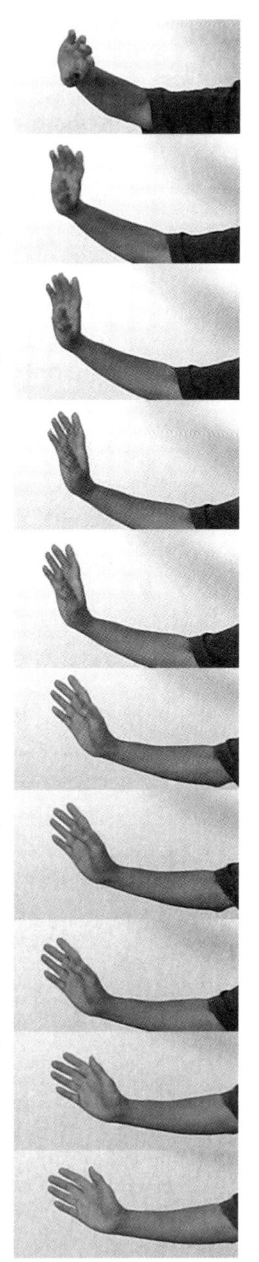

inwards. Count 1 is completed when qi is 'partially gathered' at the side of the waist; during this transition it is imperative that the weight does not shift, even imperceptibly. There cannot be a clear sense of qi flowing in the direction intended until the legs are able to give full support, and the leg not bearing the main weight has learned to twine.

This passage from 4 to 1 is a critical point; the direction of qi flow changes.

Where lies the difficulty? The change looks as though it should be simple and easy – the outward turned palm turns inwards. But it is not easy, and the beginner is puzzled by the lack of ease in performing an apparently simple movement. The movement that turns the hand lies deep within the body. Up to the end of count 4, dantian rotates in the same direction as the outwardly moving arm; the arm is fully expressing the spiral set off from the core. When qi reaches the fingers at the end of count 4, dantian begins to turn in the opposite direction, bringing about a small looping action alongside the torso. If the body's alignment is correct and the internal winding is not dissipated by a premature weight shift, then this change at dantian affects the hand, and from the hand's turning, the rest of the arm: the arm along its length acts like the spine of a snake. The dantian rotation should be so subtle that it is invisible, felt rather than seen by the viewer, and what is seen is the hand now changing its direction – the outer edge turns inwards, bringing about a rotation along the entire length of the arm; this draws the qi back from the fingers to the side of the waist, whereupon count 1 is completed.

While I have been getting occupied with this and that, Good Friday has drawn to a close, very darkly. In the gloaming, I see that the Rosa mundi leaves have come out. It may be a windy evening, chillier than it has been recently. Poor magnolia. The pseudo-morels, on the other hand, are growing sturdily in the rain, protected in the arbour; I have just been out to visit them. The old pear knows well the weather in these wild hinterlands of Tuscany.

The Way Between

In the freshness of morning I am reading again through this chapter on *chansijin*, as far as it has got. In the attempt to describe the first movement of the first exercise, we have had not only a lot of words, but a lot of little snaps – 'twipoles', I called them earlier in the book, twining tadpoles. I see too that the photos of the stances are like road signs, which say 'Siena' but may give the person reading the sign no feeling for this wondrous city, nor of the fresh and unlikely adventures along the way.

The interesting and challenging thing with Chansigong, and with the taiji forms, is what happens between. A stance has undergone becoming, and will become another stance. Is there enough vitality in it, to endure change? Is one learning to augment the vitality?

In moving from count 1 to 2, dantian continues its rotation; the direction is clear; qi from the side of the waist flows to the centre, fully gathered. In this phase of the cycle, the vitality infused by qi turning back towards the centre can be augmented, provided the stance remains unified. This is the moment for practising the 'centred' weight shift: stay intact in the transfer of weight, try not to lose the delicate insertions made at count 1 while carrying out count 2.

The change from 2 to 3 is the other critical point in the cycle. Qi turns in its direction of flow. It has to turn; the old direction, being towards the centre, has nowhere to continue once centre is reached. A key internal change chooses a new direction. There are innumerable possible choices for someone already trained in *chansijin*; to the beginner, none of these ways are obvious or easy. Three canonical choices* correspond to the three exercises we discuss here, and countless other choices correspond to others of the myriad possible forms of centred movement from this point. The change which brings about a new direction of qi flow is a deep and subtle redirecting of intent; it is a matter as much mental as physical. It hinges on the decision to express the gathered power in a particular way, a specific direction. Count 3 is the enactment of the way chosen; to achieve it naturally and effortlessly depends fundamentally on the vitality garnered at the completion of count 2. The change is, in part, a 'chest-waist change place' undulation at the core of the body, which can be effective only if the weight does not shift an iota during this phase of the cycle. A barely perceptible motion, natural and quiet as breathing, takes the flow of qi through *mingmen* – the Gate of Life between the kidneys – so that it rises up the back in an outward expression of power. In single hand exercise A the arm rises, turning across the body as

count 3 comes to completion, the palm facing down at about chest height; but when the action is true, there is no feeling of bringing the arm up from below, nor of taking it across the body, nor of turning the palm.

The continuation of the exercise from count 3 to 4 is easier since the direction is clear, as it was in the continuation from count 1 to 2. But the transition needs scrupulous attention and accuracy, in order to contain the charged store of qi. As one feels power rise through the body, the likely error is to become heady, to be carried away by the outer movement and to lead with the upper body – in other words, to fall apart. As the weight shifts, the outward twining of the arm needs to uncoil from low down in the back. If, throughout count 3, one is truly able to support the weight on the side reached at the end of count 2, then the weight shift on count 4 will be a discharge of potency. The four counts of Chansigong, correctly observed through countless rounds until the process becomes entirely natural, furnish the training for *fajin*, the release of the gathered force. Staying aware and centred, devoid of desire, the practiser brings qi to fingers, reaches the place where the single hand exercise began, and with bare attention continues to gather and refine the power through further cycles of qi flow.

Another day has passed, a real March day with scudding clouds and spells of rain. I went out to see what was happening on the terraces. Magnolia has thrown caution to the winds.

I have an idea for a different way of describing this exercise. Tomorrow.

A Celestial View

The valley is bathed in misty rain this Easter morning. No standing in the bamboos, for the second day running.

In the night I dreamt that I am standing, gazing up at birds in full flight above me, moving from left to right. Their bodies are a warm brown, with bluey grey and white on their wingtips. They are wheeling on the wind. Tiny gyrings aid their fast onward flight. They are one with the wind.

I have just been outside during a pause in the rain. These dark days suit the valley. The clouds come down from the tops, obscuring even the nearer hills. The currents of qi become more discernible, as in a Sung monochrome painting, and I find myself sinking into quiet.

Now that we have sketched out exercise A of single hand Chansigong, and no amount of switching on and off has elicited any electricity, let us try viewing it in quite another fashion.

At the very centre of your core is dantian. It is a slippery sphere, freely revolving around its own core, unencumbered by any restrictions. This by definition means being balanced in all directions. This sphere spins.

We start again at the beginning of exercise A, where qi is 'fully expressed' to the fingers, the weight on the same side as the moving arm. It is a bit tricky to pinpoint a slippery sphere, but let us attempt a foray.

We play the ball game. We now know the four counts and when the weight may shift. We simply do the exercise, one arm circling over and over as the weight goes back and forth. After this gets going and you do not need to think about it, turn your attention inwards, to the lower abdomen. Feel it round and slippery, rolling. Its rolling turns your arm, brings it across, raises it up, and sends it away.

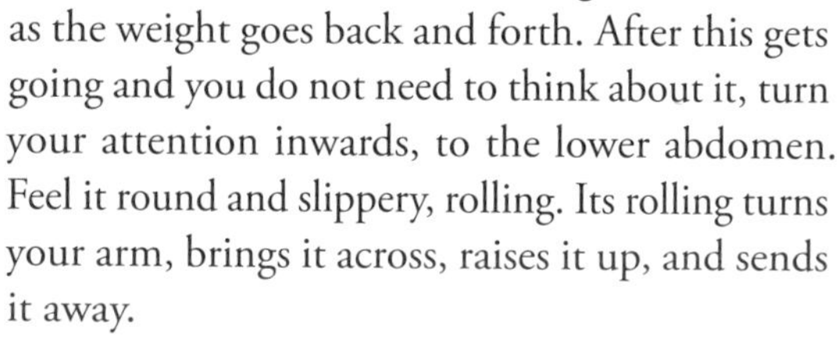

Now, with a corner of your awareness, feel what happens to the slippery ball when the arm comes down on the side of your body (the change from count 4 to 1). There is a backward roll of the ball. Its going under brings the arm, now low, towards dantian (count 2). From below, the ball continues rolling in the same direction, which means that from underneath, it comes up the front, and your arm is raised up (count 3). As it continues rolling in the same direction, your arm is sent away to the side (count 4).

If this game takes hold of you, you will feel your entire body rolling like a ball. Single Hand spirals continuously in the same direction. It is smooth, endless motion.

A friend in Bienne taught this exercise to some kids off the streets. They found it absolutely amazing. "Man!" they said. Street argot, French Swiss. "C'est vachement space!"

Well, let us return to planet Earth. Zhuangzi described it as "that hugest of clumps of soil",* instantly granting us a celestial vantage point.

5 *Knowing When It Doesn't Work*

The fifth requirement is to be able to calibrate one's level of energy through sensitivity to the qi indications that the body gives from day to day, moment to moment. This is where Chen XiaoWang's reminder needs to be heeded, that practising taiji is not like road work, or heavy manual labour which hammers away at the body. Qi flows smoothly through the movements when the mind is calm and clear, and the body light and free. When there is tiredness, as inevitably there is for one reason or another, it must be recognized and worked with. Suppose that on one day you practised intensely, and had sensations of strength and togetherness. You feel well and happy. The taiji positions are snug and compact. The next day, you go about your training in a similar way, and you notice that however you approach a movement, it does not connect like the day before. There is a heaviness about, every move is full of effort. The muscles feel sour; the body vibrates strangely, listlessly. If you now decide that what you need is to push yourself, thinking you can force your way through the unpleasant feelings, you are likely to deplete further your store of energy.

If, however, you decide not to be pushy, but practise all the same, going lightly through the form, perhaps choosing one that you do not spend much time on normally, then you will refresh the store of energy and the spirit will again lighten. The next day, or that very evening, there will be bounce once more in your taiji practice. There are many ways to conduct daily training. Regularity is important, but it is a good idea to adjust the routine from time to time, so that you do not become fixed and dependent on a particular programme. TaijiQuan is full of surprises, it is the practiser who can limit its creativity.

A Hair's Breadth

With sustained practice over the years one becomes increasingly sensitive to the feeling of flowing, and to the feeling of not flowing. And yet it is a fine line between the two, a line easy to cross inadvertently. There may be a puzzling awareness that one has lost the feeling of flow without knowing why. In my own practice this experience recurs at a particular point in single hand exercise A, at count 1, where qi from fingers moves back along the arm to the side of the waist.

At other points in the exercise, when I become aware of losing flow, I can usually alter my stance in one way or another, sometimes quite minutely, relaxing the chest or shoulder, or tautening within the relaxed arm to twine all the way to the fingers, for example. This generally will correct the fault enough for the sensation of lightness and fullness to come back. The problem at count 1, for me and for many people, is that it is very hard not to shift weight inadvertently. The amount of sheer strength which one has to put into not shifting weight is continually surprising.

There was a period when Master Chen would often say to me, accusingly, "You shift weight!" At the beginning I would protest, "No, Master Chen, I not shift weight." But he would firmly rejoin, "You do not know it, but you shift weight!"

And this at the very first count of Exercise A – how vexing! But until I had accepted his observation, I could not progress.

The two pictures on the left show the problem. In both pictures, I am in position at count 1, sitting down fairly well into the *kua*, with a decent arch between the legs. However, in the upper frame I have inadvertently shifted weight towards the centre, and missed an effective waist-side gathering of the qi; the flow is lost. This was not a deliberate demonstration of the problem; it is simply what happened yesterday when we filmed. I saw it when I viewed all the takes. Today I tried again, lower frame. It is very slightly better.

But why is it so hard not to shift weight here inadvertently?

The position is approached from count 4, where the twining right leg has just supported the weight shift to the left. As the change from 4 to 1 begins, the twining in the left arm reverses: from fully expressed outwards, it begins to gather inwards, drawing the qi to the side of the waist, *en route* to dantian. For this to happen, the delicate tautness of count 4, between the right *kua* and the left shoulder, must start to dissolve. As a result, the left leg actually has to take on more weight. If that leg was already near its weight bearing limit, then even a person who is somewhat aware of the problem will tend to shift weight inadvertently at this point, as in the upper frame shown on the left.

This has not happened, or has happened less, in the lower frame. The weight stays more on the left as it should, and qi can arrive truly at the side of the waist. Within a hair's breadth, for that is what it feels like to the practicant, lies the difference between flow and loss of flow.

Dantian Moves, Whole Body Follows

In taiji-speak we say, 'dantian moves, whole body follows'. But seeing what this idea can lead to, we had better think again! Is there confusion of the pelvis and hips with dantian? Glancing around taiji gatherings, you may see an array of people striving to move from dantian.

Dantian is where the centre of the body's mass is poised at the hub of qi. Master Chen describes TaijiQuan as a technique based on dantian as the poised centre. The dantian unit—comprising the 'waist' a little below the small of the back, and the area conjoined to it deep in the lower belly—controls the route travelled by the arm, and the consequent changes in wrist, palm, fingers.

Chen XiaoWang emphasizes that rotation of the dantian is a subtle affair. Intent sparks off a movement under the small of the back; dantian turns; qi flows in a certain direction. Dantian is the pivot. It is not a part of the body that you heave about, splitting what little unity you may have had to begin with. To be unified means that one tiny impetus from the waist turns dantian, and spiralling engulfs the rest of the body. Dantian at the junction of the qi roads is never committed. The muscles in this area are not in contraction. Thinking that power is in dantian, and pushing to move from there, jams the roads.

In each of the three single hand exercises, the dantian unit rotates in a specific way, setting off movement along particular trajectories through the arm and the legs. Qi passes through the same stations – side of the waist, dantian, upper back and fingers – but the way from one to the next varies.

Of the three routines, exercise B requires the closest affinity to one's core. To follow B's particular route requires technique that is natural and free of constraint, able to move like a silkworm as it creates liquid silk, exuding the filament. Actually one may say of every action in taiji that it must be natural and free, but attempting B makes clear the urgent need to understand silkwormhood. Only when the core is undulating softly will B begin to show its character. The penultimate Chansigong exercise ('chest-waist change place') discussed at the start of this chapter is key to the development of the technique. One must absorb this exercise so fully that it becomes one's way of moving.

When describing these 4-count exercises it is often best to start with count 4 as a lead-in to count 1. But in count 4 of exercise B, where qi moves from the top of the dorsal spine outwards through the shoulder, elbow and fingers, the pathway runs so close to that of A that for a long

while the student of Chansigong might not be able to tell the difference. B begins to differentiate itself clearly from A when count 4 (left frame above) changes to count 1 (middle frame). You soon realize there is the sensation of a new kind of twining in the arm. Whereas in A the arm arcs gradually as qi travels to the side of the waist *en route* to dantian, in B the arm coils back into itself. You feel yourself the silkworm, instinctively withdrawing or recoiling towards dantian as count 1 gives way to count 2 (right frame).

The progression from count 2 to 3 is where the worm turns. That recoil back to dantian which is of a different impulse brings out a new range of motion, more intense than the minimal core undulation of exercise A. In exercise B the torsion achieved by the closer rotation of the arm at count 1, absorbed into dantian at count 2, rises through the torso in a strong twisting action to count 3. The *jin*, twining power, is led out in this twisting.

The series below shows in sequence exercise B, starting from position 4 (qi to fingers), coiling back into itself (qi to waist, position 1); arrival at dantian (position 2), then the twist of qi up the back (position 3), which leads to the outward twining of the *jin* in the first frame (position 4).

Exercise C at first seems to resemble A. It looks like an extended version of A, involving more of a turn in the torso and a wider circling of the arm. It may not be until the first time one is corrected in the stance that one

makes the startling discovery that the turn to the back diagonal is to be accomplished without swivelling the hips. They must remain parallel, with the *kua* relaxed. The extensive spiralling is within the core of a supple and resilient body, where all parts are in free concourse, connected smoothly and firmly. The effort to achieve this can preoccupy one for several years.

Once the posture has stabilized, and one becomes a little skilful in *chansijin*, C begins to reveal its secrets. It is entirely different from both A and B, in hue, in saturation. As Schafer said of the cycles of cosmic evolution, each chimes a different celestial tune. One feels oneself like a large raptor, a bird of prey, opening the wing and sweeping the air currents with a powerful gyration from the centre. C's motion is wide and oblique, its span extending more completely across the body. The two sides are weaving together in broad swathes, creating a sensation of barely controlled turbulence.

Tied up in these thoughts, I have only now noticed that the weather outside has shifted. The sun flashes as it sets. The birds are singing.

I learn and practise instinctively, I do not really analyze movement. But when I teach, if I see the students are in need of 'words language' I look for ways to explain a move. For the writing of this book, I have been examining my practice, pausing again and again in the writing to get up and see what it is that happens in these twinings, to try and understand this perpetual becoming.

Just as interior changes are manifested exteriorly, minuscule differences in alignment, tiny variations in the angle of approach contribute to the variety of positions that can appear at the completion of the four counts in each exercise. People are different and we change from day to day. The quality of a person's energy varies; awareness of the variation guides one in shaping movement.

One day, a movement done in a particular way may flow and be true to the rules of Chansigong; for there to be flow on another occasion it might need a slightly different looping interiorly, culminating in an end position that looks somewhat different but is also true.

Double Hands

Gentle twitterings outside woke me up at dawn. The valley is soaked, all geared up for further springing. The little pine on the hill is growing sprightly, the one we call 'pseudo-Mugo'. It is one of two that grew from a bonsai kit we had bought in the local super-market, labelled 'Mugo', and germinated in the fridge. One of them is a Mugo pine, but this one looks nothing like! If the packet had not been clearly labelled Mugo, we would have said this is *Pinus sylvestris*. It sprouted from seed around the time I began to learn Chansigong.

Double hand Chansigong introduces delicious further levels of complexity compared with single. The progression from single to double multiplies the twinings.

First, the stance. It is one that occurs throughout the forms. It is a bow stance like in the single hand exercises, except that one foot is forward of the other; the back foot is turned out about 45°, and the front foot is straight, or better, a tiny bit turned in. The stance is critical for the twining.

One looks for a 'sitting' position, the torso sitting as if it were in a harness, the kind a baby sits in, and with a good inguinal crease (*kua*).

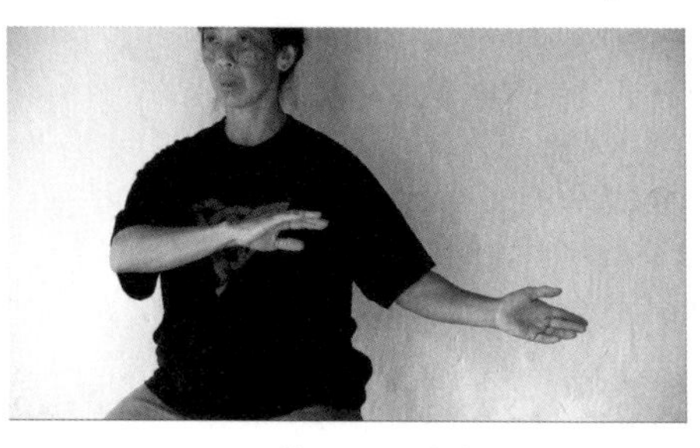

The abdominal muscles are relaxed, feeling at ease in dantian. Taking up this position (or taking down), when done correctly, is demanding for the beginner, but it is essential for relaxing the upper body while staying true to the principles of Zhan-Zhuang. Dantian feels nice and full, and the chest feels nice and empty.

All parts of the body support dantian. It takes some readjustment of the tent pegs to achieve this. The readjustment becomes a finer and finer tallying, minute tightenings and loosenings as the weight shifts, searching all the time for the correct passage through the movements. Mind balanced, listening behind. Qi sinks down. One cultivates a particular kind of attention – calm, spacious, and unharried. Only half-thinking, as Chen XiaoWang puts it, and of this half of the mind that is engaged, half is for the movement at hand, and half for attention to posture. And the remaining unthinking half – it is unoccupied, a wide unfettered awareness.

Shoulders flow to hips, elbows to knees, hands to feet. The shoulder girdle mirrors the pelvic girdle. All parts dovetail into one another, the body is unified.

The first part of the exercise is in fixed stance, no stepping, only shifting the weight back and forth in precise coordination with the spiralling arms. All that has been said regarding Single Hand A applies to Double Hands. Work on achieving a centred weight shift. Being stringently aware of when you shift weight, and when you absolutely do not, will slowly build up your bow stance, with both legs dynamically supporting the core. You continue nurturing dantian as the abode of qi. From image, it becomes a reality, you dwell within. Then your core will learn to spiral through its many articulations.

Once the core is spiralling freely, the practice of Double Hands will reveal the delicacy of timing that is essential for performing LaoJia and XinJia. There is a natural ebb and flow in the rhythm. Multiple circuits slip in and out of each other, one pausing to allow another to weave in, enfolding it for some moments before releasing and spurring it in a new direction. Spiralling activates the entire body. Feet are as hands, legs are as arms; the sides of the torso are stretchy and taut simultaneously. At the centre, dantian rides supreme, unmoving.

Like the single hand Chansigong, the double hand exercise unfolds from two critical moments when vital internal changes turn the direction of qi flow. These moments, at the beginning of counts 1 and 3, mark the two phases of a single 'chest-waist change place' action; counts 2 and 4 are the connecting passages in between.

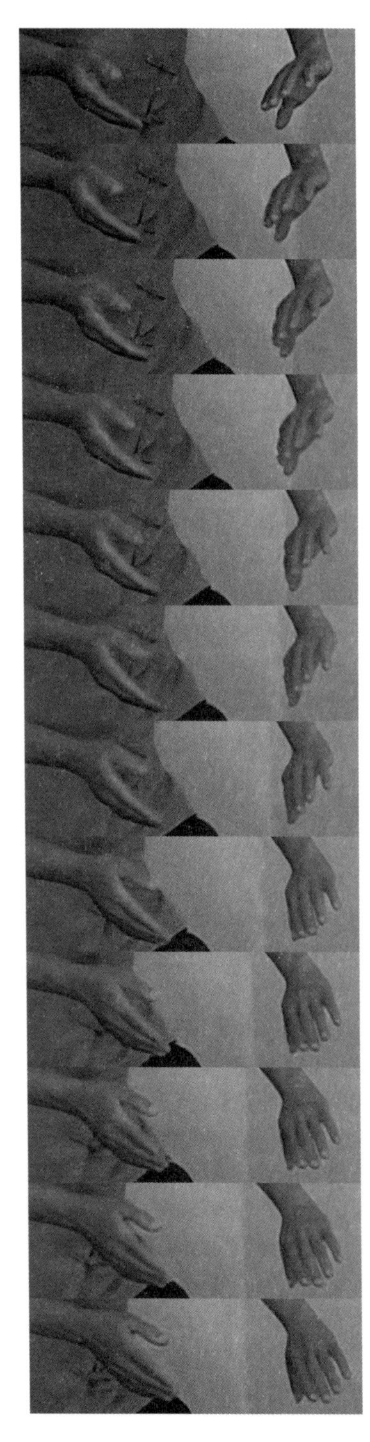

The leading hand, when it has fully expressed qi to fingers, begins to turn back towards dantian. In exquisitely precise synchrony with this change, the other side of the body turns from gathering qi inwards to leading qi out, as the following hand prepares to become the leading hand.

These changes of qi direction are orchestrated by dantian. In each count of 1 and 3, the side which begins the outward journey, from dantian up the back, is enfolded within the side that is returning towards dantian.

In count 1 the outwardly twined front hand releases its energy. A widening and loosening of the intent turns the qi which coils back along arm and waist.

In count 3, when the outwardly twined back hand changes to wind inwards, the sensation of the change is different. The back hand keeps its charge, to augment the flow towards dantian. In double hand Chansigong, where the weight shift is along the diagonal axis, the entire body's force is directed along this axis. All of the body spirals, continually leading the *jin* to the front hand, where it may be released.

In count 1, the disposition of the front elbow is crucial for allowing the qi to travel back along the arm to the side of the waist. Only through a precise degree of a fine inward twining in the elbow can the connection to waist be established. For the back arm, the crucial count is number 3, when the back elbow winds in towards the side of the torso, augmenting the flow towards dantian.

The four positions of double hand Chansigong are found gradually over some years of practice. When one can guide the qi into place at the side of the waist; when one knows its arrival at dantian and how it spirals up the back; when one is able to conduct its passage through the shoulder and along the arm until qi fills the fingers; when one can adjust oneself at any given moment to nudge the flow along these routes – then one may become free from the positions of Chansigong. The inner flowing, linking, and passing through the four stations interiorly is the true enactment of the taiji. The way, marked on a map, takes on life.

When one is skilful in guiding and shifting delicately inside, the turnings that alter the change of qi direction are taken with minimal exterior indication: little may show on the surface. One reaches the stage of practice where the positions recognized to be 1 and 3 hardly appear: the change has been made interiorly, there is no further need to assume the position.

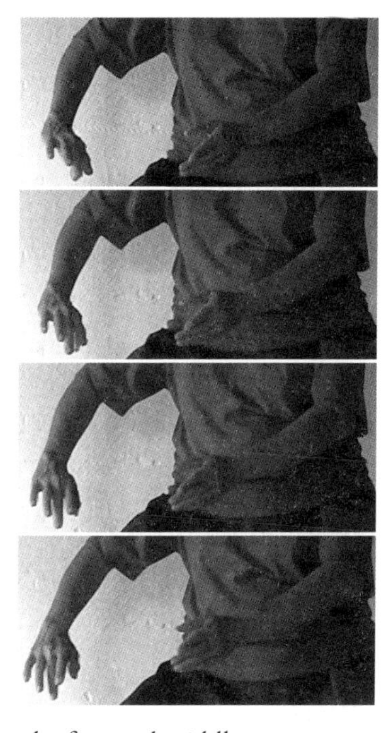

Let us look fleetingly at the transition from count 4 to count 1. The first frame shows the hands at the completion of count 4: qi has arrived in the fingers of the front hand, and on the other side of the body qi has returned to dantian. In the second frame both hands show the first twinkling of change in direction of qi flow. The change becomes more definite in the third frame: the front hand has already made the critical turn from outward to inward, while the back hand shows that qi has begun to rise up the back. In the fourth frame, with the barest of shiftings the change is complete. The direction of qi has turned, from outward flowing to inward returning; note how close the placement of the hands is to count 4 of the first picture, how tiny is the exterior manifestation of a great interior alteration. This is partly what Chen XiaoWang means when he says that the two key changes – from fingers to waist, and from dantian to back – are very delicate.

One aspect of these pictures that stands out is the way the fore and middle fingers of the right hand are 'banked'; they are not joining in very well with the qi flow. They stick out like reeds in a stream that are too stiff to go with the flow. In chapter 4 on ZhanZhuang, we explored some of the inhibiting factors elsewhere in the body which can surface in the hands. Sometimes it is one finger, sometimes another, sometimes more than one. It is common and instructive to see this problem in oneself and other people. When the inhibition becomes less, sometimes the recalcitrant finger starts quivering. That is like a reed which has begun to yield to the flow, but is still a little too rigid; it trembles, half in and half out of the current.

These *chansijin* exercises provide the framework for every Chentaiji form. Some are acutely shaped by them, none more so than XinJia and the Spear form. In the next three chapters we shall look at XinJia. When we examine the moves in the form, it will be clearer that what I have said so far about these exercises is only a first approximation to what happens in *chansijin*. The double hand exercise in particular is a training for *fajin*. The nearer one can get to a correct alignment, the more effectively the stance will channel the passage of *jin*.

I once watched Ben being corrected by Chen XiaoWang in a Double Hands position. It began with the stance as I conceived of it. At the end of the many adjustments, increasingly fine as time went on, the transformation was so great that I exclaimed out loud, "Is this still Double Hands number 2?". And for Ben who had experienced the mysteriously taxing correction, it was a revelation: the changes that Master Chen wrought had potentized the exercise. He began to realize the power that lies in *chansijin*.

The breaking down into counts and the naming of stations is an effort to simplify and make approachable motion that is as complex as nature. Every tiny variation in the stance – its width, depth, and hardly perceptible changes of angle – influences the torsion that begins just below the small of the back (the spot Master Chen pinpoints as 'waist'), which the dantian directs in a specific direction, rippling outwards from centre. In fact, each round of four counts completes a unique circuit. The more naturally we move, the more spontaneously created is the route; the arrival at dantian or fingers is each time along a subtly different pathway.

In the Chen forms with their multitude of possible spiralling actions, this is indeed what happens. The circuits are being created anew all the while one is in motion. But in order for the movements to come from centre and the body to move as a unified whole while performing multiple twinings, one needs long and exacting training in *chansijin*.

From Yang Style days my notebook contains these words from a T'aiChi classic with a very long name:

> No part of the body moves without affecting the whole… like a pleat which folds in on itself and continues to the next one with rhythm and order… Give the spirit free rein, let the breath permeate the bones…*

Like single hand Chansigong, you practise double hand *ad infinitum*, on a count of four. Together with the 'chest-waist change place' combinations,

and the leg twining routine, these exercises furnish the training for the complex interior changes required in LaoJia. LaoJia in turn is a preparation for XinJia's cascade of twinings.

Today has been beautiful from beginning to end. Now it is deep in the night, and the little owl is calling from amongst the oaks on the hill. At sunset, I saw the first swallow fly over the valley, winging its way westwards, perhaps to the Ligurian hills by the sea, where it warms earlier than here in the hinterland.

When Single Doubles

Yesterday was *Pasquetta* ('little Pasqua', the day after Easter Sunday), and friends who live in the Apennines on the other side of the pass came to visit us. Riccardo is a *fungaiolo*, and as soon as I showed him the white mushrooms from the hill that I had picked for identification, he said, "In my opinion, these are *Amanita vittadinii*." He thought they were edible. When asked if he would eat one, he replied that he would, after making out his will. Later, when we walked them down to their car, I saw that all two dozen *funghi* which had been there on the slope the day before were gone! Hunters have been about in the valley, had they picked them? Are they edible, after all?*

Earlier, Riccardo had admired the pseudo-morels, growing big and strong in the arbour, and after looking through our books, he had settled on *Helvella*, allowing for local variation.

I mentioned in chapter 6 that the sequence of Cloud Hands, *yun shou*, is the doubling of single hand exercise A of Chansigong.

As in the single hand exercise with stepping, the feet remain parallel as you step sideways – one foot steps out to the side, the other foot steps up alongside it – and like this it repeats, 'no beginning, no end', as Pytt liked to call Cloud Hands. One may indeed repeat them endlessly, travelling in both directions.

It is wonderful as a double-handed exercise, at all stages of one's training. Whereas in the single hand exercise it is not easy to free up the arms, the doubling of the movement, with both arms spinning, can build a momentum which carries one.

A person new to Cloud Hands first learns the movement, then learns to trust that the arms will keep to their pathways once the feet are in motion. It can be exhilarating, the arms moved like a windmill by strong air currents, airborne yet grounded by the steady rhythmic steps.

The secret of Cloud Hands is in the changes which take place at the critical points of counts 1 and 3. The arms, in fact the entire body, pass through them, they notch the body's parts in place. In Cloud Hands, as in the double hand exercise proper, the two sides simultaneously undergo this change: the precise moment at which the qi direction changes to flow in towards dantian on one side of the body, is the moment when it changes to flow away from dantian on the other side. There is a sense of the inevitability of change, and the innate order that embraces it.

In one's no beginning no end practice, countless observations are made daily. As technique develops, one notices within the framework of the stance and the journeying along the qi road travelled by each arm, the crisscrossing of pathways and myriad delicate interweavings of left and right, front and back, upper and lower, interior and exterior. When the legs too are spiralling freely, the experience of *chansijin* becomes profound. Chentaiji starts with a swirling point which loops around the asteroids.

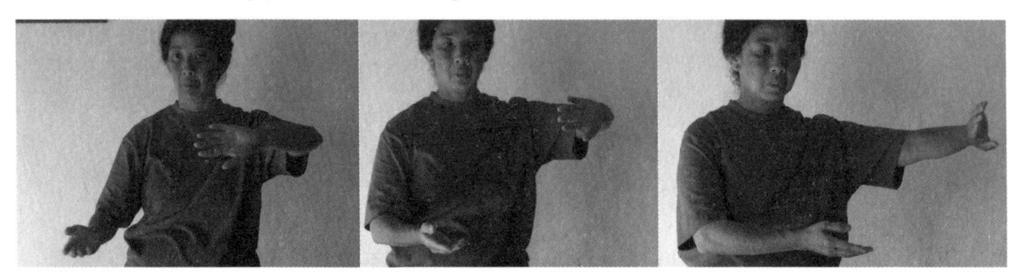

CHAPTER 9

XinJia

Now it is May. We have been back in the valley for a week, after a month in England. Each morning the Golden oriole wakes us up. The song is like a gentle tale; the other birds seem to listen too, they are more quiet when the Golden oriole (*Oriolus oriolus*) sings. The first time I heard it was on a walk on the east side of this valley, nearly twenty years ago. A hot summer's day, and a haunting call stopped me in my tracks. At first it did not even sound like bird song to me; it seemed to be a kind of human tongue, speaking a language of remembrance. I had no idea what bird it could possibly be. A few years later I heard it again; the singer was in amongst the old poplars at the bottom of our terraces, I could see a flutter every now and then. Only after dedicated periods by the window, binoculars in hand, scanning through the poplars' canopy, did I spot the bird. It is shockingly vivid, bright yellow, with black on the wings and tail, and a red beak. It is also quite large, a good ten inches. How does it manage to hide itself so well?

This year there is a new song in the valley. Hearing light squitterings from the *kako* (persimmon tree), I dash to the window and catch sight of a little bird. The singer turns out to be *Phoenicurus phoenicurus*, the Common redstart. She and her dapper mate are swooping up and down the terraces, startling us with their crimson tails.

Many years ago, on a summer's afternoon nearing the solstice, when we were new to the valley, I was standing by the stone wall just below the house. The grass we had not cut on the terrace above me was a foot high, with chicory flowers Madonna-blue standing in amongst the profusion of grasses and wildflowers. A swift and contained movement fixed my gaze: a snake appeared out of the tall grass, followed by a parallel motion nearby which I at first took to be its tail, in a strange, doubled writhing. But it was a second snake, and for a long time I watched the two twining, withdrawing and re-twining, oblivious of my presence.

This was before Chen Style TaijiQuan came into my life. Some years later, after I had learned LaoJia, we were with Chen XiaoWang in England. In Oxford we visited the University Parks; looking at the trees and the expanse of green, he decided it would be a good setting for the videotaping of a form, there and then. It was a form we had never seen before, XinJia. For me, it was a fatal moment. Here was the snakes' dance.

LaoJia and XinJia are the two long forms of Chentaiji. *Lao* means old, and *xin* means new, they are the 'old' and 'new' frames of the Chen family's style. The creation of XinJia is credited to Chen XiaoWang's grandfather, Chen FaKe. Seeing Master Chen perform it in the park in Oxford was an electrifying experience. I felt as though I had no time to lose, I could spend the rest of my life trying to fathom its depths.

Upon arriving in Sydney for our next period of study, we quickly settled into the daily rhythm established the year before – ZhanZhuang and Chansigong corrections, then correction of form gone through section by section to the end. We began with LaoJia, then the 38 Form. Master Chen wondered what I would like to learn next, and hardly daring to ask, I said, "XinJia!"

Learning it was revelatory. Its way of moving feels ancient, ab-original; an instinctive rationale threads the form together. It made me wonder, had this been a case of the old world being discovered as 'new'?

Both long forms follow the same outline, move by move, with XinJia containing greater intricacy of detail, the major stances approached more elaborately, adding up to a slightly longer form. If we were to imagine them as two works of abstract design, LaoJia would be of broad swathes of harmonious colours weaving gently in and out of one another, with a clear rhythm and order. XinJia would stand in strong contrast, the colours intense and at times of strange hues, patterns swirling in startling ways, its rhythm contrapuntal.

Chen XiaoWang in schoolboyish* mood once said of the two forms, "LaoJia like rifle, XinJia like machine-gun!" LaoJia is a wide, lazy river. Though its surface is calm, it pulls with a strong current. A few whirlpools lie along its course, as it flows steadily through gently rolling hills, all the way out to sea. XinJia is a mountain river, tumultuous, unpredictable, with narrow defiles and precipitous gorges, where one may happen upon a still pool, "flowing from an unknown source, to pour itself into an unknown sea".*

Our 1997 visit to Sydney turned out to be a XinJia-intensive. To my request that we learn XinJia, Master Chen replied that six of his students from Japan were about to arrive. If we could learn the form before they arrived, we would be able to join them in their daily lessons. And so we plunged into XinJia's torrent.

Learning a form from Master Chen in a seminar is a relaxed process; he demonstrates short sections several times over, and when you go through the moves without him, you can sneak a look at others around you. But alone with him, you had better be on the ball *cento per cento*, as the Italians say, 100 per cent (or very nearly), or you feel a real fool. At least there were two of us, and we certainly needed the combined memorizing capacity of both. He would show us a short sequence, twice or three times at the most. Then we each had to repeat it. It was nerve-wracking, but he was also very kind. There were times when he would say, "Look at that tree! It is very funny." For us Northerners, Australian trees are like beings from another planet. He would distract us, make us laugh, and relax in our efforts. And so we learned XinJia.

It begins like LaoJia. The first few movements are in principle identical. But there is a zest particular to XinJia, a quickening pulse that one feels from the very beginning, anticipating the moment when XinJia shows itself for the first time, in a subtle recoil just before the stamp of 'Pounding the Mortar'.

Now it is ten years that I have been practising the two long forms in tandem. In the early years, XinJia took a lot more out of me than did LaoJia. I would be able to correct my posture quite strongly through several rounds of LaoJia, but I could only manage two or three reps of reasonably good XinJia. There would be days when I had not the necessary energy stored for serious XinJia practice.

XinJia consists of move upon move of intricate articulations, folding at varying speeds in different directions. Only a firm fluid core gives the freedom to move lightly and swiftly. After a while I began to understand what was making XinJia so tiring for me: I was pushing against blocks. Practising it was showing me the limits of the technique that I had so far developed. XinJia, to do it well without getting tired, needs better technique than does LaoJia; I had not realized this, because I had not been listening carefully enough to the signals my body was giving me.

Chen XiaoWang had been pointing out this aspect of daily practice since the beginning. I had not taken it seriously enough. His "Natural – first principle!" necessitated awareness of varying capacities on different days, at different times of the day. I had to train with respect towards myself.

In one lesson on one day, there would be experiences of strength and connection. The next day, I would be unable to find the same feelings of flow. I would struggle, confused, not understanding why it did not feel good. Master Chen would watch me with sympathy, then say gently, "Yesterday you work very correct, today muscles tired." After a day of high energy, he would ask how many days it took me to recover. If I said that it took me three, he would respond, "Only?" I had to accept that these fluctuations in energy were natural, and that learning to work according to qi indications was actually the way to build technique.

I was slow and stubborn on this point. In thinking back to the first years of training in Sydney and in Europe, I remember the looks he would give me, when he saw me wanting to pound away at the taiji like others around me. It seems to me now, that the most important thing he wanted me to understand was how to work with qi. This required deep sensitivity to the body's state at any given moment, so as to execute the movement at hand in accordance with one's immediate capacity. The use of force which hurts is damaging in the long run; it will not serve in the development of true technique.

This aspect of working correctly was most clearly demonstrated by Master Chen's injunction that I not do the movements with force. About three years into the training, I was repeatedly told, "Kinthissa, no *fajin*!" It was most disconcerting when he began to say this in the seminars. The group in Bienne was at that time studying *paochui*, the 'Cannon Fists' form of LaoJia. This is often referred to as LaoJia's 'second routine'; it is a brief form designed to show off one virtuoso move after another, extracted from the long 'first routine'. Being reined in so persistently trained me to observe myself. Whenever I lost awareness, I was sharply reminded. I realized that every time I got pushy, I lost touch with my body. Recollecting myself, I could reconnect. I began to notice that there were not these blips when I practised alone. It was when I was in a group; whenever there was the slightest desire to show off, to prove myself, or be part of the pounding gang, I went against myself.

When some years later we had the chance to learn XinJia *paochui*, I truly appreciated the way Chen XiaoWang had taught me in that early period. This little set of XinJia variations is jewel-like, requiring for its execution the greatest freedom. Whereas in LaoJia's *paochui* the moves are somewhat clunky – a 'three to the right and three to the left' kind of feel – the *paochui* of XinJia trills and leaps, giving one the sense of a unique, authentic creation.

Apart from Chen XiaoWang's magnificent XinJia renditions, I have seen only one other person whose XinJia has impressed me. This was a woman, Japanese, one of the six, all teachers, who came to Sydney in 1997. She was of a narrow and light build. Her delicacy had a lithe power, it brought out quite another dimension of XinJia's character. I find wildness suits women. Female practitioners of TaijiQuan have a paucity of exemplars to be inspired by. Master Chen said that this woman was gold medal material, only her responsibilities in running an organization did not allow her enough training time. When I have asked him, is the training for women different from men's, his reply has been, "No, it is the same." When I enquired after women in his family who reached a high level in TaijiQuan (as one hears almost exclusively of men), he said that some had excelled in their early years, but then they had married, *etcetera*.

In chapter 2, I wrote about the art of copying. This is an essential period in learning. One must observe and try to reproduce what one sees. This stage occupies one for a good while. However, there needs to be common sense. Master Chen tries to alert his students; every now and then, he warns: "Not copy! This like handwriting!" He means that a particular detail of his movement, which he sees a student trying to imitate, is a personal detail of his own, like his handwriting, and that it is foolish to want to look like a copy of someone else, even of a master.

This Japanese woman's XinJia *xie xing*, 'Step Obliquely', continues to intrigue me, more than ten years later. The way of entry into *xie xing* needs a fineness and quickness, like a bird's darting precision. Even when someone has good technique, if there is self-conscious pride it will weigh down this movement.

From what I have said so far about XinJia, the impression I may have given is of a showy form. It can certainly be performed like that, but its real power is hidden, *xuan*, darkly threaded.*

The movement of Pound Mortar plummets through the body – the raised fist pounds the palm, the raised foot pounds the ground. In the stillness that follows the booming unification, XinJia's subterranean stirrings, which were barely glimpsed in the recoil before the stamping, begin to emerge. Tiny spirals of *jin* break surface. Close gyrations from within ripple out along the limbs, setting astir the palm and fisted hand as the body coils to the right, then to the left. The first coiling begins slowly: deep down in the torso there is a winding leftwards before the coiling manifests rightwards. The second coiling, to the left, is more inward and rapid, and requires real subtlety of command: while the body is coiled to the right, a core quivering deeper rightwards reverses the direction of the body's coiling. At the heart of these changes lies the technique of that penultimate exercise of Chansigong, 'chest-waist change place'. It needs great ease in mind and body, a carefree way of being.

I had gone to sleep last night, thinking of those half-hidden stirrings of XinJia which come after Pound Mortar.

These windings in XinJia, some tiny and visible only in a corner of the arena, while others involve entire swathes of the body, with many running in near-simultaneous cross-currents, they are all a part of one continuous twining from the form's start to its finish.

After some years of living with XinJia, the moves begin to fit into one another. The continuously twining aspect asserts itself, hooking, linking, drawing in and turning out of the stances. It is this running thread that is vital, it must be constantly churned out from dantian.

The near hills are just beginning to emerge from behind the mists, after more rain in the night. Perennial honesty glows modestly in this light. When its flower heads turn into round seed-purses, one can appreciate the local name for the plant, *monete del papa*, Pope's coins. I am glad that the orioles are still here; they are easily put off by changes in the weather, and one summer we lost them early. What they particularly do not like is *tira vento*, 'wind pulling', which these valleys, lying between mountains and the sea, are known for. Like the mushrooms, which also do not like wind, and which may be waking up now in the west woods, after rain and strong sun earlier this month.

The gyrings come out from behind the scenes. Well, they nearly do! Nothing in XinJia completely comes out from behind the scenes.

Through the second coiling leftwards one enters the complex phrase of moves known as 'Lazily Tying the Robe', *lan zha yi*. Twisting and turning, qi wends its way sinuous up the back, twines out across the shoulders, spins out to the fingers of both hands. Then the extension reverses, it becomes a taut closing, a gathering into the left. Qi has now turned back towards dantian. It pauses dramatically before opening again, languidly, to arrive at an elegant and almost coy completion of *lan zha yi*.

In LaoJia, *lan zha yi* finishes in tranquil repose. Now in XinJia, the equilibrium is delicately poised, on edge. The power is stored in the left, ready to unfurl successive waves which will lead to 'Six Sealing, Four Closing', *liu feng si bi*.

The left side of the body controls the moves that follow. It opens and folds forwards on its side of the body, eliciting in the right arm a nearly mirroring undulation. The left side then appears to settle for a moment, as though waiting, but actually it continues to coil, less visibly, charming the right to its side. When the two hands join at dantian, the body surges to the right, linked hands reinforcing the power issued from centre.

The left side then pulls back, carrying both arms to the left; they are swept up into position, and for a moment the whole body is poised: which way will it tip the balance?

Almost nothing in XinJia is symmetric. In the phrase preceding 'Six Sealing, Four Closing' (6 + 4 = 10, meaning 100% sealing, aka closing), one is tempted to think that the two arms open in symmetry. Most likely due to stiffness of the spine, people often perform this movement with the two arms equal in their spread; it is challenging enough as it is, to undulate the upper body while keeping the lower intact. When one becomes more free the motion shows its complexity. It is again the left that directs the opening and closing of the two sides, drawing in the right side a fraction of a moment later. Tightly coiling leftwards, the arms fold in, hands by the nape of the neck. From here there is a surprising final closing, slanting downwards to the right.

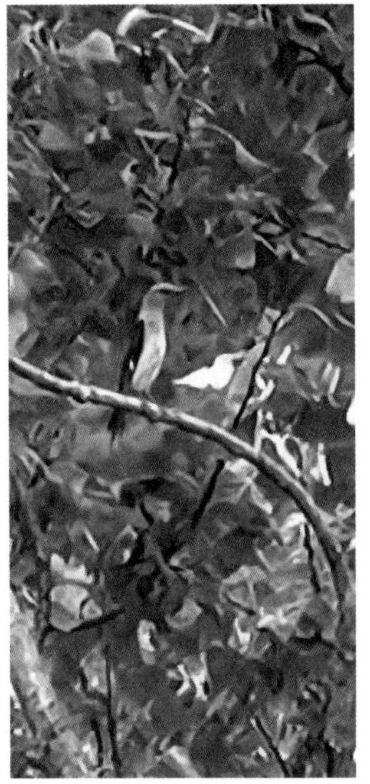

Since we have become familiar with the shy Golden orioles, we wait for them each summer. They only appear in the valley when the Black poplars on our terraces are in full leaf. These old trees have an airy canopy, yet the birds somehow conceal themselves in amongst the pendulous leaves. One sees them in rapid flight before they disappear into the foliage, or when they dart out from behind the swishing curtains. They have a startling habit of diving suddenly from a great height, out of the Lombardy poplars.

There was a flash of gold, and just in case an oriole would show itself, I scanned the trees with the video camera. Now we see to our great pleasure a young adult male in the Black poplar. He is riding heraldic the boughs heaving in the wind, his breast still pale, his head and back a warm golden yellow, his wings already a rich black with the characteristic waistcoat buttonhole spot which will soon turn golden.

Some of the minutiae that one is struck by may be due to Chen XiaoWang's aesthetic fineness. On occasion, I have seen in a room several people in the same stance of a form, after he has worked on their postures and brought each to a kind of completion. They finish looking very different from one another, to the extent that sometimes one wonders how they can all be doing the same move of the form. He has brought each person to their final position creatively, in a way that best expresses a quality particular to that person. It can be startling, when we suddenly see inner beauty given outward dimension. And where we thought the arms were in a certain predictable arrangement, they are free like brush-strokes in an original piece of calligraphy.

As one becomes more and more at home in LaoJia and XinJia, the *chansi* exercises that one has practised, sometimes laboriously, begin to illuminate the forms. One comes to recognize and experience the logic of the *chansi* that threads the stances together. At one point in the form, the arm turns in such a way that the qi is led out to the fingers; at another point, a tiny winding of the hand guides the qi back along the arm towards dantian. These moments of understanding are precious in the daily life of the practicant. Adroitness in Chansigong eventually frees up the form altogether. A stance is no longer a position of the body; it is that moment's configuration of twinings.

The rain this afternoon is light and quiet. The oriole continues to sing. The redstart pair now have neighbours on the terraces – the Red-backed shrikes, *Lanius collurio*, have arrived. They come here each year to breed, and are rather fierce in their hunting habits. The male with his black mask, elegant grey crown and red back, sits in the open on fences and trees. He has a prominent black beak. Once we were on our kitchen terrace, enjoying the peace of a summer afternoon. There was a yellow swallowtail butterfly, *Papilio machaon*, hovering nearby in fresh colours and magnificent markings. Suddenly the shrike had it in his beak, and we could only watch aghast as he flew back to his perch in triumph. I have just read in the bird book that shrikes also take small birds; I fear for the young redstarts!

The day after we came home, I spotted the hoopoes flitting along the lane. Each summer I wonder who will be back in the valley. In the early years, there was a great variety of moths. We live with our windows and doors open, and they would fly in as soon as the lights were on. It was not only the big ones that were impressive, like the catocalas, but the array of tiny moths, each exquisitely coloured and patterned, and more alluring than any lady dressed for a ball. The treat with these moths is that they stay put after the initial mad fluttering, and one can watch (and measure them!) at leisure. In recent years they have become far fewer; for several summers now, we have missed seeing the Orache moth and the Small elephant hawkmoth. Luckily the little Hummingbird hawkmoth, which the locals teasingly say is the smallest bird in the world, continues to appear when the Viper's bugloss is in flower.

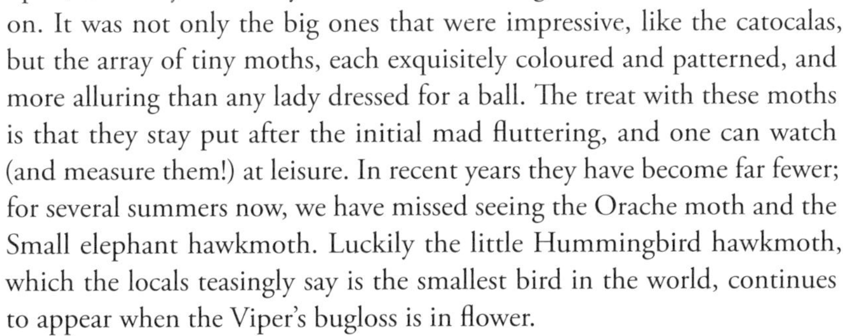

That alluring closure in XinJia is compact and slight, a slanting press, low down by the right hip. It surprised me when I first learnt it, but now it feels so natural that even in LaoJia, I find myself finishing *liu feng si bi* like this.

This movement escapes most people in both LaoJia and XinJia. It comes many times in each form, yet because of its subtle off-centre orientation, the alignment of torso and arms is far from simple. When the spine is flexible, and the training has brought forth a natural suppleness, when the spirit too is free, then one may glide into this closing.

The preparation for LaoJia's *liu feng si bi*, when the two arms are both drawn to the left and slightly behind the body, is in a way more difficult to perform than the corresponding move in XinJia. But once the hands

are gathered by the left side of the head, the closure itself in LaoJia is direct, finishing in a straightforward way, albeit off to the side.

XinJia's closure snakes across the body. The *jin* is led out by the strong outward twining of both arms, as they move from upper left to lower right. Qi arrives in the hands as they press down into a subtle diagonal. At the very end, there is an almost imperceptible change: qi from fingers returns to dantian, momentarily settling; it is a minute alteration of the twining action, requiring great delicacy in the execution. The rightness of this final position is sensed out from dantian: poised on one leg, spiralling through the body; leading out the *chansi* to one side yet keeping it balanced in all directions; the two sides of the body equal, neither side squished nor compromised; central ease.

Liu feng si bi illustrates how working on a XinJia move can improve the execution of the equivalent section in LaoJia. The serpentine looseness of the spine that one gradually acquires in XinJia helps greatly in tackling movements which are more difficult in LaoJia than in XinJia. Moreover the impression strengthens, that XinJia holds the secret of the original inspiration for movements such as *ye ma fen zong* (see chapter 11), which have become smoothed over in LaoJia. Exploring little hidden turns in XinJia gives one the insight for bringing to life those moves in LaoJia which appear to be mild and regular.

Late afternoon, the sun has come out. The shrikes' cries have not been heard for a while, but the redstarts have been to-ing and fro-ing past the house for hours. I see the female constantly alight on the wires in front of

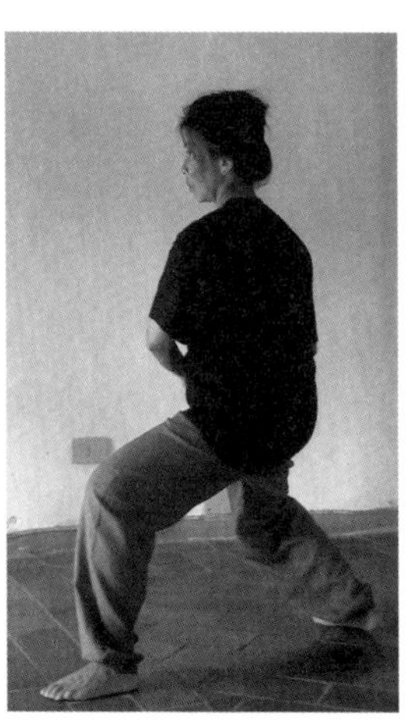

the house; as she calls *hui-tse-tse* (she speaks a southern dialect of Chinese), her head dips, and she spreads and shakes her crimson tail feathers.

For many of us coming from a Yang Style background in taiji, the most unfamiliar aspect of Chen Style is a kind of refined turbulence. We have been accustomed to broad lines and a steady pace. In Chen Style we are called upon to quicken and to release. The rhythms may

appear extravagantly variable, with tiny turnings close to the vertical axis, waves passing through dantian and chest. As technique becomes streamlined, the vortices become smaller, more contained, the local expression of a more constant underlying flow. It is like swimming in a river with a steady current. Where there are eddies, the turnings intensify, sometimes to the point of spurting force. Rippling onwards, the water flows languidly for a ways, until it cascades.

XinJia's pulse is on the wild side. This is perhaps what communicates most strongly to the viewer. A vibrant spirit throbs beneath. It curls, quivers, then appears to have let go, momentarily. XinJia's untamed rhythms.

The little owl's call is rather wavery tonight. Summer Triangle has risen in the northeast, Scorpio sparkling south. The fireflies are dancing. Soon they will gather force, the season is approaching when I like to fancy our hillsides looking from the air like Piccadilly Circus.

CHAPTER 10

XinJia 2 ~ core unfoldments

THE ORIOLE woke me up before six, in time to see the clouds break up into islets, blue-edged.

Yesterday while I was practising outside at dusk, I discovered that the redstarts are nesting in a gap in the stone wall of the kitchen, just by the window. While he thought I was not looking, the male swooped to the wall and entered a hole between the large stones. That explains why they have been so close to the house all week. So to avoid disturbing them while we were in the kitchen yesterday evening, we closed the window. This morning I went into the kitchen to put on a kettle, and found a hawkmoth on the closed window pane. It is an Elephant hawkmoth, *Deilephila porcellus*, the smaller of the kind and the first we have seen since 2000. After breakfast we waited for the redstarts and saw the male delivering a batch of food to the nest. The pair are getting used to us and are beginning to approach the house more boldly.

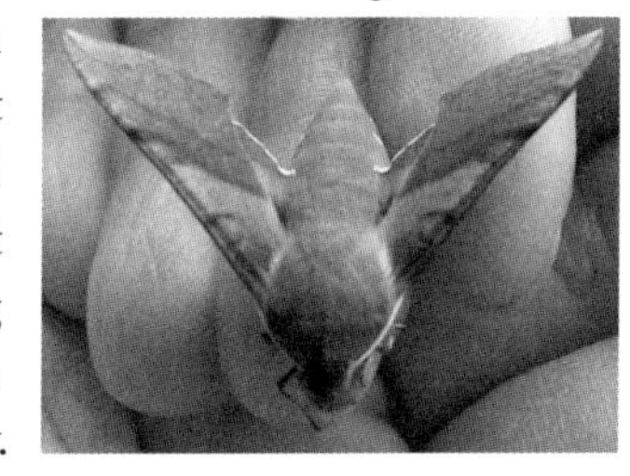

The previous chapter's discussion of XinJia ended with the sequence of moves known as *liu feng si bi*, 'Six Sealing, Four Closing'. The final position of the sequence contains the gateway that leads to *danbian*, 'Single Whip'. *Liu feng si bi* occurs seven times in XinJia, as it does in LaoJia, and on every occasion it is followed by *danbian*. The closing seals a section, and *danbian* opens the next section.

The movements that make up *liu feng si bi* and *danbian* require years of polishing. Occurring so frequently in the forms as they do, they may come to feel like mere commas, obligatory punctuation; a great many students of Chentaiji pay not enough attention to them, being attracted rather by the more obvious displays of strength scattered throughout the forms. But these turning silk movements which bind the sections of the form are intriguing, challenging and beautiful excursions in *chansijin*.

In *liu feng si bi*, in both LaoJia and XinJia, the coiling on the left side leads to an asymmetrical closure on the right. The threads for tying into position the complex knot of Single Whip lie here, in 'Six Sealing, Four Closing'.

If one understands how to approach the closure and can establish its proper positioning, then upon continuation the right arm will find its way to thread in and out of the left side, emerging with its hand hooked. This hooked right hand – the angled wrist and the thumb enclosed by the four fingers – manifests articulations set up from the centre, which are to be pulled firmly through the right arm.

The first quiver of motion is a very slight raising of the beam of the interior structure. This draws in both wings of the body, the movement of each delicately timed so that the right side curls inwards as it finds its correct route in preparation for emergence. Accumulated skill and acquired fluency in twining are needed for the body to give out just the right degree of impulse. The left side then forms itself into a container for the *jìn* which will be led out by the emerging hooked right hand.

Throughout, the hands' precision depends on exact conjunction with the legs. *Gambe! Usarle!* Springy guy-roped legs give a smooth wiriness to the coiling arms. One looks for a bounciness in the legs, with no loss of rooting. It is dantian that gives the legs their vibrancy; its free-wheeling stability invests the legs with power. Cradled as the torso is in its harness, there should be no downward impingement hampering the legs' energetic engagement. In return, the twining legs support the centre. The right hand's articulation is an outflowing from centre.

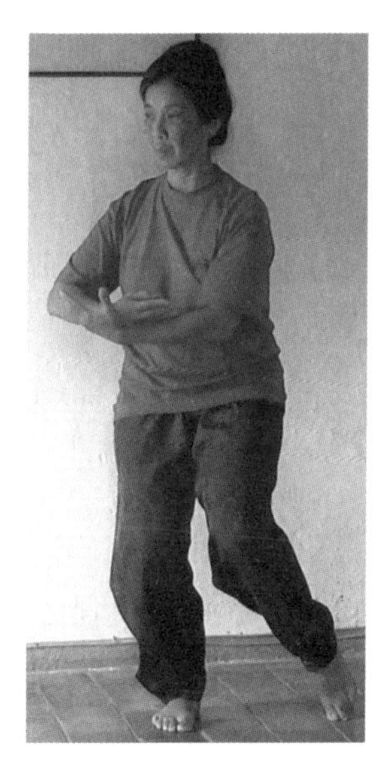

Then it is the strongly coiled right side which integrates the posture and maintains the frame so the left leg can step out with authority. The right arm extends in subtle curves through elbow to wrist. It finds at the wrist the outwirings from centre which make the articulation of hand and fingers exact. The twists and turns along the way, their interlocking, ensure the stability of the entire structure in *danbian*'s final position, where the body spans a generous girth. Searching out the Single Whip stance during practice, one learns a lot about how to negotiate through the elbow the route outwards from dantian. Much experimentation is called for, to find the precise degree of loosening and tautening. One looks for the chest and back to be open; for shoulders and hips to be joined; for balance between centre and periphery; for all parts to flow towards dantian.

In this picture of Single Whip the stance is fairly good. The right arm's twining has some intricacy, with a nice linking of parts; the energy flows through its twists and turns, back towards the core of the body. There is a sense of openness across the chest, supported by the contained bow stance of the legs. But—there is a 'but'! The left arm is not sufficiently twined, the winding outwards from centre has not been taken to its conclusion. I am speaking 'hands language' to the picture now; I know where, and how, I would take that left arm! It needs one precise tweak; this would also free up the gaze, which has not quite found a clear direction.

Of course, the way a stance is completed is also a matter of taste and choice. In Single Whip one might have periods of preferring an emphatic closure, which after a while may no longer feel right. The essential thing at the completion of *danbian* is for the qi to flow back along the arm to the side of the waist, *en route* to dantian. This may be accomplished in more than one way, the exact routing can vary. If the left arm is wound to the degree that it is in the picture above, the qi travels back along the inner arm to arrive at the waist. If there is more of a taut twining through the arm, the qi will arrive at resolution in the hand, as it does in this little picture on the left, and find its way back to the waist more along the outer edge of the arm. Ample flow through the elbow in a tautly twined arm needs better technique.

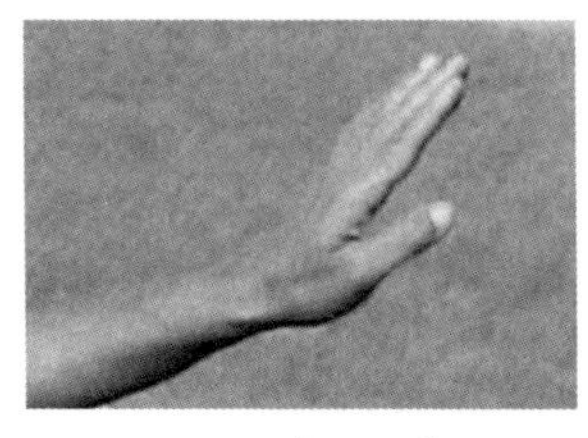

Single Whip is a magnificent array of energetic connections. In chapter 7 this part of the form is looked at in some detail, but it was only after several years of practising Chentaiji that I gained an understanding of the stance. Now I find myself relishing each opportunity to get into it. It was not always so. I remember one visit to Sydney, after I had become aware of a kind of linking in the body which is beyond simple postural considerations. I was dismayed by the frequent occurrence of this move in LaoJia and XinJia – every time, I would feel a kind of wrenching at the links. Whenever we approached yet another *danbian* in the lesson, I would think, "Oh no! Here comes Single Whip again."

This changed when I began to get a better hold of the positioning of the right side in preparation for the step leftwards. Then it began to be not such a tenuous procedure. But although the key preparation lies in finding a decent alignment in the right hip and leg, that is only the starting point. There had been clues to the mystery of Single Whip, in the placement of the hands before the sideways step to the left. The significance of the care with which Master Chen had placed my hands in that 1995 lesson dawned on me: these hands express the weftage of interior threadings.

Staying intertwined, one takes the step out to the left. Tautly coiled, the step will be an extension from an unmoving centre. While the weight remains on the right, that inner coiling begins to unwind leftwards, drawing the body to position itself over the left leg as the stance reaches completion. The left arm, with its hand in an apparently simple resting position, only feels right when the qi, after winding fully outwards from centre, returns to dantian. In the final moment, one is placed like a spider at the centre of its web.

Over the years, one is searching continually for the posture and the expressiveness of the stances. There are fundamental rules of *chansi* to observe, and with fineness of control one may explore endlessly varying possibilities without transgressing those rules. One may find that the pleasure which arises, upon arriving where one has been aiming, is momentary. Very much like throwing bowls on the potter's wheel; the finishing of one bowl points the way to the next.

When I began studying under Chen XiaoWang I found it curious that when dividing the form into sections, he would frequently break the form at the completion of 'Six Sealing, Four Closing', and he would never break it at Single Whip. From Yang Style I had been accustomed to a division of the form into sequences, with a certain number of sequences making up a part, the long form in entirety containing three parts. Each of the three main parts finished with a position known as 'Embrace Tiger, Return to Mountain', and the subdivisions came to completion with Single Whip. One would break the form at Single Whip, and step out of it happily whenever one was called upon to make a pause.

The places at which Master Chen would choose to pause are where the feet are together, but that is by no means the whole explanation. It is an energetic matter. Good places to pause are where the qi is gathered and focused in an outward direction, and one can follow the flow and step out of the position in a nimble way. As my training has deepened I have come to appreciate the ramifications in *danbian*, and now I cannot imagine how I ever used to step out of it so casually.

The only sensible way out of Single Whip is to continue with the form, and through successive twinings reach a place where one can step out of position without wrenching oneself out of the network of qi pathways. Single Whip's strong coilings resolve naturally into Cloud Hands, a progression that occurs three times in the long forms. As the weight shifts to the right one is carried out of Single Whip by a wave of twining, rising up the left side of the waist and along the inner left arm; an elegant exit. Early in the form Single Whip continues to the second Pound Mortar and thence to 'White Goose Wings Shimmering', *bai e liang chi*. Chapters 6 and 7 touched on the postural aspect of this position in LaoJia, where a minimal turning of the waist leads into a spreading of the arms. In XinJia the movement really shows its name. Have you seen a goose drawing itself up and flashing its wings in a brilliant display of white? In XinJia a core twizzle shimmers the spine in a flaring twisting upward spiral which flickers through the arms and ignites the wrists. The challenge here is to contain a rising diagonal undulation through the body without popping up in the legs. Only a strong right side can support this movement and the accompanying drop into *xie xing*. The spiralling ascent and the swift descent happen in a flash.

These movements give glimpses of XinJia's inner quality, but through 'body language' – to be seen in motion rather than described in words or shown in static images. That may be said of all movement forms, but it is particularly true of some of the movements in XinJia. The stances are impressive poses, communicable to some extent in photos, but the weaving in and out of them, and what makes them so compelling, should be seen live.

Trying to take taiji pictures for these chapters on *chansijin* and XinJia has been a lesson in itself. The effort to present a position affects the vibrancy of a movement *im fluss*, in the flow. Qi moves so lightly, by the time the body reaches a recognized stance, it has already passed through.

I see the redstarts have a strategy. The female in dialect raises a rumpus on the wire or on a nearby tree. And while we are distracted by her agitated skitties from kako to fig and back to the wire, all the while shaking her crimson plumes, the male homes straight for the gap. He stays inside for a split second and then shoots out again, leaving behind a lot of squeaking.

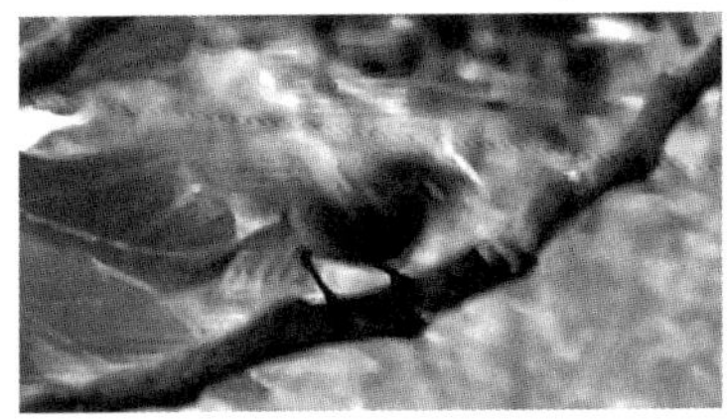

When the female brings something to the nest, she first perches at the edge and looks around to make sure that no one is watching.

From the second Pound Mortar onwards there come threadings, in and out, of twinings so variegated, that one may well start thinking the *chansijin* exercises have only sketched out simplified routes through the body, the real business of twining being far more complex. That is indeed true in some ways. But once exercises have become art, their rules provide invisible fortifications within the spontaneous and apparently effortless motion.

The names in this section of XinJia give a feeling for the complexities involved: *xie xing ao bu*, 'Walk Obliquely and Twist Step on Both Sides'; *qian tang ao bu*, 'Wade Forward and Twist Step on Both Sides'.

This was the sequence of moves so admirably executed by the lady from Japan, whom I mentioned in the previous chapter. In both long forms it is one of the telltale sequences. To appreciate XinJia's version let us look at it first in LaoJia, where it is simply called *xie xing*, though in some ways it is even more difficult there than in XinJia.

It appears that almost everyone starts out by misunderstanding how the movement should proceed. Because of the striking appearance of the leaning body one tends to barge into it, thinking, "Shoulder Down!" (our casual name for the move). One gets the body at the wrong angle, in an awkward bend. I recall the moment when I discovered I was doing it wrong, after I had been practising LaoJia for about a year. Chen XiaoWang showed me how I was bending my upper body. I was distressed. "What? I'm doing it wrong?" Master Chen replied quietly, almost compassionately, "When you do this one correct, I show another you not do correct."

I had not seen that the action of 'shoulder down' in LaoJia starts in the very same moment that the weight shift commences, from the back leg to the front leg, from right to left.

If the lean precedes the weight shift by even an instant, there will be no possibility of the weight shift catching up with it. Equally, if you make even the tiniest impulse towards shifting the weight too early, then you have Master Chen reprimanding, "Not ready! Not ready!" It took me at least a year before I caught a glimpse of what he meant by 'ready': Chansigong count 3, qi to back – you must arrive in this place before you can shift the weight. But where, in *xie xing*, is 'qi to back'?

In that lesson in Streatham in 1995, elements of which were discussed in chapters 5, 6 and 7, an overtly startling alteration which Master Chen had made to my stance was the reorientation of the hips. But nineteen years of previous training with incorrect understanding of the pelvic orientation would not be quickly dropped. And without the alignment of the pelvis into the diagonal at this juncture in *xie xing*, qi cannot arrive at the back.

It was only after a couple of years of double hand Chansigong that I developed a taste for this sideways shift with the pelvis diagonal. Then it needed still more practice, seemingly *ad infinitum*, before I began to have a sense of the moment when qi arrives at the top of the dorsal spine. The feeling is of the revolving spine meeting and joining with the right arm's spiralled power, and of the right side of the body becoming totally behind the left. There is then the extraordinary and thrilling sensation of a controlled and powerful weight shift simultaneous with the lean, 'shoulder down', the left arm enfolded in the right arm's twining. It is an unusual and beautiful movement, deeply satisfying when it happens spontaneously, well worth the years of dedication. When it becomes natural, LaoJia's *xie xing* is a wave that surges from a force beneath.

Having brought qi to the back, and having shifted the weight forwards while staying diagonal and leaning, how then is one to return to the upright? Here we delve into the details of *chansi* at work in *xie xing*. Endlessly we may discuss taiji in terms of building strength in the legs, alignment of the hips, and so on; but without an understanding of qi, the movement will not link up. The qi factor is difficult to explain, however, and until one has tasted it, it may be nothing more than inspiration. Thinking about it may

even be a distraction, if it leads one to go too eagerly in search of something unknown.

I went out for a breather, camera in hand, and found the shrike sitting in wait for his prey.

Through *chansijin* exercises we become alert to the slightest indications of uneven flow. The thread is broken when even the tiniest link in the chain becomes lax, or becomes unduly stressed. If the body succeeds in staying together through the combined shift and lean of *xie xing*, then the qi brought to the top of the dorsal spine as a result of the right side's earlier spiralling pours into the left side. Qi travels down the left arm, shoulder to elbow. At the deepest part of the lean it reaches the left hand, down by the left knee.

The instant when qi arrives in the fingers is the moment for releasing the diagonal orientation of the body. Softening the upper body to the left creates the energetic pathway for continuation of the movement. Qi turns: here, precisely, is the transition from single hand Chansigong count 4 to count 1. As the left hand starts to rise, the four fingers encircle the thumb and qi flows from fingers to waist. This draws the body upright. There is a momentary poised wait while the right arm completes its outward twining – qi from back to shoulder, to elbow, to fingers – and then both arms settle, returning qi to dantian.

Although I now put it down so factually in black and white, what I have just described is the kind of thing that comes in a flash of understanding. I can see Chen XiaoWang do this section countless times, and then on one occasion notice how he would appear to linger over a tiny detail, and I realize where the qi has arrived just in that instant. In solo practice also, the course of qi, and where it surfaces, can become suddenly apparent in unlooked-for moments.

The Amarena Gang have arrived! These are the European goldfinches, *Carduelis carduelis*. They appear round about now, in time to raid the *amarena* cherries. As I write, they are frolicking in the tall grasses. How does a fat little finch alight on a stalk of grass, and hardly bend it? They say that the old taiji masters could soften so profoundly, that a bird alighting on the hand would be unable to find the resistance that it needs in order to take off.

It was the redstarts who woke me up this morning. The hilltops are still shrouded. Making my early cup of green tea, I saw that the pink-gold moth has gone back to the window. It rested all of yesterday where we had placed it, on a stone atop the salt jar in the kitchen.

XinJia's *xie xing* is playful. It flickers this way and that. So quick and precise that one barely sees it, here too, while the body is diagonal, qi arrives at the back, at Chansigong's count of 3.

There is no 'shoulder down' in XinJia. The torso stays almost upright, at a soft angle to the legs. A slow rotation to the right gathers the qi, then a swift change of direction turns it; then there is a measured transfer of weight to the left with the centre clearly in command. When qi reaches the fingers of the left hand they draw together in a hook; the arm then twines barely discernibly, to lead the qi back towards dantian.

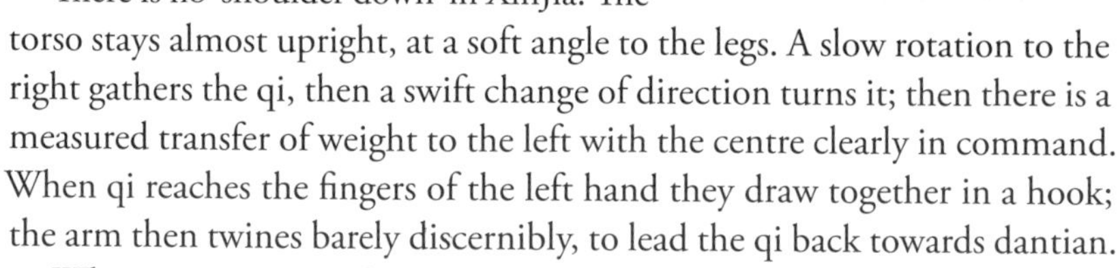

Whereas in LaoJia a clear momentum drives the shift, in XinJia the body insinuates itself forwards, taking surprising turns, hiding delicate changes in the open swirling. Body and spirit need to be quiveringly aware, balanced in all directions, in order to follow XinJia's pulsing in this section of the form.

A good solid technique is not enough. Today the male redstart has given me an aim unrealizable at least in this lifetime. I see a sudden dark streak on

the other side of the walnut – he has returned from the west with his next batch of food for the chicks. Then I cannot find where he is, in amongst the green. He has paused, waiting for the right moment. Then without warning he is at the gap in the old stones, and as my eyes register that he has entered, he has already flown.

I have come in from a XinJia rep on the pottery roof. I think the redstarts have settled down for the night, they must be pooped. There is the smell of moisture and elder, of wild and tame roses that have begun to open. There was a snark, and I looked up to see the Grey heron flying unusually high over the valley. The outline was unmistakable, retracted neck and trailing legs, and the wings with the fullness of their beat.

This morning the valley feels to be taking a breath, and pausing a moment before throwing itself into summer's arms. On a day like this I would have called Pytt, to tell her all the many things going on in the valley. She introduced me to life in the countryside. I had not grown up wandering around the Burmese jungle; nature, as a setting where one could safely fling oneself on the grass, was novel to me. She took me on my first bluebell walk. Invisible tracks in the undergrowth were brought to my attention. She took great interest in the neighbours' cows as they grazed near the little hut where she liked to be, where the garden gave way to woodland. David, her husband, called it "Pytt's Folly", and did a lovely drawing of it.

In importance in my taiji life, David was equal to Pytt. He balanced his *yin* to her *yang*. My closeness to him also had something to do with Burma. He had been there in the forties during the war, and had a fondness for the country and its peoples. Once he had been sent in from India in a glider carrying a water buffalo. The Indian command had thought it a brilliant idea to use these native creatures to clear airstrips in the jungle, for the landing of larger aeroplanes. His descriptions of the Naga Hills, the Chindwin River, the valley where two rivers from the edge of Tibet join to become the great Irrawaddy flowing a thousand miles through the heartland of Burma, and of the upland terrain further east towards China, all were precious to me. He had a keen aesthetic eye, with an instinct for taiji. Both he and Pytt would have been captivated by LaoJia and XinJia *xie xing*.

After I got into Chentaiji, Pytt would remark from time to time that if she had met it earlier in her life, she would surely have taken the chance to study it. I took this to be blessing from her, for my ongoing exploration.

The redstarts are active in a different way today. She is calling intensely, even when neither of us are about outside. He had been extremely shy of us, but now he allows himself to be seen entering and leaving the nest. Sometimes he perches openly near the house, where I can watch him for nearly a minute at a time.

I was lucky to be around one time while they were together on the wire for a few seconds. She was there first, then he appeared from nowhere to join her. She opens her beak and dips her head, fanning her red tail feathers. All the response she gets is him cleaning his beak on the wire. She appears to have a thing or two to say to him, judging from her posture.

Today I have had little appetite for practice. Brief standings here and there, and only now, at day's end, I did one light rep of XinJia in the gloaming. The oaks fringe the hill behind the house, and at this hour, in a certain reflected light, they are lit up from behind, and remind me of a painting of Magritte's.

There is value in light reps every now and then. Like eating soup when one's appetite is small. When one is not feeling much like practice, Chen XiaoWang suggests doing form 'like drunk': rolling about a bit, doing it with ease, carelessly, loosely but not badly.

I began a round of XinJia just now, sensing the evening, its sounds and smells, aware of the oaks against a northerly glow. As the rep got going, I noticed a detail, in a place where generally the right upper arm is not comfortable, and the right hand does not find its place beneath the left. Tonight the right hand came and snuggled nicely, in those tiny moves over the knee, *chu shou* and *zai shou*, that follow 'Step Obliquely'.

During that XinJia-intensive time, our second visit to Sydney, I thought perhaps Master Chen should know my Yang Style background, and risked showing him an old film of Pytt's teacher, Choy HakPang. I had once put on a video tape of someone doing Chen Style in Beijing, which a friend had brought back from China. After less than fifteen seconds of watching it, Chen XiaoWang had said, "No need look." That's why I say, "risked". To my surprise, on this occasion he watched the entire film, which shows Choy HakPang performing first the Yang Style long form, and then forms with straight sword and the large heavy curved sword. At its finish, he said, "Not many people can do like this." A compliment indeed from Chen XiaoWang.

The film was recorded in 1945, on the UCLA campus in California. I have always felt warmth for this taiji master whom I know only through this rare film. You may remember, he was one of the two gentlemen who came to the Geddes home on the Peak in Hong Kong. He taught Pytt the long form of the Yang Style. He himself had been a student of Yang ChengFu, grandson of Yang LuChan who had learned the Chen family's TaijiQuan in his youth.

Having begun to talk about him, I have just now looked in detail at this film* of Master Choy for the first time in several years. To my surprise, I see him twining! Here is an intriguing moment in the long form, after the completion of 'Deep Punch', which in Chen Style is called *ji di chui*, 'Punch the Ground'. The sequence of moves which make up the turn towards the right are known in Chentaiji as *fan shen er ji jiao*, 'Turn Over into Double Raise Foot'.

At the finish of 'Deep Punch', where both his hands are down, he begins a change in his torso which will eventually bring him around to the right in a 180° turn. The interior change starts with a twisting to the left, manifested by the left arm which spirals outwards. Simultaneous with this is a further sinking of his torso, the fisted right boring deeper towards the ground. At this point both arms are twined outwards, the left arm rising, the right arm at its lowest, close to the body. The right side now begins to take control.

The 180° turn which follows is powerful and slightly mysterious. There is a scarcely visible momentary bowing of the lower back as the windings are further intensified and redistributed through the body.

In the Chen Style, this turning of the torso creates the conditions for one of the spectacular moments of the form, as the core windings unfold into a flying double kick. Master Choy HakPang here demonstrates something completely different. In the pictures below, the energy becomes invisible as it dissolves into a focused softness.

This turn that Master Choy is performing has more in common with the equivalent section in Chen Style than any other portion of my old Yang long form. Seeing these pictures brings back to me the feeling from my Yang Style days, of a looser and wider circumference around the spine. That made for a different kind of turning, unlike the taut twistings around the core which embody Chentaiji. I wish we could know more about the fascinating process by which the Chen forms became Yang forms. It took a couple of generations to evolve. We are not even sure which form it was that Yang LuChan learned in Chenjiagou, the Chen family village in Henan.

The day has begun with excitement. The female redstart's incessant chattering and the male's monosyllabic zitters got me up this morning. There were soft zizzings from the kitchen terrace, and when I eased open the shutters, I found myself looking at two fat little birds, mottled brown, on the terrace. One of them hopped away into the wisteria. I gazed at the remaining quiet little thing, wondering who it might be. It also took a hop, and like a schoolboy at his first lessons in ABC, it elbowed itself unsteadily into the air. Could these be the fledglings? The redstart parents are certainly flapping from pillar to post this morning.

XinJia's sinuous route through the *xie xing* sequence of movements is accentuated by *chu shou* and *zai shou* which punctuate it. These delicate closings are difficult to perform, their sparseness of detail exposing any wavering at the core. The hands express the central windings that thread together the aptly named progression, *qian tang ao bu*, 'Wade Forwards and Twist Step on Both Sides'. When learning XinJia slowly, a whole term of study may usefully be spent on this section of the form that lies between the second and third Pound Mortar. The moves have a kind of complexity that does not arise in LaoJia. As with all taiji forms, the student first learns to copy the movements, and then to repeat them until they become natural. Because of XinJia's intricacy, 'learning to copy' is more demanding than usual. *Xie xing* and *qian tang ao bu* weave in and out of each other. The best way to build familiarity and ease

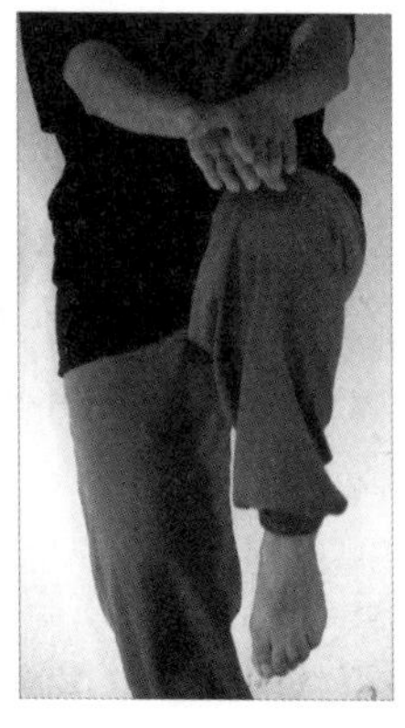

is to practise this section as a continuous sequence, over and over, like a *chansijin* exercise.

Once there is familiarity with the form, appreciation grows of the creativity that went into the making of movements such as *xie xing* and *qian tang ao bu*. The weight shifts pulse strongly. The body insinuates itself in different directions simultaneously. Sharpness is wrapped in swathes of motion. This section, so difficult to do well, is particularly hard to describe. The details are so fine, they emerge over years of practice. There is a glimpse while watching the teacher; this may be so fleeting that it is barely conscious. As one goes on practising, little shifts of awareness take place as if of their own accord. Suddenly an inch of form falls into place.

In the afternoon I was attracted down into the arbour by the tremendous activity on the terraces below the house. The redstart parents were about, their cries like a barrage of human arms trying to ward off evil from their children. I hid myself in the foliage to watch, every now and then seeing one or another of the pair, but neither of the fledglings. Here is Mama in a persimmon tree, the same tree where she was when we had first caught sight of her, open beaked. We hadn't realized then, that she was singing with all her being to the chicks in the old wall.

When I reach the bottom of the arbour, the sight of the towering Lombardy poplars in full leaf absorbs me for some moments. I steal my way through the bamboos where I practised ZhanZhuang at winter's end. Glancing back, I catch sight of something speckly brown against the profusion of green at the bottom of the arbour. It is a baby bird—I think not one of the fledglings which I glimpsed on the kitchen terrace this morning, and which were more bunting-like in profile. This one is perched in amongst the wisteria cords wrapping the old vine. It is already fluttering a tiny red tail—clearly a redstart chick! It looks at me curiously, but does not utter a peep as I approach softly, so close that I could have gathered the plump little creature in my hands.

In the early part of the form, *xie xing* and *qian tang* each occur twice. The completion of the second wading is the preparation for a punch, *yan shou hong quan*, 'Punch of Hidden Fist'. Unlike LaoJia's punch, XinJia's announces itself with no less than three jumps. They happen one upon the other and are quite confusing at the beginning, and partly for this reason are taught first without the jumps, so that the moves are practised with precision and control. When done with the jumps, it may feel amazing to the doer, but beware of the sounds emanating – they give the perpetrator away! It often sounds like a ton of bricks falling, disparate parts crashing onto the floor. Which reminds me of this:

> Whether your strength is straight or not can yet be judged with the sound of shocking.*

The 'sound of shocking' is that of Pound Mortar. This is one of the Chen moves which separates the sheep from the goats. The centre, poised over the left leg, controls the stomping action. Centre gives out force through the right leg, its foot pounds the ground: "Like punch with foot!", Chen XiaoWang says. As with the punch, the way to do it is to stay centred as one emits force. The body should not fall into the right. No splitting of the weight as one stamps; the right foot lands underneath the body, not thrust out to the side. The correct sound is unmistakable – and tells you whether your strength is straight.

Those XinJia jumps are quite particular. The usual way to jump is to shoot out of the legs, stretching the spine away from the ground. The Chen jump lifts straight up, the body compacted with the legs drawn up under. The parts of the body cohere in suspension. Within the compact frame there is softness; the challenge is to maintain this softness during the jump; it is needed for the *fajin* at the moment of landing. When Chen XiaoWang lands, there is a deep booming sound, the impact spreads through the ground. It makes everyone jump.

The oriole woke me gently this morning, but the redstarts got me scrambling out of bed. It is raining. The fledglings are practising the flying lessons they have been getting from their parents. Yesterday, just before dusk, I saw a chick sitting in the little apple tree, watching bemused as one parent after the other sallied forth from the willows, to demonstrate a most difficult technique – how to suspend itself from above by a silken thread, and hover hummingbird style in the air. There is certainly copious talking language and body language; I wonder, do they have need of the third, hands language?

One unfortunate chick may have tried to copy Papa; it landed in the deep grass below the willows and has been there all afternoon in the rain. Mama has been calling without rest, while Papa has come to give extra encouragement every now and then; I think (I hope) he is guarding the

other chick, who with luck may already be at home in the air. Today the male has slipped into dialect, the *hui* more whistle-like than the female's, and the number of *tse* repeated according to circumstance. We have been on emergency mode for hours. All on shrike-patrol.

When I went down to look, three hours ago, I found a tiny wet bird. I think this may be the other, smaller chick, and not the one I saw yesterday in the arbour wisteria. I went down again just now, as night is coming soon. The valley is wet and low with cloud. The little one has made it across, all the way to the other side of the nettle bed. When I left her to Nature she was looking up forlornly at the bank, rising above her like a mountain range. I hope we all sleep tonight.

Those XinJia jumps are still preoccupying me. I mentioned the difficulty of doing them well: they originate in dantian. The body needs not only to be centred in dantian, but to have cultivated this spot as a mobile centre of connection. The dantian then may direct the move at hand, which a flexible core translates into varying twinings. In any of the moves where there is sinking and rising, there are undulations of the spine, which can be in more than one direction. These jumps involve this kind of motion. One cannot undulate the spine by effort. It is born of first principle, "Natural!"

But what a lot of effort there is, in clearing the way to First Principle! In Sydney, during that time of XinJia in the company of the Japanese, I had a correction that I will never forget. It was in the preparation for the punch, in the last position before it, which one arrives at by way of the three jumps; LaoJia's punch has just this one position in preparation.

I had already had the 'rubble coming down' experience in the Bienne dojo the year before, while I was being corrected in 'Lean with Back'; I have spoken of this in chapter 3. I guess Master Chen thought I had had first tasters already, and set to work on me during a lesson with the Japanese instructors.

I do not remember having asked him for a correction in this stance; I may have had no choice. After adjusting my hands, which as I have mentioned before is a way that he has of working indirectly on the core of the student, he adjusted the position of my hips. Then came the critical part: the sterno-sacral alignment. It was not of the same silent intensity as the year before in Bienne. It was excruciatingly difficult; he knew he could take me further than he had in Bienne. Here, 'further' means closer to a truer alignment. The burning in the upper thighs was trivial in comparison with the immense effort involved in connecting chest to lower spine. After what felt like an eternity of manoeuvres in the deep, Master Chen gripped me behind the hip joints (Gall Bladder 30!) and held me down: I was now prepared for the punch (on facing page). A thought somehow managed to flit through my mind: "So this is what it takes, it takes all you've got."

The jumps, and the punches, and all the explosive moves, come out of this soldering of the spine. It is not compacted; the sensation is of the spine being lengthened, of greater spacing between the vertebrae. The chest giving way opens the fulcrum of the waist beneath the small of the back.

I have realized that it worries some people when they hear that a correction can be excruciatingly difficult. The word 'correction' itself gets people's backs up. This reminds me of a Chinese girl whom we met in Lhasa; she told us that her name translates as 'Correction'. She had been born at the time of the Cultural Revolution, and her parents had given as her name the theme of the time.

I wonder how else I can describe the sensations that come about from being put close to true. It is an experience to celebrate. It is a coming of age in the life of a taiji practicant.

In daily training I do not practise the punches on their own, with force. I have not the mind-set for this kind of 'punch bag training'. I enjoy immensely those moments when *fajin* erupts, as though spontaneously. I say, 'as though', because it is actually a decision: every now and then I notice, while I am doing a rep, that there is good tone throughout the body; then, when I arrive at a place in the form where there is the possibility of *fajin*, and if I sense that my body is together, feeling full and unharried, without desires, then I really *fa jin*.

On some days, this can happen throughout a rep or two. Then there follows a quiet period. There is enormous intensity in these explosive moves. It is good to be sparing with them, to let the power pool, to store it. Power is creative. Power stored makes one a contented person.

And this word, 'power'—it represents something that some people want, while others equally would shun it. To explore what I mean by it, why I choose this word, let us go back to the *Daodejing*. Late in the nineteenth century, using a romanization older than Wade-Giles, James Legge described *gu shen*, 'valley spirit':

> The 'spirit of the valley' is the something invisible, yet almost personal, belonging to the *Tâo*, which constitutes the *Teh*...*

Teh—nowadays *de*—when translated as 'virtue' as it often is, may feel distant and impersonal. But in the *Daodejing* and the *Zhuangzi* the word has a near and spacious luminosity, at the same time unfathomable. Four times* in the *Daodejing* it is paired with the word *xuan*—deep, profound *de*—endarkening it, drawing *de* close to its nameless source. Born of *dao*, we are nourished by *de*. *De* is *dao*'s overflowing, *dao*'s emanation. Its potency. Its hidden power. When we are moving along the path of our true disposition, our potential, we have *de*. The power to still. To act. To know and to hold. It is not of the body, yet it may manifest through the body. It is subtle and mysterious. Void like the valley, a vacuity, vast.

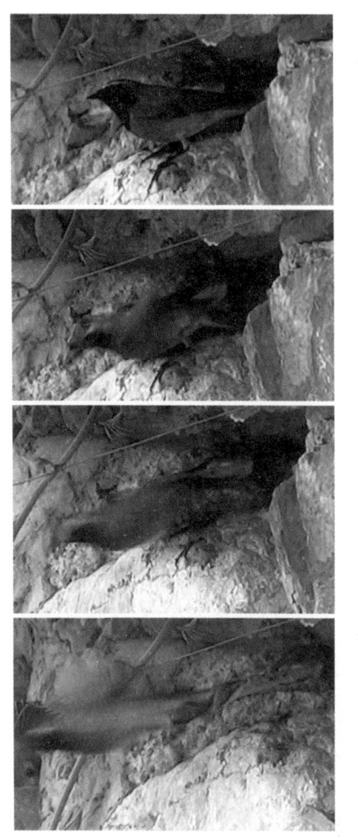

For me, Redstart Style is the tops! Now, if one really wants to learn about *fajin*, look at these pictures. The second one: see how he bows his lower spine. The third shows him maintaining the gathered force as his body rises, and the last picture ... *fa* in its ancient form means to let fly like an arrow.

Once Master Chen put on his favourite 'animal movie' of the week for us. It was of a leopard hunting in the wilderness. We watched a certain sequence over and over. It was getting quite late, we had had an intensive day of learning with him, and needed some sleep to replenish and prepare for the morning in the dojo. I said, "Now we go back, Master Chen." To which he responded, "You also? I too want to go back," reaching eagerly for the rewind button. And we had several more rounds of the 'layo-par' pouncing on a gazelle.

It is in this kind of spirit that one learns to appreciate XinJia, a combination of dedicated attention, visceral empathy and capacity for delight. Mind, body and Qi.

The details are minute, often fleetingly fast. The birds, the moths, the snake, the bat that likes to visit the house in the evenings – each accompanies me, upon this exploratory journey.

The female's calls, more staccato than ever, woke me before six this morning. The valley is soaked. A strong breeze and sudden burst of rain got me dressing hurriedly, to go and see what was happening down on the terraces. The chick was no longer on the ridge below the bank where I last saw it, and when I heard a tiny zizzing higher up, I decided to leave things to Mama. An hour later I went out again. This time I traced it by its little utterings; it has made it up over the mountain range, onto the next terrace.

The valley is darkening, storm clouds rolling in from the south. Poor chicks! Day before yesterday, possibly their first out of the nest, there was a thunderstorm in the evening, and rain all night. Yesterday, they had a lovely morning of tumbling about near the house, until one fell into the tall grasses below the bottom terrace. The female has been here all this time; Papa comes and calls, and flies fast away to the west; I wonder if it is to the other chick. If that one too is trying to copy him, he will have his hands full.

This flying business – it does take all you've got!

CHAPTER 11

XinJia 3 ~ listening

THE FEMALE redstart went on calling through the morning. I went several times down on the terraces to see if I could spot the chick. Around midday, she was hopping in the direction of her mother's calls, which were more and more *tse*, and hardly *hui*. The baby bird looked tiny but determined, fluttering red tail and speckly wings, trying to dry herself, wanting to fly as she knew her mother wanted her to.

The male appeared only a few times, also calling insistently, urging the little one to fly, but dashing away as if he could not stay long; perhaps he was guarding the other chick. By late afternoon the mother was still calling, but with increasing periods of absence. She came each time to the same spot where I had last seen the chick. The rain persisted all day, terrible luck for them. At one point I saw the male in the near wood, he also was still calling.

I decided to go west myself, to ease the anguish in my heart. The oriole's song of remembrance was too much to bear. The redstart family really let us share in their life. These May days with them were heaven-sent.

The woods always surprise me. They are oaks of different varieties, and white hornbeam, sweet chestnut, some field maple, hazel and the odd ash. Here and there are stands of aspen, which were abundant in the past but are no longer respected; were it not for their suckering habit, there would be hardly any left. Their small round grey-green leaves, scallop-edged, are put aflutter by the slightest stirring of the air, causing a strange enchantment. I am told that country folk in the past believed that the aspen trembled from a secret pain, *un segreto dolore o rimorso*. I have read that the aspen, *Populus tremula*, is important in the life-cycle of some moths such as the largest European catocala, *Catocala fraxini*, with a forewing of 4.5cm; the last time we saw one was in 2003. The aspen's roots are host to *Leccinum aurantiacum*, a fabulous *fungo* with a massive orangy-red cap atop a tall stout leg.

The long-tailed tits were looping about high up in the oaks and aspens, jangling like little children. There was a light rain, coming and going. The past and present in such thin layers. I returned from the woods with a quieter heart, and could say to the oriole who was singing sagely, "Yes…I agree with you."

Today was my birthday, and coming home from the west, I was presented with a bouquet abreast the west wall of the house, the palest dawn-pink roses and their cool scent. The woods too had offered their fruit, three *porcini* – true *Boletus edulis*, with the white-fringed dark cap and a pale net at the upper end of their fat stems. The first of the season.

This is to be the last chapter of this book of notes on taiji practice and I have the idea to try another experiment. In chapter 4 I described *ZhanZhuang* the standing qigong, from the point of view of the practitioner, and how it feels to do it. Now I will try something similar for the form practice. I will simply say what it feels like, what I notice, while doing form. Let us go inside some of the movements and fill out the picture with feelings.

I woke up around five, listening. The day's first stirrings. They begin gently, the singing of birds whose home is in these hills. Blackie sounds as though he has been holding himself back all of May, and will have an awful lot to say in the coming days. It is heavily overcast. Cloud and mist are weaving through the valley. A good day for starting the experiment.

I wrote in chapter 5 that when I first learned LaoJia, I could not copy the way the teacher's arms lifted before the body. I could see that something was happening that had not to do with breath and muscle. I still cannot say what it is, but I can try to say what it feels like. On days when the posture is integrated, and I find unity in the sterno-sacral alignment, the form dawns of itself. Qi plumps the body, the back feels full and the chest quiet. I have no sense of effort to undulate the spine, no sense of dantian rotating this way or that, nor of raising the arms. The form begins, and I am spun.

As one stands in preparation form, where the feet are separated to shoulders' width, the listening inside is like listening outside: there is a whirr of stirrings, and one becomes quiet as they shift and settle, each in their own way. The head up, listening behind...one enters a special realm. The direction, to listen 'behind', induces qi to sink and permeate the body, so that one can feel and see, and hear, the movements of the energetic interior. The mind and heart quieten.

In this brief period of standing still, in preparation for the form's start, there are many little adjustments to be made. One looks for the same posture as in ZhanZhuang, the same rebalanced interior. This 'Preparation Form' counts as the first move of whichever form one is about to do, the 'move' consisting of some moments where one reorganizes outside and inside, posturally and energetically. If form practice comes after standing, soon or immediately after, so much the better. One is searching for the same sense of cohesion throughout the body, the same alert tranquillity. A silky feeling along the torso. Centred and poised.

Sensing a breathing universe, the arms lift. Qi from chest flows down towards dantian. Shoulders give way to vibrant upper arms, buoyant elbows, a thick warmth spreading along the arms to the wrists, oozing into the hands. Fine-tuning left and right as the hands rise, micro adjustments all the way up, searching for an even flow.

The sensation is of the entire body filling, becoming more ample. There is a kind of compression into the lower body at the beginning, as qi from dantian rises up the back. This lightens towards the end, when qi from the back flows along the arms and nearly arrives at the fingers, as the arms reach their full height, just about level with the shoulders. All this happens before the body lowers itself, before the knees bend.

When it is flowing, the feeling is of breadth; of a kind of expansion within the parallel frame of legs and arms, as if the body were now elongated to the front, as if one had become a horizontal creature. Or some kind of vessel, with a spreading base.

The rising and sinking of the arms and the body being one inseparable movement, the point at which the rise turns into the descent is the subtlest of changes. Dantian gives forth, dantian receives back; the great journey of TaijiQuan has commenced. Precisely at this turning point, qi arrives in the fingers; the chest is soft, yielding to the returning flow of qi, back towards dantian. There is a stretchiness now in the arms, as the fingers come fully to life, cresting, their tips pointing forwards: connected to dantian, the undulating spine will draw them down as the body lowers into its harness. Upon arrival at the lowest point, it feels as though one is sitting on an inflated ball made from dantian and legs, balanced just right, poised to turn as one wishes.

Once the body is in its full sit, poised on a vibrant sphere which is both the lower body and the body in its entirety, two avenues present themselves. The balance until this moment has been complete, there is no partiality to either side. Now one may choose which way to go. We choose the left side: intent is to the left, a slight release of the downward pressure swivels dantian minutely to the right, the weight slips lightly right; this gives the impetus for a strong leftward turn. The legs spiral within their parallel alignment. The feet, remaining in place, anchor a twisting all the way through the body, out to the fingers.

Having taken the time to bring us slowly to this juncture, to the start of the asymmetrical twinings which initiate the form, I will try to describe how I look for the way, amidst the multiple windings and myriad sensations.

The spiralling of the arms leftwards needs to engage the entire body, from the feet all the way to the hands. A well seasoned posture allows this engagement to happen in one smooth pressing and sinking, turning and lifting, until qi arrives in the left hand's fingertips, and the right hand at dantian balances the left's furthest reach. Any tense striving creates obstacles along the way. Staying present means continually letting go of the tendencies to tighten, while keeping true to the basic posture. The feet and the hips anchor the body as it spirals. It is easy to go too far in the turning, and get hooked up on the left side. The needed degree of twist is precise – I find that I have to look carefully for it each time.

I look for lightness and pliancy, for the correct degree of turning so the left shoulder stays open and qi can arrive in the fingers; for the right elbow to find a certain inward winding so the way back to dantian is found; for each arm to be true to its side, not compromising the centre; for the arms to be looped around the back.

The turning to the right brings me near to the moment when I will plunge into XinJia's mid-stream. Everything until now has been a preparation for this. The turn is a series of tiny steps, each one notching into the next, so that it is a sinking and a turning and a spiralling, and the steps are not steps at all but a smooth progression from left to right. The mind quietly waits for qi to arrive at the waist and the back as the direction changes, from left to right. Then comes the freedom to ride across, arms swept up like sails tacking into the wind. And careful here, the left leg must dovetail into the pelvic joint. If it can do that well, then the arms can billow further, and the left leg will be articulate when it takes its forward step.

In these two turnings, left and right, the elbows are vital; they mediate the flow of qi and its precise passage. They determine the route by which qi arrives at the side of the waist and at the back, the two stations to reach before shifting the weight. In the articulation of the arm, all the way from shoulder to hand, a precise angle of the elbow joint and its connection to waist conduct the qi in the intended direction.

The ability to perform this turn from left to right depends on one's understanding of *chansijin* principle, an understanding that comes from deep practice of the first single hand exercise. This tiny phrase which initiates both the LaoJia and XinJia forms encapsulates the critical moments when the direction of qi flow changes. After one has tasted these changes, one has the code for deciphering the entire form.

When arms twine like this, it comes naturally to travel further, allowing qi to arrive at the fingers; and to balance this side, fully expressed, with the other side fully gathered at dantian. Coiled in this way, one may have the freedom to step with command.

Developing a sense of the direction of the gaze in readiness for the step is a gradual and fascinating process. The feel for it arises from a growing alertness of the spinal column.

Here in the rightward turn, the gaze is synchronous with the turning, until the entire body's weight is transferred to the right leg, when the left becomes free to step out at a 45° angle. At this moment, the gaze turns in the direction of the step, over the left shoulder, thus securing stability by sealing the rightwards coiling of the rest of the body. One steps with qi to fingers, fully expressed on the right, and qi to dantian, fully gathered on the left.

Stable in the right, the left leg steps, the gaze making clear the direction of the stance that is about to emerge. Once the left foot has placed itself heel first on the ground, the right side where the weight has remained must control and fortify the new position. The gaze softens back into the right diagonal as the body gathers itself together, qi from fingers and dantian moving to waist and back. Only then may the weight shift, and it does so with a unity that takes some years to cultivate. One tastes it, knowing it as one knows when an apple is ripe.

The next juncture is a place to explore, again and again. This is where the weight has shifted to the left, and one wishes to be both at rest and at the ready to plunge. The arms are thrown like a mantle across the back. It is the position of *jingang* the Temple Guardian. It requires uncompromising clarity; it is a good place for holding, simmering.

The process is rather as in ZhanZhuang. Staying in the stance, one settles. Releasing the breath, one lets it sink deep into the bones. As the mind accepts the moment, the body begins to relax. Whatever the condition of the posture, a little ease starts to seep through from part to part. Feeling the way through the upper body, one brings sense to the arms. Each arm is buoyantly at rest, each intimately belonging to its side of the body. The chest is soft, quietly merging with dantian as the arms find their gentle twining, the elbows slipping into connection with the waist on either side.

A little shift here and there, and again I stay, breathing and settling. As the chest yields further, the rightness of the arms feeds through little streams into the reservoir in my lower belly. This I follow, when I am quiet enough. The flowing alters the arms, for flowing moves in curves; twinings follow the natural grain of the body. Become like a tree.

Awareness of tree-being draws attention to the feet. As in ZhanZhuang, look for rooting. The ease of foot with ground begins to work upwards, again following the natural grain along the legs. As the arms twine, so do the legs, all the way into the hip sockets. Relax the joints – hip, knee, ankle, toes. A gentle bubbling upwards from the ground, percolating. Now the stage is set, for turning up the fire.

The night pierces one's being. The terraces and hillsides are aglitter with fireflies. The stars have come down to earth.

The morning brings many butterflies out, and our first sighting this year of the Scarce swallowtail, *Iphiclides podalirius*. It may have been stormy in the mountains, if the swallowtails have come down for the day from their upland pastures.

Stepping up to Pound Mortar, can one open and close the wings effortlessly? Has the long simmer balanced the ingredients enough, so there is one smooth powerful sweep? Rest further in centre, let go of aim. Have no thought…act.*

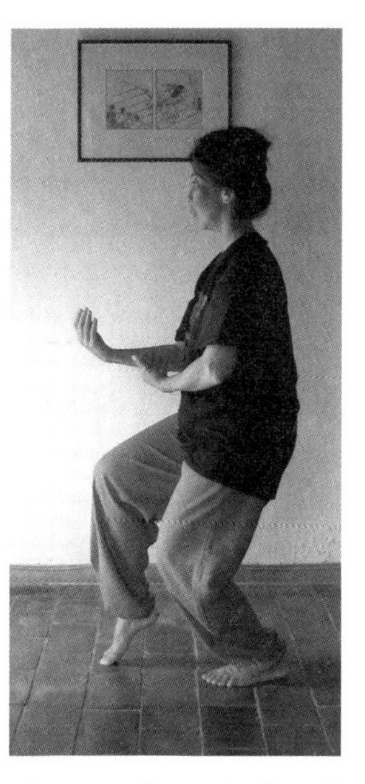

Now XinJia shows itself clearly for the first time in the form. The arms are poignant; there has been nothing like this in LaoJia. Their inwardness now is so congruent with the preceding open-close of the stepping up into position, that I have the feeling this is the only progression of *jingang dao dui* that makes sense.

The position is an expression of XinJia's interiority; not easy to comprehend or capture. The inner coiling is finely articulated, something flame-like in its vibrancy.

The sinking here can coil directly into the right hand's rising fist, the Temple Guardian poised to pound the mortar. Centre embraces the entire body. The leg's lifting is a deepening interiorly; the arms continue their twining to the point of stillness.

I have just returned from shopping in the village. I apply myself to writing with new vigour. The butcher has ordered two copies of this book, if it is translated into Italian. His wife devours books. His first wife was a theologian.

During the week after the chick's disappearance, the male redstart remained nearby. Late each evening, I would see him flying about from wood to wood, as if he was calling to his chick, warning of night's coming. Then, a couple of days ago, I saw a pair of redstarts on the wire close to the house, where the May pair were seen once together. They flew off to the oaks on the hill. Yesterday when I was out mushrooming to the west, I heard one high up in the trees. Now that their call is in my heart, I will recognize their future comings and goings.

After the second Pound Mortar comes the surprising entry into Step Obliquely, the movement which the Japanese lady did with such verve. I have again caught a glimpse of that movement, in the female redstart. It is in the way she shimmers her crimson tail. The end of her spine flickers. I have just seen her!

The way to reach the third Pound Mortar is a small hidden zig followed by a bold zag. It is at moments like this in XinJia, where the move is so instinctive, that one wonders if in fact this is the older form, re-presented later and therefore 'new' to the present generation of senior masters who grew up with LaoJia as the form in their early years of training.

The phrase of movements between the third Pound Mortar and Blue Dragon is known as *bei zhe kao*, 'Lean with Back'. The name refers to the crowning position of an intensifying series of twinings that begin with *pie shen quan*, 'Flinging Body Strike'. These are a real test. The arm movements are impossible to do until one's insides are fluid. The sequence begins in a twisting stairwell rising up the spine, hair-pin bends zigzagging around centre. There can be years of hanging on, performing laborious movements which do not take one up the stairway; an effortless rise comes when one learns to let go. Once the arms have pulled tautly into place, one is poised at the top of the stairs, ready to leap into the flinging strike. As centre jumps and centre lands, the arms wrap into position, flung back left, right shoulder on guard. Powerful revolutions around the vertical are about to come, and everything depends on the immediate securing of the stance upon landing from the jump.

This part is really fun to do, whether or not the posture has got itself together. In fact, all of XinJia is fun to do, if one is not too sensitive to one's shortcomings. But it is tempting for the student to allow herself to be carried away by ideas of power and potency. The style is bold, the moves are magnificent, and one may easily imagine that one looks great doing Chen Style.

It has been most instructive, studying the video takes of these sequences for this book. I see that everything that I have struggled to improve needed the struggling; every bit of effort was necessary. I see where the weaknesses are still, a place in a move where my 'central problem' – the left sacroiliac and its relation to the lower spine – affects the frame of the body. My left side *kua* is weak in its anchoring, especially when it is not the weight-bearing side; in the picture on the left, the right arm's extension has taken me out of centre. I see also instances where a movement is unclear, not complete in its manifestation, due to insufficient understanding of the move. It is very necessary to find out these things about oneself and one's taiji; to practise mindfully, and observe oneself dispassionately.

When the posture comes together – deep and true, flexibly compact – one may follow and express an instinctive sense in the elaboration of spirallings. The entire sequence of Lean with Back is celebratory and the final position (right) could be said to be emblematic of Chen Style; my close encounters with it in the early days have been described in chapters 3 and 6.

If asked how one builds the technique for these big Chen stances, there can be only one answer. ZhanZhuang every day for forty minutes, or more, and *chansijin* exercises for a good hour. With this as the foundation of daily training, practise the forms, LaoJia to start with, and XinJia if you like. Actually it does not matter which form; the short forms too will be effective, if they are practised lots and lots of times each day.

Practise mindfully, with ease in the heart. Practise because it is doing one good, not because it will make one a master. To become a master, or mistress, of TaijiQuan is a very long aim. Practising without expecting the day to arrive soon will be the most sensible way. Remember the road to wisdom: "Err and err and err again – but less and less and less."*

And what good does it do one, undertaking this difficult journey? Can one never have a day off? Yes, there are days when the energy is bitter in the mouth, then one should have the day off.

But about this good that it does one, what is it?

Well, it is like brushing one's teeth, better to do it than not. It is good to step aside from the madding crowd, and let the breathing settle down. There are lots of ways other than TaijiQuan for this.

It is the sweetness of Qi that is addictive. I had never tasted it before. The ease inside, spaciousness, a bubbling sense of well-being. With taiji as one's companion, this can be found any time, anywhere, without need of a single prop.

In ZhanZhuang, one discovers a wide, soft belt around one's middle. Pliable, it translates dantian's dormant strength into spinal vitality.

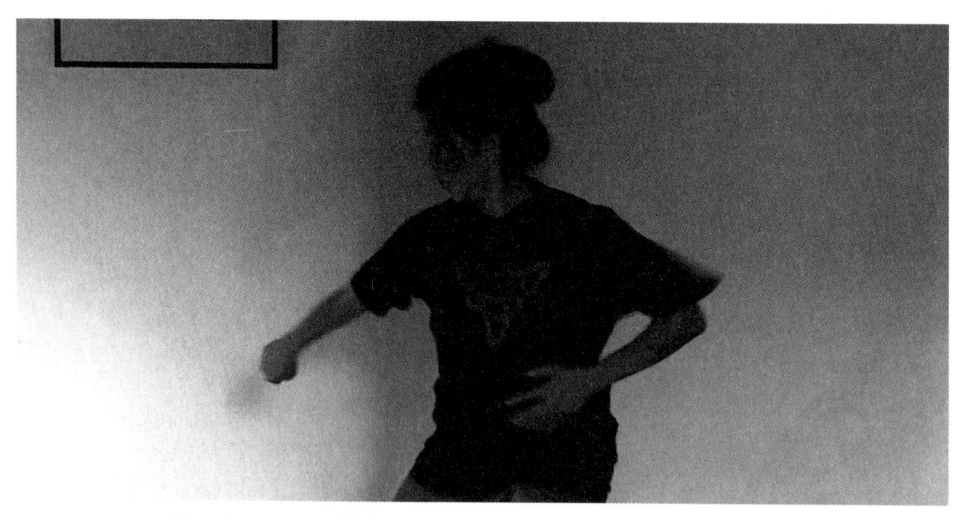

The thing with *fajin* is to be completely at home in dantian. From there, slowly cultivate an ample, resilient power. Never leave dantian. A relaxed, floppy punch is very difficult to achieve. Practise releasing with loose power, the whole body flapping softly. With gentle persistence refine it into a whip-like force, but protect the spine from whiplash: let the head follow the curve of the bow. I keep hearing Fedele, our snake brother, though he is too quick to be seen when disturbed. Hearing his 'sound of shocking', I understand better the kind of relaxation, *song*, that invests full weight into a movement. His coils thwack the ground.

The three punches of *qing long chu shui* shoot out from the turbulent waters of the Blue Dragon's heavings. The first is a fully extended high punch, surging out of Lean with Back's long windings. The second is short range and open handed, ripping out knife-like from within: soft whipping refined. The third is like LaoJia's single punch in Blue Dragon, but more intensely wound.

These are neat punches. They are progressive: each one twines into the next – each comes directly out of the *chansi* set up by the previous. All three *fajin* are executed without the weight going to the side of the body that emits force. Normally in a punch it is the movement of the body's weight that invests the punch with much of its power. We have not this recourse in *qing long chu shui*: the weight shift is minimal, from slightly left to centre. The power of the punches depends more purely on twining force coming from centre.

The 'chest-waist change place' occurs on the slant, diagonally across the body. The strong twisting action that leads out the *jin* is contained within

the parallel framework of the hips and shoulders. Containment intensifies the charge, the seed of *yin* within *yang*, central calm. It is as though, while at the periphery of the body tempests rage and seas may roil, there is continually present at dantian the sense of sitting in an upright deck-chair, in a gentle breeze. When feeling comes of the three *fajin* being one continuous series of twinings, then one has begun to understand *chansijin*.

The Blue Dragon's heavings appear to subside, but half-submerged the coilings persist. Turbulence continues until the entire body draws itself together for *shuang tui shou*, 'Push Both Hands'. The straightforward look of this move belies its difficulty. The route to it is markedly asymmetrical, involving a particularly challenging open-close motion at right angles to the direction of the final push. Spirals set off across the current must arrive at resolution.

The way into the backward steps, *dao juan hong*, is by another startling entry, redstart lady style. A flicker in the small of the back, a contained rippling in waist, arms, legs. The hands shimmer; the feet come as close to shimmering as they reasonably can. *Dao juan hong* means moving backwards with the arms swirling. *Hong* is the humerus, the bone of the upper arm; this part of the arm turns. Undulations of the spine set off diagonal ripples in such a way that a subtle slanting asymmetry draws the body continually behind itself. Once in the swirl, rhythmic precision controls the turbulence. The centre rolls, opening and closing. Elbows synchronize in *juan hong*, the centre swallows the power, retains it momentarily, then releases it afresh. The feeling is of turning oneself inside out, then turning oneself outside in, over and over, until out and in are pulled through one another, sliding past like ropes which never get knotted.

In these days running up to midsummer, there is a thrust in the last hour of night towards the dawn. Like last year in this season, I find myself waking earlier and earlier. It has rained almost every day. The valley is fully absorbed in growth. This morning, the skies are constantly aflicker with distant lightning. Thunder is on the prowl. The birds raise their voices long before dawn.

Yesterday I woke especially early, and spent a couple of hours writing. The rain let off by mid-morning, and there were several hours of sun. It gave Fedele a chance to come out. He earned his name last year by his

regularity and curious constancy. Every day he was peeping out of his slit about 9 o'clock in the morning, as soon as the stones had warmed enough. I think he is careful with his body temperature. That slit may be too small for him this year, for now he appears in the gap where he snoozed lazily last summer.

In the afternoon I found him arrayed on the wall like a heavenly constellation. He occupied me for the rest of the day, at times allowing me to come up quite close. It seems he is nearly as curious of us as we are of him. Having had several chances to watch him as he went about his day, I am realizing that the injunction to 'move like snake' in Chentaiji is no fantasy.

In LaoJia, *dao juan hong* is followed by *bai e liang chi*, 'White Goose Wings Shimmering'. In XinJia there is an intriguing series of intermediate moves between the backward steps and the shimmering. The movements express a kind of whole body tumult, a collective churning, brimming with the spirit of the valley.

In the old days, the sequences of movement in the TaijiQuan forms had more names, each little section standing out distinctly. When the naming of the moves became more systematized and compiled into neat lists of given length, some names got left out. One such name, which does not appear on the regular lists, referred to the movement that most inspired me when I first learned LaoJia. As in XinJia, it occurs later on in the form. It is a unique rising undulation moving crossways in the body that fires the arms to whip into position. The old name for this movement was 'Shake Flowers out of Sleeves'.

After XinJia's swirling backwards, the moves leading up to the elbow strike are also now nameless. At first one is in familiar *chansi* territory with double hand twinings and repeated weight shifts. Then one seems to draw closer to something that is only hinted at in Chansigong. In the familiar exercises, the coilings have a surface aspect even though they are linked to movement hidden in the kernel of the body. In XinJia the surface is almost swallowed up by the underlying. The windings become smaller and smaller, closer to a core which is not the pole around which the snake winds but is the snake itself, erupting, startlingly innumerable in its coils.

XinJia contains flickering strikes that lash out a short distance, open palmed, spat out from the interior of the body. There is very little showing of dantian's workings on the surface. Such movements are incomprehensible to the beginner, impossible to copy, but as technique and understanding grow, this kind of emission of force happens naturally.

One of these close *fajin* comes hot on the heels of the elbow strike: as soon as it locks with an abrupt tug, dantian ejects the forearm to the back, signalling the beginning of *zhong pan*, 'Central Winding'. This is an evocative name, helping one to look for the feelings special to the section. Percussive though it is at the start, there is something languid in *zhong pan*. The winding centrally involves a doubled doubling back, where the elbows are the rings through which a serpentine power wraps around one's middle.

After repeated turnings around the core, there comes a narrowing of the frame, as if the body were now aiming to fly out through an opening. This is an unusual *fajin* – the left withdraws into the right, so much so that the right side rises and overthrows the left. The 'chest-waist change place' happens more on one side, and a little behind, where it gathers force low in the body. Then one shoots for the gap; the emission of force is abrupt, released only an instant before one reaches the summit.

From the last step of the backward swirling, through to the end of *zhong pan*, one is immersed in micro-cascades of asymmetrical windings. These movements are not obvious, they are not dramatic, and they require long years of inner polishing to reveal their essence. Barely visible twists and turns extend their span until a jump erupts, like a spring wound to its springing point. This section of the form is a cornucopia of moves aslant, of rhythmic variation, of changes in direction which defy choreographic definition. The movements feel as though they were created spontaneously, and the only way to be true to their spirit is to create them anew.

The latter part of XinJia contains one move in particular that reminds me of Pytt. It is *ye ma fen zong*, 'Wild Horse Parts its Mane', which she knew as 'Parting the Wild Horse's Mane'. The spirit here goes free. It needs a seasoned technique. The movement starts at the nexus of qi pathways deep in the lower back. From there it must find its way simultaneously through both sides of the body, the twining legs wiring the arms which are to uncoil, asymmetrically but equally, to their fingertips. The openness of the stance and the fullness of extension are a challenge, because of the need to maintain compactness throughout. Running through the outstretched arms is a single finely articulated thread, looped around the small of the back.

A horse parts its mane with a quivering flick. From full extension there is withdrawal, the body coiling up again in preparation for *fajin* tight around the core, the hands moving no more than two or three inches in ejecting force, quivering flicks that should erupt with a sudden fierceness from deep within. The arms express the power that one has been nurturing in double hand Chansigong.

The way into the *fajin* defies the art of copying. One looks to the teacher, checking that this arm lies at one angle, the other arm at another angle. There may be confusion for a long time, for on each occasion the teacher's arms appear to go by a slightly different route. In moments when one forgets to worry about it, one may be surprised at how the arms find their own way to a certain poised place, an unknown place that feels mysteriously familiar, like a landscape in different season, or in a mirror. Eventually a realization dawns: the elusive path to that unnameable place is the route travelled by the arms in double hand Chansigong! We have certainly been here before, but never so tightly wound inside. The first *fajin* is an eruption in double hand position 2 (above). For the second *fajin*, on the other side, the arms pause in position 3 (below). They relax there completely, by the look of it, and strike like lightning.

Ye ma (Wild Horse, right) and *danbian* (Single Whip, below) present an interesting contrast. The stances appear similar but the internal workings and the feelings are quite different. In *ye ma* the twinings coming from below travel up the spine, with a strong spiral through the torso as they continue to wind out through the arms. The rearward side twines freely outwards as the leading side searches for a far journey's end. As the weight shifts from the back to the front leg, one is reaching for a place beyond the body; the feeling is as though the weight continues to travel.

Single Whip, in contrast, contains its power. The clue to the interior coilings lies in the right arm with its hooked hand. The entry into *danbian* is a unique movement: twining elbows fold around the waist, and the hook that emerges is one end of the belt encircling the torso. The stance is constellated energy, where the circuits are recharged for the next lap of the journey. The position comes again and again in the long forms, and the varying exits out of Single Whip are inventive phrases that one comes to appreciate after years of practice. The placement of the left hand seems to be similar to *ye ma*'s back hand. Here also, however, the feeling inside is quite different. The hooked right side does not let go of the left. The entire body is emphatic in its preparedness.

Danbian is a good place for self-cooking. Carefully enter the position, as discussed in chapter 10. Carve out a stance that is definite, with a good span between the legs, enough width to be able to search out the extension of the right leg as one simmers, but also framed and contained in the bow.

Place the weight firmly on the left side; stretch the right leg; soften the knee joint within the arched extension of the leg. Sit down in the stance, *kua* relaxed. As in the preliminary process for the Pound Mortar simmering, described earlier in this chapter, let the upper body find its rightness, the arms their own outward routing. Keep the leftward direction of *danbian* active to the fingertips, not the heel of the hand.* A hollow pole descends perpendicularly through shoulder and hip on each side, hollow for free flow. Establish the inner physical frame: vertically from right shoulder to right hip, left shoulder to left hip; horizontally from shoulder to shoulder, hip to hip. Draw the iliac wings together, look for parallel. Stretch the arms, let go within the stretch. Relax dantian. Whole body breathing. Calm down, become still. Nothing stirring the profound mirror of mind, *xuan lan*.*

Wild Horse is different; the frame shimmers. Ripples continue and amplify; the ceaseless and complex extension from foot to foot, fingertips to fingertips, works every sinew in the body. The unending opening of the stance breathes to the surface emotions held in the chest and shoulders. It wrings and unsticks, it clears out energetic impaludism lurking in the breast.* Grounding the turbulence, the body's weight falls plumb centre, *baihui* to *huiyin* a live descent.

Train in these two stances to understand the correct proportion of things. When upper and lower body are balanced, front and back unified, centre and periphery interchangeable, the sense of contained strength gives one perspective. Earth, sky, one's body—together.*

Enjoy too the smoothness of being flush with existence. Dantian sits purring. The internal organs feel to have their proper place. There is a bubbliness under the soles of the feet which gives zest. The eyes see more clearly, and with a greater tenderness. Throughout the day one feels the whole body breathing, the encasing skin porous, sensitive and protective at the same time. Mind permeates body; the body drinks in mind's kindness and clarity.

Mid-flow in the windings leading to 'Lean with Back' one finds oneself travelling in an airy element, light and viscous; easy to slice; palpably supportive. Moving through it feels to be without expense, tireless. There are sublime stretches. One enjoys them thoroughly, knowing that impermanence is the one constant, accepting the gift of well being, like Zhuangzi's True Man, and without conflict giving it back.

> The True Men of old ... did not regret it when they missed the mark, were not complacent when they hit plumb on.*

While I was preoccupied with the writing of these notes on practice, the person of Zhuangzi strode into my life. He is in a faded robe, straw sandals on his feet. It is clear from his appearance that he needs nothing. He is mocking, irreverent, and full of love. He makes fun of my attachment to correct transmission of the teaching. He laughs at my concern for my students. He does not bother to say "bearing yet not possessing",* as apparently Laozi did. He refuses to bear, let alone to possess, anything.

Zhuangzi tempers my efforts to improve my technique. He tells me that if I love what I do, then I can give myself to practice. One may apply oneself daily the whole of one's life, yet know that further depths await sounding.

I am still sounding the depths of the first movement, *jingang dao dui.* Those Temple Guardians have not relaxed their gaze, although familiarity has softened what was unremitting at the start. The arms' first lift now happens beyond breath and muscle. Whereas in the old days the parallel lift always betrayed an imbalance, there is now a truer symmetry between the arms as they rise from the depths. The sinking too feels fuller and more potent, the hands affirming the accord that will carry them through to the end. The turning to the left that comes next is twining more closely and precisely than before, but having examined the filmings for this book, I think I can let it go more freely, the posture now is intact enough for furthering. It is astonishing to think that this leftwards turn is the start of the asymmetrical twinings that will create the entire form of XinJia. Once the arms have risen and sunk at the beginning of the form, there is not a single movement in the form's duration that is truly symmetric. That is, until the very end, when the mortar is pounded one last time, and the arms are lowered.

The orioles sporting in the rain woke me this morning. They fly from tree to tree, flitting in amongst the aspens and oaks, at times hanging upside down from the willow curtains, playing hide and seek, the young ones calling each other from wood to wood.

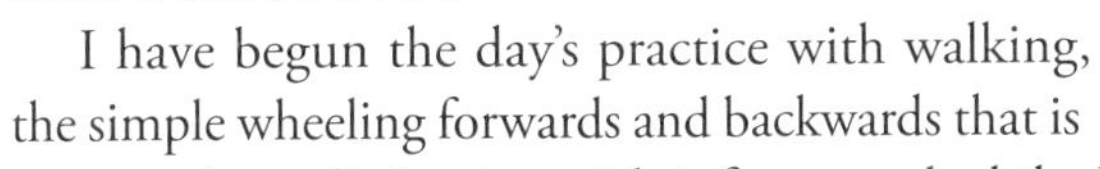

I have begun the day's practice with walking, the simple wheeling forwards and backwards that is not simple at all. Staying with it for a good while, I notice gradual changes. The body starts off sluggish in the centre, and frayed at the edges. As the hips begin to function more properly, the legs wake up, the thighs picking up with interest each step that arises. The mind is quietened by the steady rhythm, and as the breathing relaxes, a coolness bathes the chest which now flows freely within the shoulders' boundaries. The frayed feeling disappears bit by bit, with the emerging sense of parts slotting into one another, of moving with a quiet purpose, recovering harmony.

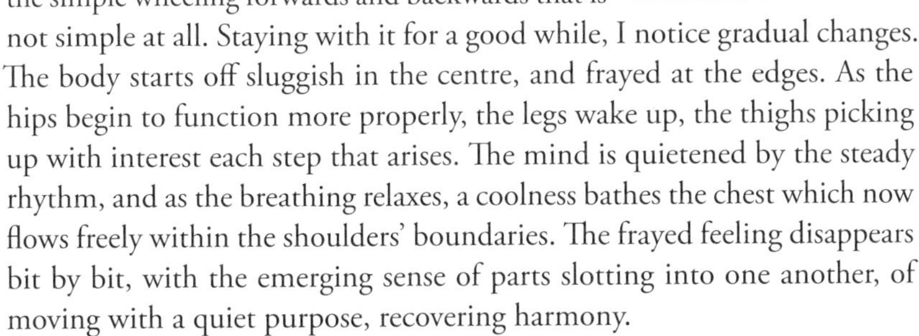

I lose count of the back and forth stepping, up and down the terrace. After a while, the core no longer wavers; the sterno-sacral line is gaining its cohesion. Each time the arm winds in and the foot steps through, there will be one correct trajectory. I look for the eye of the needle.

Finding a delicate alignment, the body becomes infused with wavelets passing up and down the spinal column. As these spread out to the limbs, the wheeling arms begin to conduct a charge. Palms plump up, fingers feel full, and the odd one that was reluctant now joins in the flow.

Something difficult to pin down, elusive, is the tiny turning deep down in the centre that opens the palm of the hand when it is low and close to the waist. This fine pulse is what conducts the charge from dantian outwards along the limbs.

Yesterday, June really shone. Fedele did not appear at his post in the stone wall. Ancient rhythms call him in these days and nights nearing the solstice.

It was full moon last night. Surrounded by hills as we are, the risings and settings of moon and sun are marked on the terrain's compass. Midsummer full moon rose at its most southerly point, well past the crest of the hill across the valley.

The morning is soft and shrouded in mist. Many orioles are in the poplars, almost hidden. I hear the musical twitterings of the young ones. Every now and then, a youngster utters a grating triple caw. In those summers when they stay through until August, we hear that harshness smoothed, as the elders teach the young ones the Golden Oriole's song.

In the pre-dawn light, they sing very close to the house. There is hardly a stir in the monochrome poplars.

Night withdraws down the lane to the west woods, accompanied by the moon and Jupiter.

Notes and References

CHAPTER 1 · MINDFUL PRACTICE

1 *T'aiChiCh'uan in England* The early flowering of TaijiQuan in America and Britain in the 1960s and 70s coincided with general use of the Wade-Giles spelling T'aiChiCh'uan, and similarly ch'i for qi, *tao* for *dao*, Hsiang Kang (or Hong Kong) for Xianggang.

4 *Schafer translates* Edward H. Schafer, *Pacing the Void: T'ang Approaches to the Stars* (University of California Press, Berkeley, 1977), p. 25.

4 *Once started ... through an infinity of time* Ibid., p. 31.

5 *The form of T'aiChi ... only through tension* Khin Thitsa (Pali modern cursive, Kinthissa), 'In Search of the Golden Needle', *New Dance*, 17 (1981).

5 *As the foot begins ... something in the mind* Ibid.

6 *In order for this spot ... hands and feet* Kinthissa.taiji.org, 2004.

8 *The twining strength is the core ... with particularity* Chen XiaoWang, *Chen Style Taijiquan* (Zhaohua Publishing House, Beijing, 1984), p. 149.

CHAPTER 2 · THE ART OF LEARNING

22 *Can you wait quietly, while the mud settles?* After *Daodejing* 15 in Gia-fu Feng's translation, "Who can wait quietly while the mud settles?" Gia-fu Feng and Jane English, *Lao Tsu: Tao Te Ching* (Wildwood House, London, 1973). This translation has no page numbers; it follows in sequence the traditional ordering of the 81 chapters of the classic.

22 *The sorting which evens things out* The title of the second of seven *Inner Chapters* of the *Zhuangzi* in A. C. Graham's translation. This chapter "contains the most philosophically acute passages in the *Inner Chapters*, obscure, fragmented, but pervaded by the sensation, rare in ancient literatures, of a man jotting the living thought at the moment of its inception." A. C. Graham, *Chuang-tzŭ: The Inner Chapters* (George Allen & Unwin, London, 1981), p. 48.

23 *Spät habe ... zu sein* The words are from Marga Bührig, *Spät habe ich gelernt, gerne Frau zu sein: eine feministische Autobiographie* (Kreuz, Stuttgart, 1988).

24 *Frame and Essence* "The Tao is elusive and intangible ... Oh, it is elusive and intangible, and yet within is form. Oh, it is dim and dark, and yet within is essence." *Daodejing* 21, trans. Gia-fu Feng in Feng and English, *Lao Tsu*.

24 *may be translated as 'Book of the Way and Its Power'* Thus following Arthur Waley, *The Way and Its Power: A Study of the Tao Tê Ching and Its Place in Chinese Thought* (George Allen & Unwin, London, 1934).

24 *Perhaps it is the mother … Call it Tao* Indeed the passage continues, "For lack of a better word, I call it great." *Daodejing* 25, trans. Gia-fu Feng in Feng and English, *Lao Tsu.*

25 *De expresses … arising from the nameless source* "All things are produced by the *Tâo*, and nourished by its outflowing operation… Thus it is that the *Tâo* … brings them to their full growth, nurses them, completes them, matures them, maintains them, and overspreads them … this is called its mysterious operation." *Daodejing* 51, trans. James Legge in *The Sacred Books of the East*, ed. F. Max Müller, volume XXXIX (Clarendon Press, Oxford, 1891), pp. 93–94.

25 *If he would lead them* "If the sage would guide the people, he must serve with humility. If he would lead them, he must follow behind. In this way when the sage rules, the people will not feel oppressed; When he stands before them, they will not be harmed." *Daodejing* 66, trans. Gia-fu Feng in Feng and English, *Lao Tsu.*

25 *Marching without* "This is called marching without appearing to move, Rolling up your sleeves without showing your arm, Capturing the enemy without attacking …" *Daodejing* 69, trans. Gia-fu Feng in Feng and English, *Lao Tsu.*

25 *The winds rise in the north … between and over them* Graham, *Chuang-tzŭ*, p. 49. Though they survive only in the patchily authentic *Outer Chapters*, Graham places these lines in the *Inner Chapters* (chapter 2) where they are cited in the eighth century meditation text *Zhiguan fuxing zhuan hongjue* by the Buddhist scholar-patriarch Zhanran.

26 *to pant, to puff … the Way and its Power* Arthur Waley, *Three Ways of Thought in Ancient China* (George Allen & Unwin, London, 1939), pp. 68–69. Also listed in near contemporaneous compilation, the Pigeon's Bath, the Monkey Dance, the Owl Gaze, the Tiger Regard (ibid., p. 67).

26 *The True Men … they gave it back* Graham, *Chuang-tzŭ*, p. 85.

26 *Death and life … to take him as their model* Ibid., p. 86.

27 *Tzu-lai … his stock* Waley, *Three Ways of Thought*, pp. 52–53.

28 Joseph Needham, *Science and Civilisation in China* (Cambridge University Press, 1954–) especially volume II: *History of Scientific Thought* (1956).

CHAPTER 3 · HELP COOK

38 *the unforgiving minute* Rudyard Kipling, *If—* following 'Brother Square-Toes' in *Rewards and Fairies* (Macmillan, London, 1951), p. 176.

38 *now TaijiQuan* Kinthissa.taiji.org, 2004.

39 *insert what has no thickness … look proudly round* Graham, *Chuang-tzŭ*, p. 64. From the third of the *Inner Chapters*, 'What matters in the nurture of life'.

40 *Knowing the secret ways of the winds … delight and use of man* A. D. Brankston, *Early Ming Wares of Chingtechen* (Vetch and Lee, Hong Kong, 1970), p. 61.

CHAPTER 4 · REASONS TO STAND

43 *south of the clouds* Going to China was important in that it placed TaijiQuan in its social context. The teacher I found in Beijing was a shepherd boy from further north who had been swept into the tide of revolution, learning to read and write only after joining the Red Army. He had a humble approach to taiji which was most refreshing. I liked being part of the group of ordinary Beijing residents who practised taiji purely for pleasure. After my time with them, I went as far southwest as I could, to Yunnan's hinterlands where China becomes the Asia of my birth: pagodas on hilltops; *bhikkhus* (Southern Buddhist monks) in orange robes part of the throng; women washing their buttock-length hair in streams alongside the paddy fields. When I reached Damenglong I found that my entire life as I had lived it so far lay to the west, or to the east, or somewhere else.

44 *When I was studying ... eventually push-hand* Feng ZhiQiang interviewed by Mak Wah Hoi, *Tai Chi & Alternative Health*, 17 (1998), p. 24.

45 *a world closer* Jacques Lusseyran, *And There Was Light: The autobiography of a blind hero in the French Resistance* (William Heinemann, London, 1963), p. 10.

48 *somewhere in China* Maggie Keswick, *The Chinese Garden* (Academy Editions, London, 1978), p. 146. I am grateful to Dr. Charles Jencks for his gracious permission to include this illustration.

52 *patterns in a perpetual dance* Joseph Needham, 'Three Masks of the Tao: a Chinese corrective for maleness, monarchy and militarism in theology', *Teilhard Review*, 14/2 (1979), p. 12.

54 *Rectilinear. Jade water* Arthur Waley, *The Life and Times of Po Chü-I 772–846 A.D.* (George Allen & Unwin, London, 1949). Bo JuYi at the Literary Examination, AD 800, is presented with five characters from a poem of the fifth century by Yan YanZhi: "Jade water record square flow". Waley explains, "Jade-bearing waters may be recognized by their rectilinear ripples." p. 20.

57 *Who said, resting in imperfection?* Sri Aurobindo, maybe not in the sense that I had in mind. "To rest in humanity is to rest in imperfection." *Essays Divine and Human* (Sri Aurobindo Ashram Publication Department, Pondicherry, 1997), p. 230. Happily resting in imperfection I had imagined Zhuangzi as the speaker.

58 *when I was two* The autograph on the photograph is by Josip Broz Tito.

62 *earth's wild symphony* The winds in the valleys of Lunigiana do not push, they pull: *tira vento*. They stretch over a week sometimes, unremitting, powerful enough to alter one's sense of the environment. Zhuangzi describing the hubbub of the philosophers conjures up the unsettling din:

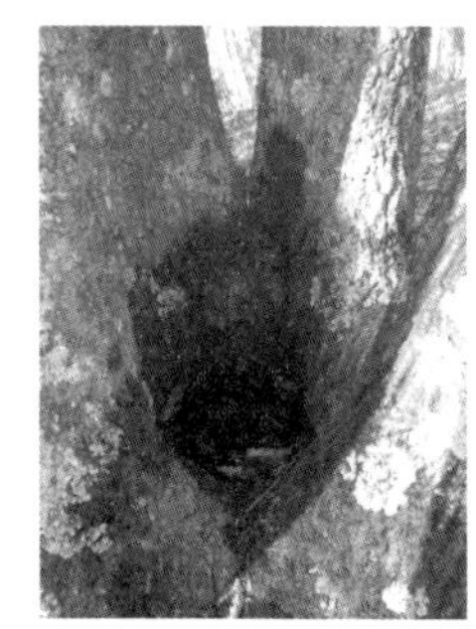

> That hugest of clumps of soil blows out breath, by name the 'wind'. Better if it were never to start up, for whenever it does ten thousand hollow places burst out howling, and don't tell me you have never heard how the hubbub swells! The recesses in mountain forests, the hollows that pit great trees a hundred spans round, are like nostrils, like mouths, like ears, like sockets, like bowls, like mortars, like pools, like puddles. Hooting, hissing, sniffing, sucking, mumbling, moaning, whistling, wailing, the winds ahead sing out AAAH!, the winds behind answer EEEH!, breezes strike up a tiny chorus, the whirlwind a mighty chorus.

Graham, *Chuang-tzŭ*, pp. 48–49.

62 *Ben shen, rooting the Spirit* In the *Lingshu* section of the *Huangdi Neijing, The Yellow Emperor's Classic of Internal Medicine*, chapter 8 is entitled *Ben Shen* (root spirit). The ideogram 本 *ben* (root) presents 木 *mu* (tree) with a horizontal line indicating the ground or that part which lies below. 神 *shen* (spirit) contains the 113th radical 礻 which informs characters "relating to transcendental matters" (in the felicitous phrase of Dr. L. Wieger, S.J., *Chinese Characters: Their Origin, Etymology, History, Classification and Signification*, Catholic Mission Press, Hsien-hsien, 1913, 2nd edition 1927, p. 29.) Claude Larre describing the older uncontracted form of the radical 示 writes:

> The spirits are not seen directly, but there is the image of somebody making a sacrifice and arranging a table with a stand…

(Claude Larre, S.J., and Elisabeth Rochat de la Vallée, *The Heart in Ling Shu Chapter 8*, Monkey Press, London, 2004, p. 13.) In the old medical texts such as the *Huangdi Neijing*, the influx of Spirit is not impersonal like the wind or the rain; it is not the unbidden blast of a remote heaven. *Shen* are near to us and they respond, maybe, to the enticement of a carefully prepared and befitting invitation. The work of the individual, or of the physician on her behalf, is to coax the spirits to bestow beneficence. They will not be drawn if there is disorder; and if they come, they may not stay.

> These Spirits are pleased to stay when they feel welcomed.

(Larre and de la Vallée, *Rooted in Spirit: The Heart of Chinese Medicine*, Station Hill Press, New York, 1995, p. 4.) The translation of *shen* as spirit(s) may give a whimsical impression of airy waftings. I suggest however that it expresses aptly the aspect of *shen* which is presented in Chinese medicine as being delicate, lively, personal; sometimes even skittish or lazy. *Shen* are of heaven, but they are operative in the body. And how does it feel, to be rooted in spirit? Imagine something which affects heaviness as light affects darkness. In taiji practice we work with bones, muscles and ligaments; an aligned, energized body attracts *shen*. The spirit in the lamp puts light in the eyes and bounce in the step, rootedly animate, 本神.

63 *Pelvic girdle contains dantian's abode* The words borrow from the title of the article by Jocelyn C. P. Proby, 'The Integrity of the Pelvic Girdle' (1986), re-printed in *Osteopathy: Principles & Practice*, ed. Russell J. White, volume 1 (Institute of Classical Osteopathy, Maidstone, 1999).

63 *thirty-six times in this direction, and thirty-six times in the other* The traditional training mandates that after a period of ZhanZhuang practice we gently lower the arms to the sides of the body. Then we cross the hands over the dantian area, "Laogong, laogong, dantian: three points, one line." We then softly circle the hands, some dozens or more times in either direction, around the coronal (frontal) axis. Initially the hands lead the dantian in a simple circling in the coronal plane. With time and practice, the interior circling becomes increasingly complex, one might almost say omni-directional. Deep structures in the body become involved, rotating around many axes simultaneously, including sacroiliac nutation and counternutation in the sagittal plane. This last may be unfamiliar. The terminology is due to Ibrahim Adalbert Kapandji, as David Coulter explains:

> Even though the sacroiliac joints are synovial joints, their opposing surfaces usually fit together tightly enough for every movement of the pelvis to affect the sacrum (and therefore the spine as whole), and for every movement of the sacrum to affect the pelvis. This view—that the sacroiliac joints

are essentially immobile—has practical value, and it was in fact the only view until the 1930s, but it is an oversimplification: the synovial structure of the healthy sacroiliac joint is now known to provide its groove-and-rail architecture with the capacity for a small amount of slippage—movements that have been called *nutation* and *counternutation* by the French orthopedist I. A. Kapandji.

H. David Coulter, *Anatomy of Hatha Yoga* (Body and Breath, Honesdale, 2001), p. 328. Coulter estimates that an "ideal" sacroiliac joint might allow up to 10° of rotation of the sacrum with respect to the ilia, from full nutation to full counternutation. That may be optimistic, or even alarming to those who view movement in the sacroiliac as more of a problem than an opportunity. But even a small degree of trained mobility in the sacroiliac—with ligamentous resilience—can have profound effects on the way we move.

Observing Chen XiaoWang as he turns dantian at the end of ZhanZhuang, from a vantage point that gives a view of both the back and the side, one may get a glimpse of the complexity of his rotations. One day in the Bienne dojo, we each had the chance to put a hand on his lower back as he moved. I felt a stirring undulation on the sides of the sacrum close to the mid-line. It had nothing to do with a swivelling of the hips. There was the merest articulation, a hidden turning of a multi-dimensioned wheel, all within the immaculate frame of the pelvis. The centre spins, the arms are drawn into the vortex in barely discernible spirals. The legs flow like water through the mill, augmenting the power.

65 *Doing Nothing* The concept *wu wei* is sometimes made more mysterious than it needs to be. A. C. Graham comes to the rescue (*Chuang-tzŭ*, p. 35):

> *Wu wei*, 'Doing Nothing' (a paradoxical expression which some translators soften by such equivalents as 'Non-action'), is a basic concept in *Lao-tzŭ* but less prominent throughout most of *Chuang-tzŭ*. *Wu wei* is refraining from trying to force spontaneous trends by deliberate action. It implies ... that when one does move, it is not 'doing' (as the execution of a reasoned project with a fixed end), but tending towards fluid goals in response to changing circumstances, as spontaneously as the unwilled processes of heaven and earth.

67 *I now work with my spirit ... many hidden openings* Gia-fu Feng and Jane English, *Chuang Tsu: Inner Chapters* (Wildwood House, London, 1974), p. 55. Graham's translation of the same passage (*Chuang-tzŭ*, pp. 63–64) runs:

> Nowadays, I am in touch through the daemonic in me, and do not look with the eye. With the senses I know where to stop, the daemonic I desire to run its course. I rely on Heaven's structuring, cleave along the main seams...

In the story of Cook Ding, *shen* invest the carver of oxen with an intuitive power beyond knowledge and reason. Graham's translation of *shen* as 'daemonic' gives us a visceral feel of the Chinese word (*Chuang-tzŭ*, p. 35, note 72):

'Daemonic' seems to me to be the modern word closest to *shen*, but I use it with the warning that its restless, anguished quality is foreign to the Chinese word, not to mention the malign associations which it tends to collect by confusion with 'demoniac'.

CHAPTER 5 · LAOJIA

76 *obrint i netejant* q.v. chapter 1, p. 11.

79 *The character of fa in its ancient form meant to let fly like an arrow* The modern form of the character 發 *fa* combines 弓 (bow) and 癶 (shoot) with 殳 (trample). Léon Wieger adds this to his collection of examples which have been "arbitrarily mutilated by the scribes" (*Chinese Characters*, p. 266):

> The modern form (to trample with a bow) is a nonsense. In the ancient primitive character, there was 矢 an arrow, instead of 殳; shooting 癶 of the 矢 arrow by the 弓 bow.

79 *Ich fühle Luft von anderen Planeten* (I feel air from other planets) The first line of *Entrückung* (Rapture) by Stefan George, included in his collection of poems *Der siebente Ring* (1907). Arnold Schoenberg quotes the line at the start of the last movement of his String Quartet no. 2 op. 10 (1908).

83 *pounding of the mortar* The Gerald Warner Taiwan Image Collection, Skillman Library, Lafayette College, includes a photograph of Atayal women in Taiwan hulling rice using a foot-operated pestle and mortar (detail below by kind permission). A similar mechanism is described by Judith Carney:

> Raising the fulcrum with the foot allowed the pestle to fall into a mortar (often just a hole in the ground or floor), where the striking action removed the grain's hulls. This device for processing *sativa* rice was in use over a broad area of Asia from India to Japan. Its use in Japan is described in *The Tale of Genji*, written early in the eleventh century.

Judith A. Carney, *Black Rice: The African Origins of Rice Cultivation in the Americas* (Harvard University Press, Cambridge, 2001), p. 112.

The best time – for practising taiji as well as for hulling rice – is the early morning, and *The Tale of Genji* describes a pair of late risers startled by the unaccustomed sounds:

> What a queer place to be lying in! thought Genji, as he gazed round the garret, so different from any room he had ever known before. It must be almost day. … That [so shrinking and delicate in her ways] she could yet endure without a murmur the exasperating banging and bumping that was going on in every direction, aroused his admiration, and he felt that this was much nicer of her than if she had shuddered with horror at each sound. But

> now, louder than thunder, came the noise of the [treadle-mortar] threshing-mills, seeming so near that they could hardly believe it did not come from out of the pillow itself. Genji thought that his ears would burst. What many of the noises were he could not at all make out; but they were very peculiar and startling. The whole air seemed to be full of crashings and bangings.

Lady Murasaki, trans. Arthur Waley, *The Tale of Genji* (George Allen & Unwin, London, 1925), pp. 106–7. In the taiji movement the practitioner's body is both pestle and mortar and becomes the pounding as well as the one who pounds.

CHAPTER 6 · LAOJIA 2

85 *the valley has disappeared* Calligraphy by Chen XiaoWang (Ryde, New South Wales, 1996). The characters are 佛 (*fo*) and 缘 (*yuan*). 佛 is Buddha, the teachings known as Buddhism; 缘 is affinity, a preordained direction. Master Chen translates 缘 in this context as 'relationship': a nearness to the Buddha's Teachings.

85 *jingang dao dui* For the names of the movements of the Chen long forms see Chen Xin, 陈氏太极拳图说 *The Illustrated Canon of Chen Family Taijiquan* (published 1933, re-issued by Shanghai Bookstore Publishing House, 1986).

86 *a succession of anterior and posterior tilts ... tuned to the overall turn around the vertical axis* To be guided through these movements is to be given a hint of mysteries that are not easily internalized or understood. Eventually, however, internalize them we must. Asked by a student about which muscles should be brought into play for a particular movement, Chen XiaoWang replied, "I give you flowing; which muscle use, which muscle not use, you must find." One day he invited us to try stepping sideways in *yun shou*, 'Cloud Hands', without losing centre. Each student in turn came forwards and stood ready to move. Master Chen applied hands-on correction until he was satisfied with the stance –"Qi now flowing"– then he stepped back a couple of paces and said, "Now start movement, do not lose centre." The instant when he saw that centre was lost, he would say, "Stop!" Sometimes, he said "Stop!" before the student had even begun to move. Banner had waved, but body had not followed. Sometimes, he said "Stop!" at the moment when the first flicker of movement appeared – evidently, the trauma of transferring from mind to muscle the intention to move had caused loss of centre. Some people were able to lift their foot and move it sideways a little, but lost centre before they had managed to take an actual step. A few people were able to take a step, but lost centre as they tried to shift weight onto the extended leg. A very few students managed to complete a whole step, or maybe even two steps. Nobody was able to take three steps.

93 *unlike ... White Crane* 白鵝亮翅 *bai e liang chi* (Chen Xin, *Illustrated Canon*, pp. 179, 233, 368)—white goose shimmer (or brightly, radiantly flash) wings.

鵝 (*e*) is the domesticated goose as distinct from 雁 (*ya*) the wild goose. In the Yang form the white goose 白鵝 (*bai e*) is replaced by the more rarefied white crane 白鶴 (*bai he*)—understandably so, as the form migrated from the Chen family village in Henan to the capital Beijing where it attracted the interest of merchants and intellectuals, Qing government officials, members of the Imperial guard and one of the grandsons of the Daoguang Emperor.

CHAPTER 7 · LAOJIA 3

102 *access point* TaijiQuan shares some terminology with Acupuncture. It is an interesting question to what degree the two traditions are speaking of the same things when they refer to points and channels. Sometimes the taiji practitioner is working with interior configurations that may be related to but are not the same as Acupuncture points, which occur where channels come close to the surface of the body and are thus accessible to treatment by needle.

CHAPTER 8 · LOOPY CHANSIJIN

125 *transverse arch* Caution is advisable regarding the transverse arch of the foot. Gray's Anatomy (15th edition) refers to the "appearance" of an arch which "can scarcely be described as a true arch":

> In addition to [the] longitudinal arch the foot presents a transverse arch, at the anterior part of the tarsus and hinder part of the metatarsus. This, however, can scarcely be described as a true arch, but presents more the character of a half-dome. The inner border of the central portion of the longitudinal arch is elevated from the ground, and from this point the bones arch over to the outer border, which is in contact with the ground, and, assisted by the longitudinal arch, produce a sort of rounded niche on the inner side of the foot, which gives the appearance of a transverse as well as a longitudinal arch.

Henry Gray, *Anatomy, Descriptive and Surgical* (Bounty Books, New York, 15th edition 1977), p. 213. But even that may be going too far:

> The concept of a transverse arch at the level of the metatarsal heads was a common belief in the past. It was accepted as one of the major structures in the mechanism of energy absorption. It is still described in textbooks and was in Gray's anatomy as recently as 1995 (38th edition). In recent years, with the introduction of various pressure platforms, the existence of a metatarsal arch has been questioned. ... We believe that our findings, the first quantitative study, will help to clarify the situation. ... A transverse arch during the stance phase was found in 22 feet (3% of the population)... The 95% confidence interval for the proportion of subjects and patients with a metatarsal arch in the population is thus between 1.8% and 4.3%.

E. J. Luger *et al.*, 'Patterns of weight distribution under the metatarsal heads', *J Bone Joint Surg [Br]*, 81–B/2 (1999), pp. 199–202. My experience is that in lively feet the transverse arch is more frequently found. The arch is also important in Yoga:

> The foot has three arches: the inner (longer) arch, the outer (shorter) arch and the frontal or transverse arch. ... The transverse arch is supported mainly by the M. Peroneus longus which runs from the outer side of the knee down the outer leg and diagonally across the sole of the foot to the big toe. These three arches must be raised to rebounce the weight of the body back upward against the downward pull of gravity. ... To lift the three arches, the distance between the big and little toe has to increase by abduction of these toes.

Dona Holleman, *Centering Down* (Tipografia Giuntina, Firenze, 1981), p. 35.

130 *canonical choices* Basic exercises train a set of transitions which in skilful combination cover the range of possible movement.

132 *that hugest of clumps of soil* Graham, *Chuang-tzŭ*, pp. 86 and 88.

142 *No part of the body moves ... let the breath permeate the bones* The T'aiChi classic with the long name is *Shih-San Shih Hsing-Kung Hsin Chieh*: Treatise on the Thirteen Kinetic Movements As They Relate to Mental Comprehension. The text was associated (by the cheerfully lenient historiography to which T'aiChi aspirants were accustomed in the 1970s) with a fifteenth century reformulation by Wang Chung-Yüeh of earlier compilations. My notes would have come from the translations provided for Sophia Delza by Koo Hsien-Liang, Hubert Wang and Sally Ch'eng:

> Like a pleat which folds in on itself and continues to the next one with rhythm and order, so the movement goes forward and back with rhythm and order and continuity.
>
> Breath permeates bones; give spirit free rein and the body will be calm. Be attentive all the time. Deeply remember: one single movement suffices to effect the whole body movement; there is no isolated quiet without enveloping the whole being.

Sophia Delza, *Body & Mind in Harmony: T'ai Chi Ch'uan: An Ancient Chinese Way of Exercise to Achieve Health & Tranquility* (Cornerstone Library, New York, 1974) p. 184. The book was first published in 1961 and the publisher's claim (on the cover) that it is the first and foremost book on the subject (in English, presumably) may have some validity. Sophia Delza was a pupil of Ma YuehLiang, master of the Wu Style. She and Gerda Geddes had been contemporaries in Shanghai.

143 *edible, after all?* My *fungaiolo* friend has reconsidered the identification of this specimen, offering two other species for scrutiny, *Amanita ovoidea* (the common name is *farinaccio* referring to the cap's mealy texture) and *Amanita strobiliformis*. The latter possibility I have considered on several occasions and have never been certain. Riccardo says, "Reported edibility ranges from 'excellent' to 'disgusting' and 'dangerous' (this because they could sometimes

be confused with poisonous white amanitas)". These poisonous pure white or whitish amanitas include the Destroying Angel, *Amanita virosa*. A few of the poisonous amanitas are fatal; the most dangerous whitish one (in fact with a green tinge, sometimes quite unearthly at dusk; this may get whitened by the elements), is *Amanita phalloides*, Death Cap. From summer through to late autumn, after good rains and sunny spells our woods display an enchanting array, the toxic mushrooms alongside the delectable *porcini* and chanterelles growing in amongst the vivid and variously coloured *russulae*. These are mostly harmless, and some of the greeny purply kinds are firm and pleasant. Among the many-hued reds however there are several fragrant but poisonous kinds, sometimes smelling of coconut, often startlingly hot on the tongue. An uncle of Riccardo's who knows his woods intimately, and knows which of the piquant reds are edible, uses some of these like chillies. The most sought after mushroom here is an amanita, *A. caesarea*, prized since Roman times. The *ovolo* is usually found singly, rusty red head thrusting out of its white sack-like volva atop a bright yellow leg. The fragile gills, also yellow, are distinctive. That the Romans valued this mushroom above all others sheds an intriguing light on them, for the young *ovolo* tastes like the purest mountain water.

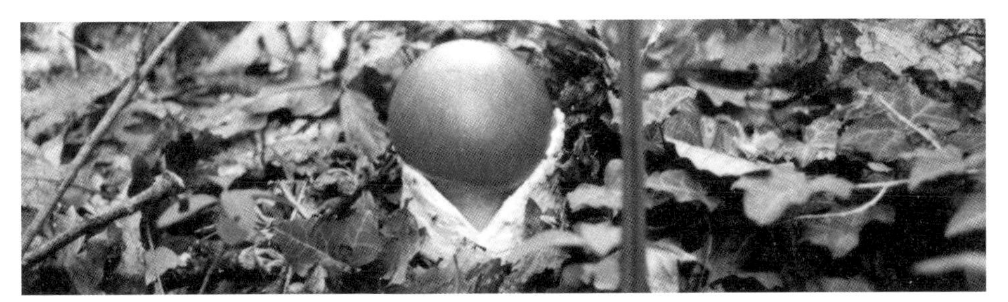

CHAPTER 9 · XINJIA

146 *in schoolboyish mood* Chen XiaoWang, teaching XinJia in Hamburg, in November 1998. Students came from all over Europe to this meeting. Asked by a visitor from Poland about the difference between LaoJia and XinJia, Chen XiaoWang replied, "LaoJia like rifle, XinJia like machine-gun!"

146 *pour itself into an unknown sea* After Somerset Maugham's description of the Salween which he encountered while travelling through Burma, Siam and Indochina in 1923.

> It became the Oriental river of my dreams, a broad stream, deep and secret, flowing through wooded hills, and it had romance, and a dark mystery so that you could scarcely believe that it rose here and there poured itself into the ocean, but like a symbol of eternity flowed from an unknown source to lose itself at last in an unknown sea.

W. Somerset Maugham, *The Gentleman in the Parlour – a Record of a Journey from Rangoon to Haiphong* (William Heinemann, London, 1930), p. 69.

149 *xuan, darkly threaded* Describing the ideogram 玄 (*xuan*) Sandra Wawrytko writes, "The character rendered here as 'profoundly dark'... depicts a piece of silk thread which has been dipped in dye." Sandra A.Wawrytko, 'The Poetics of Ch'an: Upaayic Poetry and Its Taoist Enrichment', *Chung-Hwa Buddhist Journal* No. 5, July 1992 (Chung-Hwa Institute of Buddhist Studies, Jinshan), p. 354. The character occurs twice in the last line of *Daodejing* 1, "Profoundly dark and ever profoundly dark, The gateway to infinite wonders" (trans. Charles Wei-hsun Fu and Sandra Wawrytko, ibid., p. 350).

CHAPTER 10 · XINJIA 2

168 *film of Master Choy* I am most grateful to Frank Choy for his permission to include pictures from this rare film of his grandfather, Master Choy HakPang. In 1989 Ben and I went in search of the Choy family in San Francisco, and found Frank Choy teaching together with his father, Master Choy KamMan. Contact with three generations of masters of the art is inspiring, particularly so when I am told by the grandson that he continues "the honing" of the skills passed to him by his father and grandfather. The film is included in the compilation *Tai Chi Chuan*, © Chinese Martial Art Association, 1971.

172 *Whether your strength … the sound of shocking* Chen XiaoWang, *Chen Style Taijiquan* (Zhaohua Publishing House, Beijing, 1984), p. 150.

175 *constitutes the Teh* James Legge, *The Sacred Books of the East*, ed. F. Max Müller, volume XXXIX (Clarendon Press, Oxford, 1891), p. 51.

175 *Four times* The pairing *xuan de* occurs in *Daodejing* 10, 51, and twice in 65.

CHAPTER 11 · XINJIA 3

182 *Have no thought … act* In my experience Chen XiaoWang has never consented to guide a person through this movement. Instead, having made the most thorough preparation possible, he places himself in front of the student and says, "Follow me!"

185 *Err and err … less and less* Piet Hein, *Grooks* (Hodder Paperbacks, London, 1969), p. 34. Grook (Danish, *gruk*) is a form of short, rhymed epigram.

195 *not the heel of the hand* As technique develops and sensitivity grows, nuances in the *chansi* become more finely differentiated. Qi passes lightly and swiftly, through hidden openings; skill is to be at one with the current, forgetting the water. *Chansi* is a delicate interplay between extension and yielding. The routes outward are numerous and no two instances of Single Whip are the same. The way each *danbian* finishes in the left hand depends on what leads up to it. The first Single Whip occurs early in the form, and the next one not until a third of the way through; the variety of intervening movements tunes the body, and gives the second *danbian* a different character from the first. Always there

must be balance between centre and periphery; *chansi* is the route created between the two. A forcibly flexed left wrist will block the flow. Search for the way outwards along the tautest route, a charged flowing; balance this with a plentiful return to centre. Qi to fingers, qi to dantian, nearly same time. Deep inside, let go; dwell in dantian. When shoulders meld with hips, a stretchy net spreads across the back, weaving through the dorsal vertebrae. This net secures the entire frame.

195 *xuan lan* Profound mirror-mind. This reference to the pairing of *xuan* with *lan* in *Daodejing* 10 needs qualification. We may recall (cf. note to chapter 9, p. 149) that 玄 (*xuan*) has the senses 'dark' and 'profound', and by extension 'hidden' or 'mysterious'. The meanings of 覽 (*lan*) range from 'vision' to something approaching 'insight'. Arthur Waley (*The Way and Its Power*, p. 153) translates *xuan lan* as 'vision of the Mystery':

> Can you wipe and cleanse your vision of the Mystery till all is without blur?

More colloquially Gia-fu Feng (Feng and English, *Lao Tsu*) translates *xuan lan* as 'primal vision':

> Washing and cleansing the primal vision, can you be without stain?

In contrast James Legge (*The Sacred Books of the East*, ed. F. Max Müller, volume XXXIX, Clarendon Press, Oxford, 1891, p. 54) has a robustly Victorian understanding of the passage, whereby the dark and mysterious aspects of *xuan* indicate delusionary thoughts which are to be discarded:

> When he has cleansed away the most mysterious sights (of his imagination), he can become without a flaw.

Be that as it may, there is an alternative reading of 'mirror' for *lan*, and thus 'mysterious or hidden mirror' for *xuan lan*, or as Sandra Wawrytko has it (*The Poetics of Ch'an*, p. 354) "profoundly dark mirror ... or the inmost heart/mind". D. C. Lau translates as follows (*Tao Te Ching*, Penguin Classics, 1963, p. 14):

> Can you polish your mysterious mirror [*footnote*: i.e. the mind] and leave no blemish?

In 1973 two silk texts of the *Daodejing* were uncovered at Mawangdui in Hunan, where they had been buried since 168 BC. Both texts vary from the received text at this point, but in different ways:

> [One text] has 監 *chien* "to survey, examine, superintend", which is written the same as 鑑 *chien* "mirror" except for the absence of the metal radical. Transcribers have thus taken it to mean the latter *chien* (mirror). [The other text] replaces 覽 *lan*, "insight", with 藍 *lan* which has the nonsensical meaning of "blue, indigo", but is written similarly to the two *chien*s, except it has the plant radical #140 above it, rather than the metal radical to its left or below. Hence transcribers read this *lan* also as *chien* (mirror).

Dan Lusthaus, 'Ch'an and Taoist Mirrors: Reflections on Richard Garner's "Deconstruction of the Mirror..."', *Journal of Chinese Philosophy*, volume 12 (1985) p. 178. For *xuan lan* I may settle for 'profound mirror-mind', and when I find myself undecided between 'mirror' and 'mind' I need look no further than Zhuangzi for a thoroughly practical resolution:

> The utmost man uses the heart like a mirror; he does not escort things as they go or welcome them as they come, he responds and does not store.

Graham, *Chuang-tzŭ*, p. 98.

195 *impaludism lurking in the breast* Marsh, *palude*. Impaludism is a general morbid state to which inhabitants of marshy districts may succumb. Ariosto describes a city surrounded by fishy marshes, sandwiched in the flow of the Po, where the people long for lashing waves and fierce winds:

> la città ch'in mezzo alle piscose paludi, del Po teme ambe le foci, dove abitan le genti disiose che 'l mar si turbi e sieno i venti atroci.

Orlando Furioso, 3/41.

195 *Earth, sky* "Earth, sky, your body—together." Chen XiaoWang says this from time to time when he is teaching, usually at the end of a good long standing. The words in their bareness effect a merging, a deeper union: *xuan tong*, the profound, darkly mysterious oneness with *dao*. The pairing of *xuan* with *tong*, occurring in *Daodejing* 56, Arthur Waley renders 'mysterious levelling' (*The Way and Its Power*, p. 210) and Gia-fu Feng 'primal union' (Feng and English, *Lao Tsu*).

196 *The True Men of old … were not complacent when they hit plumb on* Graham, *Chuang-tzŭ*, p. 84.

196 *bearing yet not possessing* There is a main thread running through chapter 10 of the *Daodejing* which leads us beyond TaijiQuan's form towards its essence. It calls us to embrace the One, never to leave it, to hold fast to union as in ZhanZhuang; to gather the energies as in Chansigong, attending child-like to breath and qi, softly and wholly. Clear, unblurred, reflecting with utmost lucidity—*xuan lan*. Can we respond yieldingly to Nature's comings and goings?

> Rear them, then, feed them,
> Rear them, but do not lay claim to them.

Daodejing 10, trans. Waley, *The Way and Its Power*, p. 153. To give forth, to nurture—to bear yet not to possess—this is *xuan de* 玄德.

A minute description of the battles of Gorey, Arklow, and Vinegar-Hill, tegether [sic] with the movements of the army through Wicklow-Mountains, in quest of the rebels, who were supposed to have been encamped at the seven churches

Archibald MacLaren

A minute description of the battles of Gorey, Arklow, and Vinegar-Hill, tegether [sic] with the movements of the army through Wicklow-Mountains, in quest of the rebels, who were supposed to have been encamped at the seven churches. ... Written by Archibal
MacLaren, Archibald
ESTCID: T093794
Reproduction from British Library

[Dublin?] : Printed in the year, 1798.
40p. ; 8°

Gale ECCO Print Editions

Relive history with *Eighteenth Century Collections Online*, now available in print for the independent historian and collector. This series includes the most significant English-language and foreign-language works printed in Great Britain during the eighteenth century, and is organized in seven different subject areas including literature and language; medicine, science, and technology; and religion and philosophy. The collection also includes thousands of important works from the Americas.

The eighteenth century has been called "The Age of Enlightenment." It was a period of rapid advance in print culture and publishing, in world exploration, and in the rapid growth of science and technology – all of which had a profound impact on the political and cultural landscape. At the end of the century the American Revolution, French Revolution and Industrial Revolution, perhaps three of the most significant events in modern history, set in motion developments that eventually dominated world political, economic, and social life.

In a groundbreaking effort, Gale initiated a revolution of its own: digitization of epic proportions to preserve these invaluable works in the largest online archive of its kind. Contributions from major world libraries constitute over 175,000 original printed works. Scanned images of the actual pages, rather than transcriptions, recreate the works ***as they first appeared.***

Now for the first time, these high-quality digital scans of original works are available via print-on-demand, making them readily accessible to libraries, students, independent scholars, and readers of all ages.

For our initial release we have created seven robust collections to form one the world's most comprehensive catalogs of 18th century works.

Initial Gale ECCO Print Editions collections include:

> ***History and Geography***
> Rich in titles on English life and social history, this collection spans the world as it was known to eighteenth-century historians and explorers. Titles include a wealth of travel accounts and diaries, histories of nations from throughout the world, and maps and charts of a world that was still being discovered. Students of the War of American Independence will find fascinating accounts from the British side of conflict.

Social Science

Delve into what it was like to live during the eighteenth century by reading the first-hand accounts of everyday people, including city dwellers and farmers, businessmen and bankers, artisans and merchants, artists and their patrons, politicians and their constituents. Original texts make the American, French, and Industrial revolutions vividly contemporary.

Medicine, Science and Technology

Medical theory and practice of the 1700s developed rapidly, as is evidenced by the extensive collection, which includes descriptions of diseases, their conditions, and treatments. Books on science and technology, agriculture, military technology, natural philosophy, even cookbooks, are all contained here.

Literature and Language

Western literary study flows out of eighteenth-century works by Alexander Pope, Daniel Defoe, Henry Fielding, Frances Burney, Denis Diderot, Johann Gottfried Herder, Johann Wolfgang von Goethe, and others. Experience the birth of the modern novel, or compare the development of language using dictionaries and grammar discourses.

Religion and Philosophy

The Age of Enlightenment profoundly enriched religious and philosophical understanding and continues to influence present-day thinking. Works collected here include masterpieces by David Hume, Immanuel Kant, and Jean-Jacques Rousseau, as well as religious sermons and moral debates on the issues of the day, such as the slave trade. The Age of Reason saw conflict between Protestantism and Catholicism transformed into one between faith and logic -- a debate that continues in the twenty-first century.

Law and Reference

This collection reveals the history of English common law and Empire law in a vastly changing world of British expansion. Dominating the legal field is the *Commentaries of the Law of England* by Sir William Blackstone, which first appeared in 1765. Reference works such as almanacs and catalogues continue to educate us by revealing the day-to-day workings of society.

Fine Arts

The eighteenth-century fascination with Greek and Roman antiquity followed the systematic excavation of the ruins at Pompeii and Herculaneum in southern Italy; and after 1750 a neoclassical style dominated all artistic fields. The titles here trace developments in mostly English-language works on painting, sculpture, architecture, music, theater, and other disciplines. Instructional works on musical instruments, catalogs of art objects, comic operas, and more are also included.

A Minute Defcription of the

BATTLES

OF

Gorey, Arklow, and Vinegar-Hill,

Tegether with the *Movements of the* ARMY through *Wicklow-Mountains*, in queft of the

REBELS,

who were fuppofed to have been encamped at *THE SEVEN CHURCHES.*

To which are Annexed,
The *Capture* and *Execution* of feveral *Traitors*, four of whofe Heads are expofed to *Public view* in *Wexford*.

Interfperfed with many curious Anecdotes, worthy the Reader's notice.

WRITTEN BY
ARCHIBALD M'LAREN,
late Serjeant in the Dunbartonfhire Highlanders, who was an Eye-witnefs to moft of what he relates.

Author of the Coup de Main, Siege of Perth, Siege of Berwick, American Slaves, Highland Drover, What News from Bantry Bay, &c. &c.

PRINTED in the YEAR, MDCCXCVIII.

FIRST when I formed the idea of publiſhing this Pamphlet, I drew out a rough ſketch of Facts as they occurred to my memory, and in that imperfect ſtate ſent it to the Preſs, fearing that had I taken time to reviſe and correct it, I might be removed far from the reach of a Printer. Now it being publiſhed, I am ſenſible that the Reader will have many opportunities to ſay that the language is capable of great improvement; nay, more, I am conſcious that errors in the diction will occur to myſelf when I ſee it in print: but as I profeſs to relate Facts, I hope all thoſe who prefer truth to elegance, will eaſily pardon any inaccuracy in my ſtile, for "if partially affied or leagued in office I write more or leſs than truth, then am I no Soldier." When I was taking in ſubſcriptions, I remember to have fallen into converſation with ſeveral perſons who ſeemed very apprehenſive that partiality would ſway my Pen. Now if any of thoſe doubtful ſouls ſhould deign to turn over the following pages, I am perſuaded that every circumſtance unfavourable to Croppiciſm will be received as partiality or falſehood: for no man will willingly believe what he does not wiſh to credit. Some of them will be apt to cry out "oh did not I tell you that he would be partial, don't you see how he endeavours (as far as the line of his slender abilities will allow him,) to throw a fair gloss upon all the actions of the Loyalists, while he attempts to lash (in a strain of ill-digested ridicule) all the advantages gained by the Sons of Liberty.——— Gentlemen, I humbly beg your pardon.

Though I must confess I have related the naked truth on both sides, I must also confess that I have not treated your friends with that respect you wish: I have past no high encomiums on a worthy set of people who have not only spent the last winter in forming the most harmless associations, but also commenced their summer career by assembling their thousands with the laudable design of overturning all decency and good order, and to enjoy themselves, the amusement of Piking to death, all those who adhered to their King and Constitution.

But gentlemen, I know you are furnished with arguments sufficient to confute any thing I can say, therefore I shall afford you but one answer, so well known to all that even Children not only speak but sing it in the streets, which is "*Croppies lie down*" take a sleep and forget your idle dreams of folly and vanity, awake to sense and reason, honesty and loyalty, and then I am your humble servant to "applaud you to the very Echo, till Echo shall applaud you back again."

INTRODUCTION.

NOW, before I enter upon the Battle of Gorey, I ſhall endeavour to give a ſhort deſcription of the commencement of the Rebellion near Dunboyne. Although the Croppies had during the winter been very buſy with their private levies, yet they did not think proper to put their hoſtile intentions in practice, untill a few days after the capture of Lord *Edward Fitzgerald* Among their firſt exploits, was their ſeizing a few Carr-loads of Baggage, belonging to Lord *Rhea's* Highlanders, and killing two or three of the Guard who were walking careleſsly by the Carr ſides unſuſpicious of danger. This affair which happened at Dumboyne, cauſed ſuch an alarm at Dublin that many ſcouting parties were ſent to the country. I remember ſeeing two Carr-loads of Pikes and old Muſkets brought into the Royal Square one morning: under the arms, covered with ſtraw were the Bodies of three men, who had been killed in a ſkirmiſh with a party of Soldiers. The Bodies were hung up to public view for a whole day in Barrack-ſtreet, and afterwards buried in ſome obſcure corner. Several Country people comminging to market, brought us intelligence that ſome hundreds of Croppies with Pikes and Firelocks were aſſembled in a large field near the Black Bull ſome miles beyond Dumboyne. In conſequence of this information, General Craig, with the 5th Dragoon-guards, the Dunbarton and Anguſshire Fencibles, the Londonderty and Cavan Regiments of Militia, a Detachment of the Flying Artillary, and ſome Yeoman Cavalry, marched out in queſt of this Hodge-podge army. Having proceeded five or ſix miles beyond Dublin, we found all the Cabins deſerted and the doors ſecured by Padlocks, which we were forbid to touch. A few miles from the Black Bull we diſcovered three of the Anguſshire Fencibles murdered by the road ſide. They had belongedto a detachment ſtationed at Lutrells-Town, whom Lieutenant Armſtrong, of the Royal IriſhArtillary had led out to recover the Baggage taken from Lord Rhea's Highlanders, but as their number conſiſted of no more than Eighteen including ſome Yeoman Cavalry, they were overpowered and forced to retreat, leaving five or ſix of their companions dead on the field. As we advanced, the Rebels who were apprized of our coming, retreated. The Cavalry in front had ſeveral times a full view of them, but loſt them in the duſk of the evening · however in a little they met a young Boy whom they queſtioned but he pretended to be entirely ignorant until they called for a rope to fix about his neck, the poor fellow intimidated by these threats (which they by no means intended to put in execution led us through several foot-paths, and brought us to a large Mansion-house, where he said we should find their Camp. As we entered the Haggard, a fellow from the top of a Hay-stack called out "Who's there," and being answered, "A Friend," he tumbled down and asked for the Pass-word (as he termed it) which they gave him in a bullet through his body. Another Sentry fired his piece, and would have run away but they prevented him The Cavin and Dunbarton Regiments rushed into the field on the right of the house and form d a line of Battle, imagining the enemy to be in their front; but learning that the Camp (if a parcel of Hay and straw deserves such a name) was in the rear they faced about, but most of the Croppies had taken to their heels when they heard the report of the Sentinel's piece. By this time, the Cavalry and some foot who had taken a circuit round another field, were advanced in front of the house. These mistaking us for the Enemy fired upon us, but General Craig and Colonel Scott who got between us and called out not to fire, (as we were friends) prevented any mischief. Some of the Rebels who had hid themselves behind the ditches and in the garden, thought to escape under favour of the night, but the Cavalry soon dispatched them. One of the Sentinels who was killed, had a Firelock belonging to the Rhea Highlanders; and about the field were scatered several pieces of Tartan Hose taken among the Baggage. In the Camp we found some Barrels of Butter-milk, and Bags of Potatoes, the only provision laid in for the lower ranks, but in the house, great quantities of Tea, Sugar, Porter, Spirits and Wine, were found by the Soldiers. We lay upon some Hay and Sraw till day light, at which time we observed three Men with Pikes on their shoulders, walking at their leisure towards the house: I suppose they had been out foraging and mistook us for their friends: some of our Soldiers who were in too grear a hurry to fire, prevented our taking them. Among the slain was one tall Man with a pair of White Breeches with Marine Bottons. Another fellow of a very decent appearance, was found concealed among some Pigs in a Stye, when dragged out he was interrogated, but would give no satisfactory account with respect to the number or intentions of the Rebels; he was therefore shot upon the spot. A young Girl was shot in the house by accident.——On our return to Dublin we set fire to all the Croppies houses by the way side. Dumboyne also was burnt to ashes.

THE

BATTLES

OF

Gorey, Arklow, and Vinegar-Hill.

WHEN the Dunbarton Regiment, to which I belong, marched from DUBLIN I was on the Commander in Chief's guard, and of courſe remained behind, however, as far as I am able from information, I ſhall give a conciſe account of their excurſions, as far as they are connected with the affair at GOREY, which I have engaged to deſcribe; but when I come to treat of the Battle of ARKLOW, (in which I was a party concerned) I ſhall be more capacious in my deſcription.

The firſt night the Regiment arrived at WICKLOW, and being informed that an Officer and ſome Privates of the Royal Army had been killed at a place which the Soldiers called the DEVIL'S GLEN, they next morning (with a detachment of the Ancient Britons, and a few Yeomen) went in queſt of the Rebels who had committed the murder. When they had entered the GLEN, they diſcovered ſome ſculking parties, of whom they killed to the amount of Eighty and then returned to WICKLOW, from whence they proceeded to ARKLOW, and from Arklow to Gorey, where they were joined by the Londonderry and Armagh Regiments, of Militia, the Tyrone and Suffolk Light Companies, the Ancient Britons, and a detachment of the Antrim Militia, all under the command of Gen, LOFTUS On the 4th of June this Army moved in two Diviſions, having received intelligence that the Rebels were encamped upon Carrigrew-Hill. The Diviſion under Colonel WALPOLE kept to the right, and General LOFTUS, with the Dunbarton Highlanders and 5th Dragoon

A Guards

Guards took to the left. The Rebels who had that morning left Carrigrew-Hill were advancing to Gorey, when they met a woman who told them that the King's Troops were at hand upon which they concealed themselves behind the ditches on each side of a narrow Glen through which the Troops must pass. Colonel Walpole marched on without the least suspicion and was in the centre of his enemies when they started up on every side of him. Finding himself thus surprised he opposed his Cannon and Musketry to the Fire and Pikes of the Enemy; the contest lasted twenty minutes, but one of the Cannons being dismounted, the Colonel killed, his men overpowered by superior numbers and on the point of being surrounded, were forced to retreat; the Rebels turned their own Cannon upon them.

General Loftus, who had advanced farther on the left, heard the firing and supposed that the Enemy had been beat, he therefore turned off to the right with a design to intercept them in their retreat, but when he reached the Scene of Action, the first object that caught his eye, was Colonel Walpole lying dead, and stripp'd to his Flannel [illegible] the place was covered with the bodies of the slain, some of whom had the marks of twenty pikes in their faces legs and breasts, which leads me to imagine that the Croppies delighted in exercising their wanton cruelty. In an adjacent Field our Troops discovered a great number of Stolen Horses, a few of which some of our Sergeants (though reluctantly) were obliged to [illegible] lest the Rebels should return and take them. General Loftus seeing no Enemy, moved on for Gorey, which route he expected the Rebels to have taken. In the course of this march the Soldiers observed a great number of dead Croppies whom their friends [illegible] to the houses as they past. As the [illegible] Army came opposite to Gorey-Hill, the Rebels fired a [illegible] the Bullet fell a little to the [illegible] The General who did not think it prudent to attack them in such force, marched off for Cornew thus ended the Battle of Gorey, in which we lost 25 men, and the Rebels 150, and which the Soldiers called Gorey Races, because each strove to out-run his fellow. The Rebels got possession of Gorey, and our Flying Troops retreated to Arklow, which flattered the sons of Rebellion with the fairest prospect of future success, but when their minds were raised to the very pinacle of insolence their blooming hopes were blasted like an unwholesome Pear, that withers ere it ripens.

On Thursday the 7th of June, those of our Regiment who were left behind, received orders to hold themselves in readiness to march. Before ten o'Clock at night, the Old Custom-house Yard was filled with Coaches, Chaises, Jaunting-Cars, &c. At Nine on Friday morning we moved off fully resolved to dedicate the last drop of our Blood to the service of that Government which had so generously indulged us in so unprecedented a manner. Now Reader, if this simple Narrative, after an hundred years have elapsed, should fall into *the hands of some Lover of Antiquity*, presumptuous thought! and yet who knows,—come imagination lend your pleasing assistance, suppose a copy of this should fall into the hands of some Miser who has no heart either to use or loose the smallest article, my poor Pamphlet may be buried with some lumber in a Garret till some Spend-thrift heir of this penurious family hath dispersed his Grand-Sire's hoarded store, at length my Pamphlet catches his eye, he snatches it up, runs to the Whiskey-shop and after spending half an hour in expatiating upon its merits, (though he never read it) sells it to the Land-Lady for half a glass to drown remorse; some tippling orator reads (or attempts to read it) Gods! how his audience will stare, when they hear that Government had indulged the Soldiery with Coaches, Chaises, Jaunting Cars, &c. they will not believe it— well let them live in their incredulity, you and I, reader, are convinced of the truth of it, so we'll

proceed

proceed with our H ſtory As we paſt the Royal Exchange our good friends he Yeomen honoured us with three cheers, and 'Succeſs attend you, Boys' reſounded throug' tre Crowd It is impoſſible for me to expreſs my ſenſa ions up n his occaſion, b it every lover of hi K ng and Country may par ly conceive it In a few hours we lo ſight of Dublin, a City of which I ſhall t ink and ſpeak (as long a I can think and ſpeak) with the u moſt reſpect a d gratitude.

Ah Dubl n dear !——
Though Fate may force me from thy S ght,
No Ill but Death can blo' Thee from my mind.

Nothing worth notice occurred till we came to Bray. This town ſeemed to us (whoſe m nds were filled with the idea of ſweet Dublin,) exceeding diminitive. All the male inhabitants bore arms and thoſe of the lower or er, though dreſt in their ordinary garb, had pieces of blue or red Rags prefixed to the front of their hats as Ba ges of their Loyalty, and to diſtinguiſh them from t e Cropp es. Here we met a Corporal of the K ngs County, who was very communicative: he told us that two days previous o our arrival, they had hanged a man, "there (ſaid he) is the Houſe of a Rebel; we demoliſhed it becauſe he had ſome Amunition concealed in a back room — e ſent h m on board a Man of War — we ma e pre ty well by plunder, and if I be ſerved till I d e' — n tru h he continued his ſtory very long and migh have con nued till he had fallen aſleep, (for withou the lea't offence to his honour, I believe he was ſome Whiſkey-ſtrick or had taſted of the R ver Ergine) but our Drum beat, I took Coach; the Corporal fo owed me to he Carriage Door and reſumed h s H ory, but the unfeel ng Coach-man drove off and left t e Tippl ng Hiſtorian in the very middle of a ſentence In our route to Wicklow e ſaw the rema ns of ſeveral Ho ſes that had been burnt, partly by the Soldiers

Soldiers and Yeomanry from Bray, and partly by the Rebels when they found the inhabitants unpropitious to their cause. It was past Twelve at Night ere we arrived at Wicklow, and as no beds could be had at that time, we took up our Lodging at a Quakers Meeting-House, where we lay untill morning in our Blankets: I am persuaded that had many of our young Soldiers wrote home from this place to their Mothers, they would be apt to inveigh most bitterly against the hardships of War, and yet on our march through Wicklow Mountains, which took place some weeks thereafter, when we had neither Houses nor Tents to screen us from a severe Air and a deluge of Rain, the very best of us might be ready to mistake a Quakers Meeting-House for a Terestrial Paradise. From Wicklow we proceeded on our way to Arklow, where we arrived about the middle of the day. I was told that some few days ago this had been a flourishing little Town; but by this time alas! it bore the most evident marks of that devastation which is always the Concomitant of War. At some Shops where the Painting on the Sign-boards promised all manner of Groceries, we could not purchase so much as a Half-penny worth of Tobacco*,—Shelves, Boxes, Counters, Barrels,&c were all converted into Fuel for the use of the Soldiers who were then the Tenants. Taverns, licensed to sell Wine and Foreign Spirits, could not afford one Noggin of Whiskey,—some of their best Parlours, once the scenes of Conviviality were now become the habitations or stables of Horses; every thing of value being either destroyed or carried away; for the Rebels who had no regular supply of Provisions were under the necessity of plundering indiscriminately both friend and foe.

Having marched through the Town, we took up our ground on the left of the Durham Fencibles a few yards beyond the Barracks. Here we had scarce thrown off

our

* In Country Towns, Grocers sell Tobacco.

our Knap-ſacks when an alarm was given that the Enemy was approaching owing to the report of a Rebel-Deſerter; but ſo little credit was given to his aſſertions that a Regt. in the Field was making preparations to puniſh one of their men, but the arrival of ſome Yeomen Cavalry who declared that the Rebels were within a mile of us, ſuſpended the opperation: then all was in a buſtle, the Aid-de-camps and Brigade-Major galloped about and call'd for the General; the Soldiers began to examine their Flints, and thoſe who had got their Loaves ſerved out were willing to eat as much as poſſible leſt the Bread ſhould fall into the hands of the Croppies, ſo great an averſion did we bear to thoſe unprincipled gentry, who had even dared to entertain the preſumptuous idea of deſtroying our Glorious King and Conſtitution. The Inhabitants who had remained in Town, fled to their Boats which lay ready upon the Beach to receive them. General Needham drew all the Troops out of Town and formed them to the beſt advantage. The Cavan Regt. with the Gorey diſmounted Cavalry, the Arklow Yeomanry and ſome detachments from other Corps under the command of the brave Colonel Maxwell, extended a line from the centre of the Town along the Ditches almoſt to the Fiſhermen's Huts on the left near the Sea. On the right of the Cavan, the Durham Fencibles were drawn up in front of the Town, with two Field pieces. Detachments of the Armagh and ſome others occupied the end of the main Street adjoining the Kings High way on the right of the Durham. The Antrim, with ſome other detachments were ſtationed in the Barracks on the right of the Armagh near the River in rear of the Town. The 4th Dragoon-Guards, the Ancient Britons, and ſeveral Corps of Yeomen Cavalry were drawn up on the Dublin road on each ſide of the Bridge. Theſe were the different poſitions of the army, when the Dunbartonſhire Highlanders were ordered out about a Quarter of a Mile in front of the Armagh, to line the Ditches on each side of the main road where the Enemy was advancing: it was my chance to be of this party.—When the Croppies appeared with their green Rags fixed to Pole-heads in imitation of Colours; they fired, which compliment we returned. As I did not think my Halbert a proper weapon to annoy the Enemy at a distance, I exchanged it for a Firelock; and here I appeal to all those who were present if I did not by example and precept exert my utmost power to animate my brother Soldiers. I speak not this through ostentation, but merely to prove that though my Halbert has since been transferred to other hands it was not for cowardice, a crime reckoned in ancient times the greatest disgrace of all disgraces in a Soldier.

I remember to have seen one fellow who stood in the centre of the road, neither advancing nor retreating, but seemingly encouraging others; several shots were fired at him without effect; but at length he was brought to the ground. When we had exchanged about a dozen rounds, an Aid de Camp from the General ordered us to retreat and join the Armagh in the Street. This we did in seeming confusion, and the Rebels (no doubt) thinking that we fled, came on with great vaunting, setting up a loud Huzza. One fellow (an Officer) inspired with the spirits of Whiskey, (of which they had drank very copiously at a village called Coolgreene) galloped in front, having something resembling a stand of Colours in his hand, (Serjeant-Major Fisher, of the Dunbartons has it in his possession) and waving his Hat, called out "Blood and Wounds my Boys, come on, the Town is our own." But ere the Fool hardy Hero was aware, he turned the corner of a House which brought him almost to the mouth of a Field-piece, surrounded by some hundreds of Soldiers, ready to fire or receive him on the points of their Bayonets. At so unwelcome, and perhaps so unexpected a sight, he [illegible] G[illegible] Steed, and [illegible] himself like Young Hamlet when [illegible] his Father's Ghost,

but

but a volly of small shot laid his Horse sprawling in the dust and broke his own Thigh; though he fell under his Horse he had cunning enough to lie still, and might probably have passed for a dead man, had he not, like Sir John Falstaff in the Battle of Shrewsbury, raised his head to take a peep round about him: this being observed, four or five Bayonets were plunged into his body. In the midst of his agony he stretched out his arm to shake hands with one of the Soldiers and exclaiming at the same time, "Oh Blood and Wounds, Soldiers, dont, dont." But the Soldier sent a Bullet through his head, which soon put a period to the Life and adventures of this drunken Knight of the green Banner.* Another Cavalier who came coursing at his heels having his Horse shot under him, ran into a House, where in the hurry of Battle he might have lain concealed, had he not had the temerity to fire a Pistol at Corporal M'Dougald. The Corporal gave him a sleeping dose which made his spirits evaporate in fumes of Whiskey: and his noble soul which refused to pay his reckoning upon earth, was sent to settle his accompts in the region of—— I dont know where.

Reverend shade of the Renowned Father Murphy, pardon my dilatory Pen which has so long delayed to relate thy great, thy glorious, thy Quixote or mad-like Atchievements.—Father Murphy was sensible of the insufficiency of human strength, he therefore, had recourse (or pretended to have recourse) to miracles; for he had been long in the practice of teaching his adherents that he could catch or ward off the Balls with his hand. Oh wonderfull Iron-fisted Father Murphy! had it been thy lot to have entered the list in a Boxing match, with Feutrel, Humphry, Big Ben, or Mendoza, they had not so long reigned the vincer, the pride and admiration of the humane Rabble. Father Murphy

* He had a Green Banner in his Hand

Murphy could ward off the Bullets, and yet as he rode in front, encouraging his Troops to advance, an unmannerly Grape Shot obtruded itself upon his skull, before the good man had time to put forth his Hand to stop it. Some of his followers who saw him fall, dragged him into a House, perhaps with a view to restore him to life, or probably to conceal him, lest his death should discourage the poor Gulls whom he had deluded. The House, or Cabbin was adjoining several others, which served as a shelter to the Rebels who fired from behind them. Our Troops, to deprive them of their sculking places, set fire to one Hut; the flames communicated with others and reached that in which the remains of the Mob deceiving Father Murphy lay, and there I shall leave him till I have given a further description of the Battle; and then if I can spare as much time, I shall return again to satisfy the Reader who must certainly be very anxious about the fate of so great a man. Though the Rebels were deprived (as I said) of their sculking-places, yet they still continued to pour in fresh Troops, (if I may be allowed the expression) but a Six pounder which served as a Base to the music of the Musketry, made many of them dance back in quick time.

Having thus failed in their attempt upon the main Street, they extended a long irregular line in front of the Durham and Cavan, (as I said) with a design to turn our left flank, but those two Regiments, with the Mounted Corps and the Artillery [illegible] Croppy [illegible] under the [illegible]. However their Musketmen kept up a brisk fire from behind ditches, (which covered them up to the very chin) and sorry I am to say with too much success, for three brave fellows of the Durham and one of the Londonderry fell [illegible] to their Loyalty. Farewell, brave Comrades, [illegible] the tear of pity [illegible] your memory [illegible] my Heart [illegible] I leave one sigh for Serjeant Devine.

Reader, poor Serjeant Divine had ſerved in the Cavan Light Company, he left a Wife and ſome Children in Dublin,—when he had imprinted the parting kiſs upon her trembling lips, he requeſted Heaven to bleſs her "Take care of the Children, my love (ſaid he) till my return —but alas! he ſhall never return, moſt hapleſs widow, the Meſſenger of Death hath pierced his Braſſy Breaſt-plate, and ſpilt that Heart blood which flowed for you, his King, his Country, and his Children May his memory be ſacred to every Lover of Loyalty He fell! but he fell like a Soldier Beſides the killed, ſeveral were wounded Colonel Maxwell had his Horſe ſhot under him, he had likewiſe ſeveral Bullets through his Hat but I hope Heaven has reſerved him for a better fate than to fall by the hands of ſuch miſcreants.

Two Field pieces taken from the Londonderry at Gorey, were played upon us, from an eminence oppoſite the Durham and Cavan, but as the chief management of theſe Pieces was entruſted to a Serjeant of the Antrim who had been made their Priſoner, we ſuſtained no damage for ſome time, for at every ſhot, he pointed with ſo much elevation that the Balls whiſtled over our heads but being obſerved by one of his officers, he was ſo far obliged to rectify this ſeeming miſtake, that the very next Shot ſtruck one of the Durham Field-pieces and ſmaſhed the Carriage to pieces, which pleaſed the Croppy officer ſo well, that he cried out "a Hundred Pounds for a Soldier," meaning, I ſuppoſe, that one trained Soldier was better than many of his [illegible] followers Another Shot ſtruck the Halbert out of the hands of a Serjeant of the Cavans; ſome forced their way through the Tents, and others ſtruck upon the roofs of Houſes And here if the Reader [illegible], I ſhall relate (though it may ſeem rather [illegible]) the adventure of one Biller [illegible] to the River, being ambitious to [illegible] and dip a Bucket in the

water

water, at that instant a Cannon shot fell within a yard of her and splashed some quarts of dirt and water in her face. Being seized with a temporary blindness, she took to her heels and tumbled over a large Pig, which got up in a fright and carried her some yards before she fell from his back

When the Dunbarton Detachment hod retreated according to orders, the Enemy advanced on the right of the road in front of the Barracks, (which was well surrounded by a strong wall) but they did not seem to relish their entertainment, for they turned their backs before they completed their visit As the General was riding up Street, a man of seeming respectability, came and told him that the Rebels were making full speed for a lane which led (on the right of the Barracks) from the River to the centre of the Town. To check their progress, the General ordered out a Subaltern, Serjeant and twelve men. Though I hate Egotism truth compels me to say I volunteered upon that duty, under the command of Mr Dauglas whose conduct did not in the least disgrace the memory of the ancient Heroes of that name he bears As we turned down the lane to take possession of our post, we observed some hundreds of the united gentry advancing towards us, but we sent so many leaden messengers to forbid their visit, that many of them (to speak in a military stile) fell back but the reader may take it in the literal sense if he pleases. When their design of forcing the lane had miscarried, they attempted to ford the water, but in this they were also disappointed However that it might not be said that they came upon a Fool's Errant, they retreated across a Field to a Protestant Clergy-man's House, which they burnt, destroyed and drank all the Liquor in the Cellar; and set up such a hallowing and hooping as might be mistaken for the music of Savages, at an Indian sacrifice Having got rid of our impertinent visitants, I requested Mr Dougl s to let me go where the Battle was still carried on, but

he

he would by no means [illegible] that time, allow me to leave my post. However, in a few minutes thereafter I was ordered up to the Tree to observe how matters went on. As I passed through the Lane, an old woman popt her head out at a Cabin door, "Holy Jesus (said she) the sound of the guns since the break, shall I fly or shall I be burnt alive?" I told her to fear nothing, for all was in our favour. "Heavens be praised (cried she) Take a drink of water. I wish it had been Wine or Butter milk for your sake." I thanked the matron and accepted her offer. When I came to the Street, several Horsemen were galloping about with orders. At the windows I observed some well dressed women, who were very anxious about the fate of the day, for they asked with seeming impatience, "How are they going on now? For God's sake, shall we get the better of them?" I told them we should; and one of them called me to take a drink of Grog, but she durst not open the door, so she put out a Bowl out of the window about a foot above my head, and as I happened to be [illegible] of the Cup [illegible], I was obliged to [illegible] Toy at the four Cripes [illegible]

The [illegible] at the [illegible] town and I was [illegible] on [illegible] towards [illegible] I my way through [illegible] ground [illegible] d [illegible] with a P[illegible] I [illegible] the [illegible] of [illegible] When I [illegible] reached the [illegible] I found the Troops [illegible] way be[illegible] to the front of the spot where the [illegible] Cripes had by this time entered [illegible] the Fishermans Houses; [illegible] of Fire, [illegible] endeavouring [illegible] other way [illegible] Street by the end of the Bridge under cover of the [illegible], but [illegible] was [illegible] by some detachments from different Regiments, [illegible] proved [illegible], for Colonel Sir Watkin W[illegible] with some of the 4th, and 5th. Dragoons, a part of his own Regiment, and ſome Yeoman Cavalry, made a charge which they attempted to reſiſt with their Pikes, however it was but an attempt, for they were obliged to fly, though Captain Knox loſt his life in the conteſt. The Foot on the right ceaſed firing while the charge laſted, but when the purſuit cropt, they commenced again. By this time the Sun was almoſt ſet, and the Rebels began to retreat in every direction. I remember we took a tall fellow priſoner he proteſted his innocence, and ſhewed us a Protection he had from Dublin, but the Soldiers were for diſpatching him; however I did what I could to ſave his life, and ſucceeded ſo well that a Serjeant of the Tyrone or Londonderry, took him to the General, tho' next morning I ſaw him lying dead in a brook below the Barracks ſome of the Arklow Yeomanry ſwore that he had been Tarr'd a few days before

The United men made the beſt ſhift they could to draw off the Cannon, but I'm told by a Soldier of our Regiment, who was their Priſoner, that two dozen men might have taken both Pieces, their ammunition as well as their courage being all expended, and indeed they much dreaded a purſuit, and ſaid that if ſuch a thing was to happen, they would leave the Curs and ſhift for themſelves. I returned to my Poſt and ſtood all night (as did the reſt of the Troops) under arms. Though many of the moſt head-ſtrong of the Rebels were for renewing the attack at night, ſome of the more moderate diſſuaded them from their purpoſe; which was perhaps no difficult taſk, as the gentlemen probably only wiſhed to diſplay their courage by words. Be that as it will, we only ſaw a few of them dancing round the flames of a Houſe which they had ſet on fire the oppoſite ſide of the River. An hour after day-light we joined our detachments, after which I took an opportunity of ſurveying the road and adjacent fields. I confeſs I was ſhocked at ſeeing ſuch a number of miſerable wretches brought by their own

folly

folly to an untimely end; ſome were ſhot through the head, ſeveral through the breaſt; others had half of their faces torn away by the Cannon Balls; ſome were ſtript quite naked by the Soldiers, while others were ſuffered to lie in their rags, becauſe they were not worth the taking. I remember to have heard two wounded Rebels in a ditch, conſulting how to make their eſcape, but two Yeomen with their Swords, put an end to their conſultations. Dead Men and Horſes were lying in heaps in the Fields, on the Roads, and in the Ditches. Oh, Ireland! why were you ſeduced to your own deſtruction?

As I was returning to the Barrack my Noſe was accoſted with a diſagreeable Smell, upon enquiery I found it to proceed from the body of Father Murphy, whoſe Leg and Thigh were burnt into the very Bone. "My Gorge was turned;" I could eat no meat for ſome days. His Head was fixed upon the wall of a Burnt Cabin. Farewell Father Murphy, may folly die with you. But perhaps the reader may think that I have treated this venerable character with too much levity, and the more ſo as he was a Roman Catholic. This leads me to a degreſſion, Reader; I believe that different ſentiments in Religion depends upon circumſtances; for inſtance, had I been born in Conſtantinople, I might have been a Mahomatan; had I made my firſt entry in France or Spain, I might have been a Roman Catholic; had I been a native of England, I might have been a Lutheran, but as I happened to behold the firſt ray of light in Scotland, I am a Preſbeterian, but not [illegible] but what I believe that any man who acts according to the dictates of his conſcience, may be a good man, though of a different opinion from myſelf; on the other hand, if a man acts in open contradiction to what he profeſſes, let him be Turk, Roman Catholic, Lutheran, or Preſbeterian; that man, no his profeſſion, becomes the object of my redicule.

In

In the Battle of Arklow we had one Captain, one Serjeant, and Six Privates killed, and about twenty wounded. The Rebels loſt between Five Hundred and Two Thouſands. The General having order'd that we ſhould raiſe Entrenchments round the Camp, we worked moſt of the day at leveling or raiſing Ditches, and from Eleven at Night till Four in the Morning, ſtood under Arms: the fatigue was very great, but as we took it for the good of the ſervice, we bore all without murmuring. On the Monday after the Battle, a Yeoman found an old ſervant of his own wounded in a ditch, and while he was bringing him to the General, had it not been for the interpoſition of an Officer, the Soldiers would have killed him. On the ſame afternoon two men were found among Straw, in one of the Fiſher-men's Huts. Tueſday forenoon a Court Martial ſat, and in the afternoon the three were hanged upon three trees in the centre of the Town. The Yeoman's Servant ſaid he would die by the Green; and ſtrange to ſay, yet true it is, that as he hung, a ſmall piece of a green branch fell into his boſom, and remained by way of a Poſie. Every day we had falſe alarms. One morning a party of Dragoons made an excurſion almoſt to the Rebel Camp, and brought home a Centinel, who was hanged the day following. Mr. Burke, a Yeoman taken by the Rebels, arrived from Gorey; it was immediately reported that he came as an ambaſſador from the Croppies, with an offer to lay down their arms. Let that be true or falſe, certain it is, that after undergoing an examination he was ſent to the Guard-houſe, and ſo great was his apprehenſions, (from the menaces of the Soldiers, who told him he was inſtantly to die) that I ſaw him upon his knees begging for Chriſt's ſake that they would not be too precipitate, but give him time to write to his Captain who would clear him from all ſuſpicion. Every day the Piquets or Foraging parties diſcovered ſome dead bodies in the fields or ditches; and indeed the ſtench was was intol-

erable

erable, for two days had elapsed before the slain were buried, nor were their funeral obsequies attended with much ceremony, some being dragged by the heels, others, with cords about their necks were drawn into the [illegible] and the [illegible] thrown upon them. I saw Father [illegible]'s head, three days after the Battle, [illegible] before the tents. I am still seized with a fit of spitting when I recollect one circumstance; we were forced to have recourse to the River for drink, as well as for water to cook our victuals till several dead Men and Horses were seen floating upon the water a little above the Town, and yet General Needham's servants would not suffer us to touch the Well in the yard. However we discovered a Fountain, called the Soldiers' well, which (though at some distance) supplied us with water.

I believe none but a savage could look without pity on some of the wretched women, begging and starving through the streets, several of them with Children at their breasts. I gave one of them a few crumbs of bread and some [illegible] bits of flesh, which she devoured with the voracity of an Hawk; on another I bestowed a penny and she repaid me with a prayer worth a shilling. It is well known that Soldiers in time of War, (notwithstanding all orders to the contrary) will plunder; Hens, Chickens, Ducks Geese, and even Pigs they take as a prey to themselves. Now Reader, I could lay the price of one of [illegible] that you think I mean to say our army did the same—I beg your pardon, I tell no such tale, let that Fly stick in the Wall, says an old Scots proverb.

On the 19th of June we left Arklow, and after marching a few miles we halted on the way side. Various were the reports that flew from right to left. Some said the General [illegible] had surrounded the Rebels, and that we only waited till they were drove in upon us, others said that they were still upon Gorey-Hill. However, after two or three hours halt

we

we renewed our march, in the courſe of which the Horſemen killed about fourteen or fifteen fellows, whom they found ſculking behind ditches with Pikes in their hands. We entered Gorey without the leaſt oppoſition, the Rebels having abandoned it with precipitation a few hours before our arrival. The afternoon brought on a deluge of rain—The Troops quartered themſelves the beſt way they could in the houſes, moſt of which were deſpoiled of their furniture. We found a Howitzer which was ordered to be ſpiked. Books, Papers, &c were ſcattered about the ſtreets; and great quantities of Pork, Beef, and Mutton lay ſtinking in many of the houſes which the Croppies had occupied. Some Yeoman Cavalry diſcovered an emaciated wretch concealed below a parcel of hay; they brought him to the General, his arm was tyed in a handkerchief with a piece of red tape, and his ſhirt ſleeve bloody, being aſked where he received his wound, he anſwered in a whining tone " at Arklow," the General ordered them to let him go; but another fellow taken near the ſame place was not ſo lucky; as he was found with a Pike in his hand, ſome kicked him, others ſtruck him, and two Yeomen with ſwords knocked him down and clove his ſkull, Captain Hardy of the Durhams, with one ſtroke of his ſword ſevered his head almoſt from his body.

On the 20th ſome Light Troops marched through the town, we followed them, and arrived at Oulart, where we encamped. here Major Lumbart with a hundred and twenty-ſix of the North Cork were cut off by the rebels. The detachment marched from Wexford early on Whitſunday morning. The rebels who deſcry'd them at a diſtance, concealed their main ſtrength behind the ditches on the height, and thoſe who thought proper to appear, on the approach of the detachment pretended to fly, 'tis ſaid the Major ordered his men to purſue them, and not to fire till they were within a few yards of them. The rebels who had by this time began to rally, received their enemy's fire with some loss then rushed on with their Pikes while their companions, in sedition started up from their ambuscade and surrounded the detachment, who after selling their lives as dear as possible, were cut to pieces except seven who survived to carry the doleful news to Wexford. I have heard different accounts of this affair but I believe this is the most likely to be true. Now, I know that we have many who impeach the army with cruelty, and I would advise those wise people (whose pretended sagacity proceeds from their ignorance) to consider that though the Croppies had been fair enemies and no rebels after their barbarity at Oulart the laws of retaliation would justify the greatest severity that could be practised against them. In the neighbourhood of this place some of our men found a serjeant's coat, a silver laced hat, and several other articles belonging to the North Cork, which the inhabitants had left in their precipitate flight upon the approach of the King's Troops.

We had not been above an hour at Oulart when an Express arrived from General Lake to General Needham, in consequence of which we were ordered to strike our Tents and begin our march in the dusk of the Evening with positive injunctions to observe the most profound silence. The occasion of this movement was, that the Commander in Chief had designed to collect as many troops as he thought expedient to surround Vinegar-hill, the reduction of that place being so necessary for carrying on his operations against Wexford, the head-quarters of the rebels— Generals Johnson and Eustace with a column from Ross, (where they had lately gained a most signal victory over the sons of rebellion) were already arrived in the neighbourhood of Enniscorthy. Lieutenant-General Dundas, Major-Generals Sir James Duff and Loftus had also brought their columns close to the scene of action, where they lay impatient for day-light.

In

In order to co-operate with these troops we marched all night and arrived about day-break within a mile and half of the hill on the left, where we lay for about an hour, rolled up in our Blankets in the ditches by the road's side. I was just beginning to dose when I heard one of our men cry out that they had a fair view of Vinegar-hill from a piece of rising ground a little to the right of us. I instantly started up and repaired to the place above mentioned, from which I could easily discern the rebel flag and tree of liberty displayed from an old wind mill near the summit of the hill (but the hill is by no means so high as some people imagine) it is said that upon this, and an adjacent height they had 30,000 men (including those at Enniscorthy) but I am doubtful if they could muster quite so strong, for though the day previous to the attack, many were employed in casting musket bullets to the amount of 6000, and in making other necessary preparations for a vigorous defence, yet I am told that hundreds slunk away and took a french leave of their fellow rebels.

When our men (General Needham's army) saw the rebel flag, they showed the most eager desire to begin the attack, but it was near six o'clock before we were put in motion, and even then instead of marching straight forward we were ordered to take a circuit of at least five or six miles, which made it impossible for us to be up in time. This we much dreaded, because ere we had marched two miles from our last ground we heard the cannonading from General Johnson's column who, began the attack upon the town of Enniscorthy near the Foot, and a little to the right of Vinegar-hill, Lieutenant-General Dundas commanded the center column, supported upon the right by Major Generals Sir James Duff and Loftus.

All the field pieces attached to the different Regiments which composed those columns commenced firing by pouring out thick showers of grape shot among their enemies. The night before the attack, the Croppies had planted a field-piece at the foot of the hill with which they no doubt promiſed to perform wonders, but the day of the battle, it was dragged up to the top where it was made to contribute its part (in concert with ſome other field-pieces) to vomit forth the thunder of rebellion againſt his Majeſty's liege ſubjects. The Croppies' muſket men lined a ditch that ran along the foot of the hill, and kept up a very ſmart fire which did ſome damage to our troops.

Alexander Hatterick of the Dunbartonſhire Highlanders who was taken at Gorey, told me that they had the impudence to entertain ſome hopes of a victory. Several of them aſked his opinion and when he gave his advice to retreat he narrowly eſcaped being piked, however the thunder of the Royal Artillery had a wonderful effect in making them change their tune, a large party of them attempted to force their way on the right of the hill, but the Light Brigade under Colonel Campbell who occupied that poſt ſaluted them with a ſhower of hail ſtones ſomething harder than boiled peas, drove them back, and purſued them to the [illegible]. In their retreat they were ſeverely galled by the grape ſhot which flew from the field-pieces belonging to the Dunbartonſhire Regiment, under the command of Lieutenant Dougald M'Dougald.—General Needham's army (of which I made one) was by this time advanced on the left almoſt to the foot of the hill, where we were commanded to order arms and ſtand at eaſe. I jumped upon the top of a ditch from whence I could obſerve the confuſion among the Croppies, I remarked in particular one fellow galloping up and down upon a white horſe in apparent diſorder, and though I am told the Gentleman was a Commanding Officer, I am apt to believe that he would willingly have given his commiſſion to be out of the reach of the unmannerly bullets which threw up the duſt about his horſe's heels.

As

As soon as the Light Brigade had gained the summit of the hill, a general foot-race commenced among the Croppies, and happy was the man who could sit down some miles hence and thank his legs for carrying him so far out the reach of danger. When the enemy retreated the cavalry pursued and made great havock among them, though some of them had the impudence (when they got on the inside of a ditch) to turn about and fire upon their pursuers.

It was thought by some of the soldiers who are perhaps none of the greatest politicians) that General Needham had orders to let the Croppies escape as government might be unwilling to cut off so many deluded wretches in the very midst of their sins. The reason they assign for this opinion is, that had the General advanced a little sooner and drawn a line from the left of General Dundas's column to the river, it would be impossible for the rebels to escape to Wexford, but this is but mere conjecture and very immaterial to us whose sole business was to obey. I cannot say but it gave me infinite pleasure to see the rebel flag pulled down, may it always meet with a similar fate whenever it is advanced.

The King's County and 89th Regiment ran up the hill with great impetuosity every man firing as he thought proper and so eager were they to get at the enemy, that the swiftest man was the foremost regardless of any order. Colonel Scott marched up his Regiment in line, and took possession of a great quantity of ammunition, &c. left by the rebels. He received the thanks of General Dundas as well as of General Loftus, for not suffering his men to break their ranks and General Dundas reported the conduct of the Colonel and the Regiment to the Commander in Chief at Vinegar hill in the handsomest manner. I am told that some of the soldiers found a great quantity of plate and other valuable articles which the rebels had collected in their marauding excursions through the

Country

Country. In this battle two subalterns, two serjeants and sixteen privates were killed, two field officers, two captains, two subalterns, one serjeant and sixty-two privates wounded.—The loss of the rebels was computed to about 1200 men. After the battle we saw a young woman with a hat and green band lying dead by the way side Another who came to visit her husband had the mortification to see him killed before her face and in addition to her misery her daughter a girl of eleven years of age had her arm shot away almost by the shoulder. Several instances of this kind could I give, but let the following suffice As we past we saw a woman wounded in a ditch, surrounded by three or four children She told the General and other Officers a pitious tale, how her husband had been forced to join the rebels, and how she herself had been wounded. She begged the soldiers to shoot her, but they would not contaminate their arms with a woman's blood. She asked for a drink of water and they gave her grog which revived her drooping spirits for a little The General took the children and sent them to Dublin to be taken care of, and death took the mother to be sent to the grave—to be buried and forgotten.

Now reader, having heard those pityful stories no more sad than true, by way of variety I shall entertain you with a whimsical circumstance which took place after the battle, as General Loftus, Colonel Scott and Captain White were riding out to discover a convenient place for an encampment some of the soldiers who had mistaken them for enemies fired upon them; one of the bullets went through the ear of Captain White's horse Not much discconcerted by this accident they rode on and were mightily surprized to see a fine saddle horse without a rider galloping after them, the Colonel observed that he was a mighty good looking horse, Captain White said he was a fine Croppie but upon a closer inspection the Captain exclaimed, by God it is my own horse, and in reality so it was. Now that the reader may not be in the dark with regard to this affair, I shall thus account for it; Captain Whites servant who had rode behind them was so terrified at the hissing of the bullets that he alighted and hid himself in a ditch but the horse who was the better soldier of the two disdained to flinch, so he galloped after his master.

General Needham's army after receiving a little refreshment of Bread and Whiskey, took the route for Wexford, in pursuit of the flying enemy the road for a mile or more was strewed with dead bodies That evening we arrived at Mr. Hays mansion where we encamped all night Several prisoners were brought in, one of whom was shot near the Park Gate, others were set at liberty by the General's orders, I saw one man taken upon a white horse; the soldiers had him down upon his knees two or three times to shoot him but as he evinced evident symptoms of insanity they dismissed him. In the morning we continued our march for Wexford, some miles to the westward we saw a great dust ascending from the road but Colonel Skerret who had recourse to his perspective glass told us that it proceeded from our own troops who were marching to Wexford by the Carrick-ferry road. Having past Castle Bridge we halted, and Lieutenant-Colonel Bambridge with some horse and foot returned to Mr Dixon's house, where he found a hat with a green cockade and band. When we halted it was reported that Wexford Bridge had been burnt by the rebels. in consequence of which a light horse man was detached off, who returned with orders for us from General Lake (who was arrived in town) to return to Cullart Camp. On our retreat I saw Mr. Dixon's house (from which I suppose the hat had been taken) all in flames A few miles from Castle Bridge we set fire to a Malt House belonging to the Arch Rebel Fitzgerald.

In

In the evening we encamped at Owlart.—Next morning I saw a large pit where some of the brave but unfortunate North Cork were buried; their legs and arms were bare, and a few of their fingers and toes were eat by the pigs, but we covered them decently with earth. At Owlart there lived a woman who had three daughters, she had a son also who was wounded at Vinegar hill, he returned to his mother's house to be cured, but the soldiers dragged him out and shot him in a potatoe garden where he was afterwards buried. Two Militia Soldiers watching their opportunity, caught one of the dumb girls and her mother whom they ravished. The father coming to their assistance was used with the utmost brutality. The mother and daughter came to the Camp and by the General's permission pointed out the ravishers, who were condemned to receive a severe flogging.

The rebels who had retreated from Vinegar-hill, fled to Ferry Carrick.—Lord Kingsborough who had been prisoner at Wexford was solicited by the rebels to bring about an accommodation, for this purpose his Lordship deputed an Officer of the North Cork and one of the rebels to advise the Croppies not to approach the town till matters were adjusted, he at the same time allowed Captain M'Manus to repair to General Moore who was advancing to Taghmon, with terms of submission from Mr. Keughe and some of the inhabitants of Wexford, but ere those destined for the rebel Camp had reached Carrick Ferry, one Timothy Whalen a vagabond rebel, shot the King's Officer from behind a ditch. The report of this being carried to Wexford. The rebels under Mr. Perry after murdering 79 prisoners upon the Bridge, and hearing that General Moore was approaching, fled towards Gorey. Their intention was to have murdered the remaining prisoners the following day in their usual manner, which was to strip them naked, Pike and throw them over the Bridge.

The

The King's Troops entered Wexford without the leaſt oppoſition which was a joyful ſight to every loyal ſubject. Father Roche from the Rebel Camp had the impudence to ride into Town with propoſals but he was immediately taken into cuſtody. Fitzgerald with the Rebels under his command fled towards Kilkenny and left the County of Wexford to the King's troops. Father Roche was tried, executed and his body thrown over the Bridge—Captain Keoghe the Rebel Commandant at Wexford was a half-pay Officer and had ſerved the King in the American War. After the retreat of the Rebels he remained in Wexford having ſome property which he was unwilling to loſe. He was tried, executed for a traitor, and his head fixed upon a Croppie Pike upon the Seſſion Houſe though he attempted to exculpate himſelf before his Judges. Mr Grogan a gentleman of a conſiderable fortune was alſo ſeized, hanged and his head placed upon the Cupola. I remember one day when I came in from Carrick Ferry where our regiment was encamped, I ſaw four men led to execution. Jack Murphy walked without hat, ſhoe, or ſtocking, with his hair hanging looſe about his ſhoulders, he requeſted the prayers of the public and hoped they would ſuffer his wife to take care of his body. Sutton and his Son two of the four were either acquitted or pardoned I cannot tell which. When the ropes were fixed about Murphy and Pender's necks, the ſoldiers were ordered to hoiſt them up, after Pender was drawn up I was aſtoniſhed when I heard him attempt to ſpeak in a mumbling tone for the ſpace of two minutes, this was owing to the rope not being properly fixed. I am ſure he died in great pain. Begnel Harvey the Rebel Commander in Chief, after his defeat at Goffe's Bridge took a boat in company with Mr Colclough and his wife, and putting on board all the ſpecie and plate he could collect, made off for one of the Saltee Iſlands, where they con- cealed in a cave waiting an opportunity of ſome veſſel

 to

to carry them to France, but the boat being discovered, a party of the Military was sent after them—As two of the soldiers entered the cave, Harvey who had a double barrel gun, asked if they had brought many men to take him, upon being told that resistance would be in vain, he surrendered and was carried with his two companions to Wexford, where he was tried, condemned executed and his head put up upon the right of Mr Grogan's—He said he could have beat the army if the cowardly B—g—, his men had supported him at Goffe's Bridge, he was a middle aged man of a low stature and puny appearance

Captain Kelly a farmer's son who had been wounded in the leg at Vinegar-hill, was taken, tried and executed, he denied having any command among the Rebels, and requested the prayers of the public—His head was the fourth and last fixt upon one of the Rebel Pikes under Captain Keughe's head on Wexford Session House.

About this time a report having been propagated that some thousands of Rebels were encamped at the Seven Churches, we marched from Carrick Ferry and arrived at Enniscorthy where we joined the Hessians and other corps under the command of General Moore. I saw a man that evening hanged but as I was told that he had often sat in judgment upon some loyalists whom the Rebels had put to death, I could not look upon his exit without that degree of pity which we generally bestow upon the comman run of malefactors.—It was melancholy to observe such a number of poor people's houses burnt to the ground in the sububs of Enniscorthy, as well as some comfortable if not elegant buildings in the town. We left our camp at Enniscorthy the following morning, and encamped that evening in a field near Cornew, this town had also been burnt to ashes Here we saw General Lake and the 89th Regiment of Foot, we continued our route through Hacketstown which the Rebels had
burnt

burnt, only one houfe had efcaped the conflagration. At the end of the town as we marched out, I counted eighteen dead horfes half buried in a ditch by the road fide, the ftench proceeding from thefe carcafes was moft abominable, I was told that they had belonged to the Rebels who had made an unfuccefsful attempt upon the town when our Troops lay there — This evening brought us to the foot of Wicklow mountains where we encamped in the rear of General Lake's army; before we had pitched our tents we were wet to the fkin and all the night poured down a heavy rain upon us, next morning the army divided; General Moore with the Dunbartons, Heffians and Light Brigades, &c. afcended the mountains, the other army proceeded towards the Seven Churches with all the Artillery and heavy baggage by the King's high way to the right of us,

We marched, or rather climbed up a large hill, while a flanking party of the Heffians kept on our left among a number of rocks which we would imagine to be inacceffable to any creatures but goats — To our right on the brow of the mountain we obferved three Rebels with Pikes upon their fhoulders; at fight of us they fled with precipitation When we had gained the fummit of the mountain we halted, being greatly fatigued with marching through a foft boggy ground into which we funk at every ftep almoft to the very knees; although it was covered with a kind of flowery weed which looked at a diftance like a field of clover — The General ordered each man an allowance of Bread and Whifkey but it took fome time before this order could be complied with as the few cars we had being at the foot of the hill, from whence they were obliged to be dragged up by men and horfes againft a fteep uneven rocky path — The Heffians took three prifoners at this place. After we had refrefhed ourfelves, we marched acrofs the mountain; and a little before fun fet defcended into a long deep valley, on both sides of which hung large rocks of white and spotted marble.

By the help of the twilight we could discern a dozen of men walking on the top of the rock and keeping pace with us all the way. Just as we had forded a [illegible] Being ro Bridge, a shot was fired from the face of the rocks on our right without doing any damage. It was near midnight when we arrived at a [illegible] containing one farm house, and a few [illegible] — we lay all night in our blankets within [illegible] of the Seven Churches, and as no provisions had accompanied us, each Regiment was permitted to slay the cattle to satisfy our hunger. [illegible] killed a young heifer and cut the flesh from the bones which they left like a skeleton upon the [illegible].

A poor countryman having complained that his cabin had been destroyed, the Colonel gave orders that nobody should give him any further molestation, [illegible] after this a Hessian came and offered to [illegible] the sticks from the [illegible], the centinel told him it was [illegible] orders "I don't care damn for orders I [illegible] boil cow" said the Hessian, [illegible] offended at the interruption, for, he looked [illegible] liberty to plunder, as his undoubted privilege. When we expected to have been led on to the Seven Churches, we received orders to trace the ground [illegible] the day before. On our retreat eight or nine [illegible] appeared upon the top of the rocks, and kept pace with us for three or four miles, but when a few Hessians who had ascended the hill, had fired upon them, then they took to their heels.

The afternoon [illegible] a heavy rain which lasted all night and rendered our situation very uncomfortable, for though we had now descended into the champaign country, yet were we obliged to lie all night in our blankets round a turf fire. Instead of returning to [illegible] as we expected, we were ordered to march

for

for Bleſſingtown; the next night we lay within Lord Tyrane's demeſnes Colonel Scott iſſued very particular orders that no body ſhould do any damage to the plantation or to any other part of his Lordſhip's property Two Heſſians who ventured too far upon a marauding ſcheme were Piked by the Rebels, but as their conduct was quite contrary to repeated orders, the loſs was not much lamented.

When we came to Bleſſingtown, we found our baggage and tents, which had arrived by the Eaſt road, with General Lake's army Perhaps no people in the world are greater dabblers in news than ſoldiers. If they ſee a Light Horſe-man galloping towards the Camp, every body cries out " the route is come."— In ſhort no heathen Diviner was ever more ready to draw concluſions from the flight of birds or entrails of beaſts, than they are to form routes, battles, heiddays, invaſions, &c from the moſt trifling circumſtance As we approached Bleſſingtown, ſome of our falſe prophets foretold a march to Dublin, this ſoon ſpread through the Regiment, where it was received with joy and believed without heſitation; but, to our mortification, we were ordered to return to the place from whence we came; I muſt confeſs we were exceeding ſorry to part with General Moore, who is certainly a humane ſweet tempered gentleman, but, when we underſtood that the ſole command of the march was to devolve upon Colonel Scott, nothing in the world could give us more pleaſure. About a mile from Bleſſingtown he halted the Regiment, and gave us a friendly caution againſt plundering and every other ſpecies of irregularity which might diſgrace the name of a ſoldier—I have marched in England, Ireland, Scotland and America, under ſeveral Commanders; but, I never knew (reader think not that partiality guides my pen) a commanding Officer who paid more attention to the honour and welfare of his men, though he would by no means ſuffer a ſoldier

to

to leave his ranks or run into a houſe under a pretext of getting a drink of water; yet he would halt the Regiment when ever we came to a clear ſpring, and ſit down himſelf upon a ſtone or bank, till we were refreſhed (if we had Whiſkey it was ſerved out) then continue his march in a manner not to fatigue the ſoldiers—That morning we left Baltinglaſs, a woman came and complained that one of our men had robbed her of ſome wearing apparel, the Colonel deſired her to point him out, ſhe ſaid ſhe could not, but that he was blind of an eye Michael Horgan, a native of the north, being the only cyclop in the expedition, the ſuſpicion fell upon him: he was called to the front and being ſearched, behold, a ſhabby blew cloak was extracted from his Haverſack, ſhame and indignation were painted upon the Colonel's cheek; he ordered the delinquent to be ſtript of his coat, bonnet, and knapſack, and (as if he had thought him too deſpicable for military puniſhment) ſet him adrift, cut him off from our liſt like an infectious member who might be apt to corrupt the whole body of the Regiment.

From Baltinglaſs, we came to Tullow, and as no beds could be had, we were obliged to ſleep all night in a church In this town I ſaw the head of one Father Murphy fixed upon the Seſſion Houſe, I was told he was brother to the ball-catching Father Murphy who made his exit at Arklow. From Tullow we marched to Newtownberry, where we met our old friends and acquaintance, the Cavin, and where for once more, I was forced to break through one of the golden rules of my grandmother, which was never me, "never to ſleep in Church" Our next ſtage was Enniſcorthy, and, would you believe it, by yea and nay I was obliged to take up my quarters in a Quakers meeting-houſe; having ſuſpended my portable baggage on a pin that ſtuck in the wall, the ſpirit moved me to viſit Vinegar-hill and the adjacent fields,

where

where I was aston'shed to see the skulls of some who had been kil'ed (and it was not then a month since the battle; as bare as if they had lain three years in the grave; but, my wonder ceased when I was told that the pigs had fared most sumptuously upon some of the dead carcases which lay half buried in the ditches; this may serve as a momento to the lovers of pork.— Among others I saw the bodies of two young boys who had been killed in the time of the battle, their legs and arms were uncovered, as well as their little short waistcoats made of coarse cloth, with mettle buttons, near them lay an old man with a black silk handkerchief about his neck, and an old scratch of a brown wig lying at his head, his ribs were quite visible through his withered skin, I wonder no body took the trouble to cover them—when I mention wounded women and boys killed, the reader must impute their misfortunes to accidents, for, bullets once set loose have no respect of persons

In the neighbourhood of the hill, I saw an old house which brought to my remembrance, a circumstance I forgot to mention in its proper place, and though it does no great honour to some of my brother soldiers, I shall here relate it that the reader may see the evil effects of war; after the battle some soldiers got hold of a Croppies wife, whom they dragged into a house, and shame to say four and twenty brutes (ambitious to disgrace a red coat) had connection with her, even the blear-eyed Michael Horgan, the blue cloak merchant meant to have been one of the number—As I past I saw him coming out at the door and exclaiming "blood and wounds I've lost my turn" I began to expostulate with him upon the impropriety of his conduct, knowing that he had a wife and children in Dublin, but he cut me off short with 'blood and wounds man, Kitty and I have made an agreement; she gives me liberty to do what I please, and I give her the same when I'm from home, I could not help
laughing

laughing at this family compact, though I despised the abominable wretches who had made it.

Next morning being Saturday, we arrived at Wexford—in the evening I saw the grey-headed Mr Kean, who had cut so many capers (in his green carriage) at Corrig, led out to execution, he requested most earnestly that he might not be hanged, to bring a disgrace upon his family, "let those brave fellows shoot me, said he I'll warrant they'll soon dispatch me," but as this request could not be granted, he solicited the prayers of all good christians—he was then executed and his body thrown over the Bridge. Now, reader though justice prompts me to acquiesce in their sentence as Rebels, think me not disloyal, if my heart commands my eye to drop one tear when I consider them as men and fellow-creatures—Oh! sons of Erin! easy fools! why were you seduced by the prince of darkness, for sure no other power could have inspired such hellish born thoughts—but you are forgiven so let your past faults be buried in your future acts of loyalty—Let us unite our hearts and hands, and, when we meet to consult the Public Safety whether it is over the flowing bowl, the sparkling glass the humble noggin or salubrious draught of butter-milk—let friendship, love and brotherly affection adorn our meetings.

ERRATTA.

Page 14, for rebel deserter, read a rebel deserter—15, for Coolgreene read Coolgreene—16 for don't done, read don't don't—for drunken king, read drunken knight—for ho! I don't know where, read ah! I don't know whither—for human rabble, read humane rabble—20, for the south of the town, read south side of the town.